# Star Testing Astronomical Telescopes

## A Manual for Optical Evaluation and Adjustment

# Star Testing Astronomical Telescopes

## A Manual for Optical Evaluation and Adjustment

## Harold Richard Suiter

Published by:

**Willmann-Bell, Inc.**

P. O. Box 35025
Richmond, Virginia 23235
United States of America

Published by Willmann–Bell, Inc.
P.O. Box 35025, Richmond, Virginia 23235

Copyright ©1994 by Harold Richard Suiter
First English Edition
Second Printing May 1995

Printed in the United States of America

**Library of Congress Cataloging-in-Publication Data.**
Suiter, Harold Richard.
    Star testing astronomical telescopes : a manual for
optical evaluation and adjustment  /  Harold Richard Suiter. – 1st
English ed.
        p.    cm.
    Includes bibliographical references and index.
    ISBN 943396-44-1
    1. Telescopes – Testing – Amateurs' manuals.    I. Title.

    QB88.S85    1994
522'.2'0287 – dc20                                     94-30450
                                                              CIP

95 96 97 98 9 8 7 6 5 4 3 2

# Foreword

In writing this book, Dick Suiter has created an important resource for amateur astronomy. This is a book that will help every telescope maker, every telescope owner, and every serious observer learn what a fine telescope is truly capable of, and how to obtain from their own telescopes the best possible images. If you are an amateur astronomer, whether a raw novice or expert, this book is important because it tells you how to get the most from your telescope.

What makes the star test so remarkable is that it's both very easy and very sensitive. The star test is so simple that you're probably already using it—even if you aren't fully aware of doing so. Every time you observe, indeed, every time you look through your telescope you see how starlight comes together to form a star image. This book teaches you how to interpret what you see in an objective and meaningful way.

To perform the star test, you simply observe a star with a moderately high-power eyepiece, giving careful consideration to the image on both sides of focus. The patterns you see in the focused and out-of-focus star images tell you whether your telescope is aligned for maximum performance, whether the atmosphere is steady, and when the telescope has cooled and is ready to do its best. The star test takes only a moment, and because it is so helpful, star testing becomes a normal part of your observing routine.

I first corresponded with Dick Suiter over a dozen years ago, when I contacted him for a short star-testing article that was eventually published in *Astronomy*. Since then he has continually impressed me with his ability to meld abstruse theory with practical telescope making. The book you now hold is no exception: Dick has combined sophisticated computer modeling with down-to-earth advice that you can use to learn more about your telescope. The hundreds of illustrations he has created allow you to recognize the entire range of factors that can influence telescope performance. That makes this book heavy-duty stuff in a form that anyone can understand.

To give you an idea of how star testing can help you, let me describe how I have used star testing to get top-notch performance from my first big telescope, a 20-inch f/5 with a Dobsonian mounting. At the time I built it, Dobsonians were fairly new, and the total information then published about making these large, alt-az instruments would have barely filled a pamphlet. I made everything bigger, thicker, and stronger than necessary. Although my newly completed telescope's light grasp was marvelous, of course, its star images were often mushy until the too-heavy structure cooled.

The first year I used the telescope, I star tested regularly and, from the air currents I saw in the extrafocal images, deduced that both the mirror and tube were cooling too slowly, and that the mirror cooled more slowly than the tube. I installed a fan behind the mirror to pull air down through the tube and over the mirror. It worked wonderfully! With the air currents greatly reduced, star testing now revealed a bit of spherical aberration, although hardly enough to interfere with most deep-sky observing. I debated for some time whether this problem deserved attention and ultimately had the primary refigured.

The result was extremely satisfying. With the cooling fan and a nearly perfect mirror, my big Dob now gave excellent lunar and planetary images. It outperformed precision apochromats in giving crisp, brilliant views of Saturn and Jupiter (although—to be fair—the apos were smaller). During the 1988 opposition of Mars, not only did I see Deimos and Phobos for the first time, but also enjoyed the best views I'd ever had of the planet itself. Careful star testing now revealed that at times the optics appeared slightly pinched. I traced the problem to the mirror cell, and found that if I shook the telescope, the mirror would settle in its cell and outstanding images would be restored.

You too will benefit when you become sensitive to your telescope's optical performance. If you find that your telescope has a few problems—and what telescope does not?—it is best to deal openly with them. Would-be astronomers who refuse to acknowledge such problems tend to stop using their telescopes, and eventually lose their interest in astronomy. Once you recognize that a problem exists, you can possibly use the star test to correct it. Often, it's nothing that careful collimation will not solve. If your telescope has properly adjusted and excellent optics, the star test will confirm that fact and you can turn your attention to other observing issues.

It is not often that a single book has the potential to open the eyes of a whole generation of amateur astronomers. I believe Suiter's *Star Testing Astronomical Telescopes* is such a book. It will enhance the observing pleasure of every amateur astronomer who reads and takes this book to heart.

Richard Berry
Lyons, Oregon

# Table of Contents

Foreword iii

An Introduction to the Author xi

Preface xiii

1 Introduction 1
  1.1 Telescope Evaluation . . . . . . . . . . . . . . . . . . . . . . 1
  1.2 Testing the Surfaces . . . . . . . . . . . . . . . . . . . . . . 2
      1.2.1 Sources of Errors . . . . . . . . . . . . . . . . . . . 4
      1.2.2 Measures of Optical Quality . . . . . . . . . . . . . 6
  1.3 The Star Test—A Brief Overview . . . . . . . . . . . . . . 9
      1.3.1 Diffraction Rings . . . . . . . . . . . . . . . . . . . 10
  1.4 The Reason for Star Testing . . . . . . . . . . . . . . . . . 14

2 An Abbreviated Star-Test Manual 17
  2.1 Some Necessary Preliminaries . . . . . . . . . . . . . . . . 17
  2.2 Optical Problems in Turn . . . . . . . . . . . . . . . . . . 18
      2.2.1 Secondary Mirror Obstruction . . . . . . . . . . . 20
      2.2.2 Misalignment . . . . . . . . . . . . . . . . . . . . . 22
      2.2.3 Atmospheric Motion and Turbulence . . . . . . . . 23
      2.2.4 Tube Currents . . . . . . . . . . . . . . . . . . . . 24
      2.2.5 Pinched or Deformed Optics . . . . . . . . . . . . 25
      2.2.6 Spherical Aberration . . . . . . . . . . . . . . . . . 26
      2.2.7 Rough Surfaces . . . . . . . . . . . . . . . . . . . . 28
      2.2.8 Zonal Aberrations . . . . . . . . . . . . . . . . . . 31
      2.2.9 Turned Edges . . . . . . . . . . . . . . . . . . . . . 31
      2.2.10 Astigmatism . . . . . . . . . . . . . . . . . . . . . 32
  2.3 Concluding Remarks . . . . . . . . . . . . . . . . . . . . . 33

**3  Telescopes Are Filters**      **35**
  3.1  Perceptions of Reality . . . . . . . . . . . . . . . . . . . . 37
  3.2  A Comparison to Audio . . . . . . . . . . . . . . . . . . . 38
      3.2.1  Aperture Diameter/Size of Speakers . . . . . . . . 39
      3.2.2  Colored Filters/Equalizer Filters . . . . . . . . . . 41
      3.2.3  Image Processing/Signal Processing . . . . . . . . 41
      3.2.4  Scattered Light/Audio Noise . . . . . . . . . . . . 43
      3.2.5  Spatial Frequency/Audio Frequency Responses . . . 45
  3.3  The Modulation Transfer Function (MTF) . . . . . . . . . 46
  3.4  The MTF in Use . . . . . . . . . . . . . . . . . . . . . . . 49
      3.4.1  MTF Associated with Defocusing . . . . . . . . . . 51
      3.4.2  Stacking of MTFs . . . . . . . . . . . . . . . . . . 52

**4  Diffraction**      **55**
  4.1  The Coordinates of Light . . . . . . . . . . . . . . . . . . 57
  4.2  The Consequence of Filtering . . . . . . . . . . . . . . . . 61
  4.3  Waves Are Reborn . . . . . . . . . . . . . . . . . . . . . . 63
      4.3.1  Diffraction and Focusing . . . . . . . . . . . . . . 65
      4.3.2  Fresnel Zones . . . . . . . . . . . . . . . . . . . . 66
      4.3.3  Fresnel Zones with Defocus . . . . . . . . . . . . . 68
  4.4  Nodes and Antinodes . . . . . . . . . . . . . . . . . . . . 70
  4.5  Other Aberrations—The Pupil Function . . . . . . . . . . 74

**5  Conducting the Star Test**      **77**
  5.1  Defocusing and Sensitivity . . . . . . . . . . . . . . . . . 78
      5.1.1  Focuser Motion Related to Defocusing Aberration . 78
      5.1.2  Sensitivity of the Star Test . . . . . . . . . . . . . 81
  5.2  Artificial Sources . . . . . . . . . . . . . . . . . . . . . . 82
      5.2.1  Distance of Artificial Sources . . . . . . . . . . . . 83
      5.2.2  Diameter of Artificial Sources . . . . . . . . . . . 86
      5.2.3  Using a Reflective Sphere Instead of a Pinhole . . . 88
      5.2.4  Setting Up a Nighttime Artificial Source . . . . . . 90
  5.3  Performing the Test . . . . . . . . . . . . . . . . . . . . . 91
      5.3.1  8-Inch f/6 Newtonian Reflector . . . . . . . . . . . 94
      5.3.2  16-Inch f/4 Dobson-mounted Newtonian . . . . . . 97
      5.3.3  6-Inch f/12 Apochromatic Refractor . . . . . . . . 98
      5.3.4  8-Inch f/10 Schmidt-Cassegrain Catadioptric . . . . 100

**6  Misalignment**      **103**
  6.1  Kinematic View of Alignment . . . . . . . . . . . . . . . . 103
  6.2  Effects of Misalignment . . . . . . . . . . . . . . . . . . . 104
  6.3  The Aberration Function of the Misaligned Newtonian . . . 106

6.4   Filtration of a Misaligned Newtonian . . . . . . . . . . . . 107
6.5   Aligning Three Telescopes . . . . . . . . . . . . . . . . . . 108
      6.5.1   The Newtonian Reflector . . . . . . . . . . . . . . 109
      6.5.2   The Refractor . . . . . . . . . . . . . . . . . . . . . 121
      6.5.3   The Schmidt-Cassegrain . . . . . . . . . . . . . . . 125

**7   Air Turbulence and Tube Currents               129**
7.1   Air As a Refractive Medium . . . . . . . . . . . . . . . . . 129
7.2   Turbulence . . . . . . . . . . . . . . . . . . . . . . . . . . 130
      7.2.1   The Aberration Function . . . . . . . . . . . . . . 131
      7.2.2   Filtering Caused by Turbulence . . . . . . . . . . . 136
      7.2.3   Observing Turbulence . . . . . . . . . . . . . . . . 136
      7.2.4   Corrective Action . . . . . . . . . . . . . . . . . . . 138
7.3   Tube Currents . . . . . . . . . . . . . . . . . . . . . . . . 139
      7.3.1   The Aberration Function . . . . . . . . . . . . . . 139
      7.3.2   Filtering of Tube Currents . . . . . . . . . . . . . 140
      7.3.3   Observing Tube Currents . . . . . . . . . . . . . . 142
      7.3.4   Corrective Actions for Tube Currents . . . . . . . 143

**8   Pinched and Deformed Optics                  145**
8.1   Causes . . . . . . . . . . . . . . . . . . . . . . . . . . . . 145
8.2   The Aberration Function . . . . . . . . . . . . . . . . . . 147
8.3   Filtering of Pinched Optics . . . . . . . . . . . . . . . . . 147
8.4   Diffraction Patterns of Pinched Optics . . . . . . . . . . . 148
8.5   Fixing the Problem . . . . . . . . . . . . . . . . . . . . . . 150

**9   Obstruction and Shading                      153**
9.1   Central Obstruction . . . . . . . . . . . . . . . . . . . . . 153
9.2   Spider Diffraction . . . . . . . . . . . . . . . . . . . . . . 157
9.3   Shading or Apodization . . . . . . . . . . . . . . . . . . . 160
9.4   Dust and Scratches on the Optics . . . . . . . . . . . . . 166

**10 Spherical Aberration                         169**
10.1 What Is Spherical Aberration? . . . . . . . . . . . . . . . 170
10.2 The Hubble Space Telescope . . . . . . . . . . . . . . . . 172
10.3 Generalized Spherical Aberration . . . . . . . . . . . . . . 173
10.4 The Aberration Functions . . . . . . . . . . . . . . . . . . 174
10.5 Correction Error (Lower-Order Spherical Aberration) . . . . 176
      10.5.1 Filtering of Spherical Aberration . . . . . . . . . . 176
      10.5.2 Star-Test Patterns of Correction Error . . . . . . . 178
      10.5.3 Estimation of the Severity of the Problem . . . . . 179
10.6 Testing for Correction . . . . . . . . . . . . . . . . . . . . 191

10.7  Higher-Order Spherical Aberration . . . . . . . . . . . . .  192

    10.7.1  Star-Test Patterns of Higher-Order Spherical
Aberration  . . . . . . . . . . . . . . . . . . . . . . .  194

    10.7.2  Filtering of Higher-Order Spherical Aberration  . . .  194

10.8  A Compact, Uniform Standard for Optical Quality . . . . .  196

10.9  Tolerable Errors  . . . . . . . . . . . . . . . . . . . . . . .  198

**11  Circular Zones and Turned Edges**                                 **201**

11.1  Causes of Zonal Defects  . . . . . . . . . . . . . . . . . . .  201

11.2  Interior Zones . . . . . . . . . . . . . . . . . . . . . . . . .  204

    11.2.1  Aberration Function of S-Zones . . . . . . . . . . . .  205

    11.2.2  Filtering of S-Zones  . . . . . . . . . . . . . . . . . .  205

    11.2.3  Detecting Interior Zones in the Star Test  . . . . . .  207

11.3  Turned Edges . . . . . . . . . . . . . . . . . . . . . . . . .  209

    11.3.1  Aberration Function . . . . . . . . . . . . . . . . . .  211

    11.3.2  MTF of Turned Edge  . . . . . . . . . . . . . . . . .  211

    11.3.3  Image Pattern of Turned-Down Edge . . . . . . . . .  211

    11.3.4  Signal-to-Noise Ratio of a Turned Edge  . . . . . . .  215

    11.3.5  The Width of the Turned Edge . . . . . . . . . . . .  216

    11.3.6  Remedies for Turned Edge . . . . . . . . . . . . . . .  217

**12  Chromatic Aberration**                                            **219**

12.1  Dispersion . . . . . . . . . . . . . . . . . . . . . . . . . . .  220

12.2  The Achromatic Lens  . . . . . . . . . . . . . . . . . . . . .  222

12.3  Residual Chromatic Aberration . . . . . . . . . . . . . . . .  224

12.4  The Apochromat . . . . . . . . . . . . . . . . . . . . . . . .  226

12.5  Testing Refractors for Other Aberrations . . . . . . . . . . .  227

12.6  The Star Test for Chromatic Effects  . . . . . . . . . . . . .  227

    12.6.1  Wedge, Assembly Errors, and Atmospheric Spectra .  228

    12.6.2  Star Test for Conventional Astronomical
Visual Doublets . . . . . . . . . . . . . . . . . . . .  229

    12.6.3  Star Test of Apochromats or Advanced Refractors .  231

    12.6.4  Chromatic Effects in the Eye . . . . . . . . . . . . .  232

    12.6.5  The Eyepiece . . . . . . . . . . . . . . . . . . . . . .  232

12.7  Conclusions and Remedies . . . . . . . . . . . . . . . . . . .  232

**13  Roughness**                                                       **235**

13.1  Roughness Scales and Effects  . . . . . . . . . . . . . . . .  236

13.2  The Terminology of Roughness  . . . . . . . . . . . . . . . .  238

13.3  Medium-Scale Roughness, or Primary Ripple  . . . . . . . .  239

    13.3.1  The Aberration Function of Medium-Scale Roughness  241

    13.3.2  Filtering Effects of Medium-Scale Roughness  . . . .  242

13.3.3  Star Test on Medium-Scale Roughness . . . . . . . .  243
13.3.4  Roughness and Turbulence  . . . . . . . . . . . . .  243
13.4  Small-Scale Roughness, or Microripple . . . . . . . . . . .  246
13.4.1  The Aberration Function of Small-Scale Roughness .  247
13.4.2  Filtering of Small-Scale Roughness . . . . . . . . .  247
13.4.3  The Great Unknown . . . . . . . . . . . . . . . .  248

14 Astigmatism                                                  251
14.1  Astigmatism in Eyes and Telescope Optics . . . . . . . . .  251
14.2  Causes of Astigmatism . . . . . . . . . . . . . . . . . . .  253
14.3  Aberration Function of Astigmatism . . . . . . . . . . . .  254
14.4  Filtering of Astigmatism . . . . . . . . . . . . . . . . . .  256
14.5  Star-Test Patterns  . . . . . . . . . . . . . . . . . . . . .  258
14.6  Identification in Newtonian Reflectors  . . . . . . . . . . .  258
14.7  Refractors or Schmidt-Cassegrains  . . . . . . . . . . . . .  263
14.8  Remedies  . . . . . . . . . . . . . . . . . . . . . . . . . .  264

15 Accumulated Optical Problems                                 265
15.1  Breaking the Camel's Back  . . . . . . . . . . . . . . . . .  265
15.2  Fixing the Telescope . . . . . . . . . . . . . . . . . . . .  269
15.3  Errors on the Glass . . . . . . . . . . . . . . . . . . . . .  272
15.4  Testing Other Telescopes  . . . . . . . . . . . . . . . . . .  273
15.5  When Everything Goes Right . . . . . . . . . . . . . . . .  274

A Other Tests                                                   277
A.1  The Foucault Test  . . . . . . . . . . . . . . . . . . . . .  278
A.2  The Hartmann Test  . . . . . . . . . . . . . . . . . . . .  284
A.3  Resolution of Double Stars  . . . . . . . . . . . . . . . . .  286
A.4  Geometric Ronchi Test . . . . . . . . . . . . . . . . . . .  289
A.5  Interferometry  . . . . . . . . . . . . . . . . . . . . . . .  298
A.5.1  How Do Interferometers Work? . . . . . . . . . . .  298
A.5.2  The Point-Diffraction Interferometer . . . . . . . .  302
A.6  The Null Test . . . . . . . . . . . . . . . . . . . . . . . .  304

B Calculation Methods                                           307
B.1  Diffraction Concepts . . . . . . . . . . . . . . . . . . . .  307
B.2  The Fraunhofer and Fresnel Approximations . . . . . . . .  310
B.3  Image Calculations for Symmetric Apertures  . . . . . . . .  312
B.4  Image Calculations for Nonsymmetric Apertures  . . . . . .  314
B.5  The Programs . . . . . . . . . . . . . . . . . . . . . . . .  316
B.5.1  Symmetric Pupil Function . . . . . . . . . . . . . .  316
B.5.2  Asymmetric Pupil Function . . . . . . . . . . . . .  317

B.6   Verification of Numerical Procedure . . . . . . . . . . . . . 317
     B.6.1   Comparison of APERTURE and ASYMM . . . . . . . . . 318
     B.6.2   A Numerical Comparison with an Analytic Solution   318
     B.6.3   Comparison with Published Patterns . . . . . . . . 320
B.7   Numerical Limitations on Programs . . . . . . . . . . . . 320
B.8   Difficulties in Printing . . . . . . . . . . . . . . . . . . . 324

**C  Minor Axis and Offset Derivation**      **327**
   C.1   Derivation . . . . . . . . . . . . . . . . . . . . . . . . . . 327
   C.2   Test Case . . . . . . . . . . . . . . . . . . . . . . . . . . 330
   C.3   Approximations . . . . . . . . . . . . . . . . . . . . . . . 330

**D  Labeling of Diffraction Patterns**      **333**

**E  Eyepiece Travel and Defocusing Aberration**      **337**

**F  Glitter in a Shiny Sphere**      **339**

**G  List of Common Symbols**      **341**

   **Glossary**      **343**

   **Bibliography**      **353**

   **Index**      **359**

# An Introduction to the Author

I will never forget the first time I met Dick Suiter. I had built my first telescope, an 8-inch Newtonian on a Dobsonian mount, in a single weekend. The 'scope wasn't a model of the craftsman's art. I had misplaced the hole for the focuser a couple of times and covered up my mistakes with pieces of cardboard. The telescope was haphazardly finished with some sky-blue house paint that had languished in my garage for several years.

My first forays into my backyard to use the telescope were unsuccessful. I couldn't find any actual astronomical objects with it, and I was about to forgo astronomy as a hobby.

A friend suggested that I visit Perkins Observatory with my telescope. He had heard that members of the local astronomy club, the Columbus Astronomical Society, set up their small telescopes in the shadow of the observatory's gigantic dome. A dozen or so telescopes dotted the observing field that night. Among the group was Dick Suiter, who had earned the reputation as a local expert on telescope optics. Hoping that all my observing problems could be attributed to bad optics, I asked Dick to test my 'scope.

He shone a red flashlight on the blue paint. "It isn't much to look at," I said, embarrassed by the poor workmanship.

He turned the 'scope on its mount. "Doesn't matter. Works okay," he said. He taught me how to align the telescope and turned it to a bright star. He looked through the eyepiece and began slowly to rack it in and out. After what seemed an eternity to me (it was actually just a few minutes), he finally pronounced judgment: "A bit overcorrected with a slightly rough surface. Good edge. It'll do."

"How can he tell all that just by looking?" I thought, as he turned the 'scope to the Ring Nebula in Lyra. All further skepticism was washed away by the splendor of the view.

A month later, I was using the star test to evaluate other people's telescopes. It's that simple to learn. I built 50 telescopes, all Dobsonians, over the intervening years, and I've star-tested each one to evaluate the optics.

All those experiences taught me the value of the star test. Other tests are too complicated for the beginner or require special equipment—I've always meant to build a Foucault tester, but there never seemed to be any point. Others are painfully insensitive to the subtle problems inherent in some telescope mirrors. (I've seen some truly awful mirrors "pass" the Ronchi test.) The star test is all I've ever needed.

Dick is the last person who would say that star testing is the only useful test of a mirror. For example, it doesn't provide the quantitative data necessary during the early stages of mirror figuring. However, it is extraordinarily useful in the final stages, where a careful mirror maker is looking for visual verification of the Foucault data.

When our group was working on the Columbus Astronomical Society's 16-inch mirror, we got the mirror as well figured as we could using the Foucault test. Then, night after night, Dick set up the optics in a makeshift mount in my backyard. With rouge and infinite patience, Dick made a few passes with the polishing tool, star tested it, and made a few more passes. The end result is the best amateur-made mirror I have ever used. (The views of Jupiter's cloud belts are to die for.) The mirror's final figure was verified in the telescope under the stars. And that is as it should be.

The star test's greatest problem has always been the lack of simple, widely available instructions on how to do the test and a clearly articulated argument for its advantages over other methods of evaluation.

You hold those instructions and that argument in your hands. Some of you who are convinced that other methods of testing are superior will, I think, be impressed by Dick's lucid and irrefutable arguments for the star test's sensitivity and utility. The star test offers a unique combination of simplicity, elegance, and power.

Practically every amateur astronomer I know learned the star test from Dick or learned it from someone who learned it from him. With this work, Dick's patience and talent for explaining the technique will get the wider audience they deserve.

The most important lesson that Dick taught me that night at Perkins Observatory was that a good set of optics, well mounted and superbly aligned, is a doorway to infinite worlds. When the star testing was completed, Dick and his friends showed me dozens of star clusters, nebulae, and galaxies in my dog-eared, homemade instrument. My life was changed that night so long ago. I hope yours will be enlivened in the same way—with the help of a fine telescope pointed upward at the stars.

Tom Burns, Director
Perkins Observatory

# Preface

This book is about one method of testing the optical quality of telescopes. It goes by the informal name of "star test," although it would probably be more accurately named "point source" testing. The reason stars are used as test objects is not because there are so many, but because stars appear infinitesimally small. Thus, they act like true points. The job of the telescope in this case is to map one point in distant space to one point on the image. Stripping the complexity of imaging to this minimal task, we have some hope of discovering how the telescope fails or succeeds.

The point-source test was first used to fabricate a telescope in 1722 when John Hadley used it to make the earliest astronomical Newtonian reflector. Hadley employed a variant of the star test, since his source was a nearby pinhole, but all the essential elements of the star test were used. He drew the eyepiece to both sides of the image and judged the behavior of light in focus by what he saw on each side (King 1955).

However, the star test has never enjoyed popularity as a sole method of testing during fabrication. Even after Hadley's example, other tests were preferred. The star test usually doesn't yield surface profiles, and it is not a convenient indoor evaluation technique. That does not mean that its use in telescope making hasn't had a few outspoken adherents, but the star test's most popular function is final evaluation of a completed working telescope.

Mathematical calculation of the appearance of an image is possible, but that doesn't mean it is easy. Diffraction calculations, though conceptually simple, are almost intractable computationally. Only a few canonical examples were calculated using analytic (i.e., "paper-and-pencil") methods. Diffraction had to wait for the modern electronic computer before cases of general interest to telescope users were solved by any but the most hardy and persistent optical theorist.

This difficulty explains the comparative rarity of good instructions for viewing various aberrations. Each defocus position requires a separate, lengthy calculation. It is no wonder that diffraction patterns resulting from aberrations were seldom calculated before the ascendancy of computing xiv

machines.

Instead, observers relied for a full century on the encyclopedic experience and drawing skill of one individual, H. Dennis Taylor. In 1891, he published a tiny book with a set of star-test drawings reproduced photographically and pasted in the frontispiece (Taylor 1983).[1] These drawings have been reprinted many times since, and Taylor's descriptions have been summarized in a number of books (e.g., Twyman 1988, Bell 1922, and Ingalls 1976).

Taylor's little book is heavily oriented toward the refractors that dominated the astronomical community of his time. It doesn't deal with problems appearing more commonly in reflectors, such as obstruction and turned-down edge. As such, Taylor's drawings have led observers to thirst for more. Among other goals, this book is an attempt to modernize and extend Taylor's star-test descriptions. It fills in much of the reflector performance that was neglected in his seminal work.

During the century since Taylor's book was published, there have been few works dealing exclusively with the star test. W.T. Welford (1978) published one review article in which he summarized the sparse literature on the technique. He again had to fall back to verbal descriptions, because he didn't possess a method for graphically rendering the complex star images.

One of the enabling factors of this book is a computerized graphics-arts language. The diffraction images calculated here are composed in the language called PostScript, by Adobe Systems, Incorporated. PostScript allows one to calculate the brightness of a pixel and place it in the image at its precise location. No diffraction figure in this book has been drawn by hand or otherwise represents a fallible retouching effort. This claim does not imply that the images seen in this book are perfect. They have my contrast preferences and the inevitable sampling errors, as well as the imperfections of not precisely knowing what will be printed on the final page. At least, all errors are *uniformly* applied to each pixel of the frames. The calculated images in this book are as near to optically correct as the publisher and I can make them. The goal all along is to convince you that these images are authentic, if not genuine.

With this emphasis on graphics in mind, the book has also been printed on expensive glossy paper. This paper type is customarily reserved for photographic plates and is typically used for only a few sheets. Glossy paper is used here because it offers a gloriously wide dynamic range. This paper is very dense and packs more tightly than ordinary book paper. As a consequence, this volume is superficially thinner than its 380-odd pages would indicate. I hope this compactness will also allow testers to transport

---

[1]More recent editions do not have this plate. They reproduce the photo on a printed page.

the book to observing sites more readily than they otherwise might.

This book has been written for the amateur astronomer with a telescope of small to moderate size (apertures less than 20 inches or so). The book may occasionally be useful to professional astronomers and optical experts, although the former usually have to deal with the imaging peculiarities of huge telescopes and the latter may have already formed diverse opinions about many of the topics. When faced with the choice of rigor versus clear exposition, I almost always opted for clarity. Thus, the book resembles more a personal viewpoint than an authoritative document.

I have attempted to keep the less instructive aspects of Huygens-Fresnel diffraction theory to the rear of the book. However, I was unwilling to throw them out entirely. Otherwise, most of the book would have resembled a cold assertion, leaving the reader to believe or disbelieve me. I was also unwilling to completely remove equations from the central discussion, but I try to limit them to elucidating important topics. The reader need not understand the mathematics in the body of the text to use the star test effectively, but fullest comprehension of causes and effects will reward those who have studied these discussions. Appendix B is only for those wishing detailed knowledge of the way these complicated figures have been generated. It is by no means "required." Appendix D, on the other hand, is helpful to casual readers because it contains the labeling description for the star-test figures. It explains the manner in which I "jack-knifed" the focal region to fit on a printed page. Be sure to consult it when you finally encounter these figures.

Some may accuse me of trying to light a fire beneath manufacturers, but that is not my intent. My motivation is almost the reverse. Too long have manufacturers been forced to make inferior telescope optics because their customers buy telescopes the way they buy a sack of potatoes—based on price alone. If buyers can't determine optical quality, other less important factors (such as price) become the only criteria in their decision. What I'm doing is placing a reliable testing method in customers' hands. The star test will allow them to determine that Brand B, which costs a little more, is *indeed a better product* than Brand A. Manufacturers can return—with some relief, no doubt—to making quality optics, and their customers will be able to tell the difference.

I would like to thank the host of people who have helped me with this book. I can't list all of them here, but I would like to mention the following contributions especially:

Bob Bunge, Peter Ceravolo, and Bob Gent for kindly supplying me with various references.

Ray Lim for locating typographical errors in the difficult mathematical appendices.

E. Wolf and R. Kingslake for going out of their way to help me get reprinting permission on one of the figures in Appendix B.

Skilled mirror-maker Bill Herbert for his Foucault and Ronchi test photographs.

Editor Tom Burns for converting my meanderings to reasonably coherent English.

Diane Lucas, Richard Berry, Michael Brunn, Richard Buchroeder, Roger Sinnott, and Bill Zmek for the unenviable job of doing detailed technical reading on my manuscript.

Thanks to these people, the book is more accurate and much clearer. (Of course, any errors that remain are strictly my fault.)

H.R.S.
Panama City, Florida
April, 1994

# Chapter 1

# Introduction

## 1.1 Telescope Evaluation

I'm going to tell you a little-known fact. Telescopes are easy to test. All that is required is a good high-magnification eyepiece, a conveniently placed star or illuminated pinhole, and some experience. In fact, telescopes are so easy to test that I recommend you check the optical train of your telescope *every time you use it*, as a monitor of alignment, proper optical support, and atmospheric conditions.

You will notice that the methods proposed in this book are a great deal different from the methods telescope makers use. Telescope *fabrication*, as contrasted with telescope *evaluation*, requires that corrective measures be indicated. Hence, telescope makers favor methods that lead to profiles of the optical surfaces, or at least the errors in the slope of those surfaces. They can use such information to decide where they must remove slight amounts of glass during the next figuring step.

Such methods demand specialized equipment, and more importantly they require skills best learned at the elbow of an expert. Optical shop tests tend to require delicate visual interpretations, and someone usually has to physically demonstrate the test to a person unfamiliar with it.

Telescope evaluation, on the other hand, is a test of a finished product. It requires little or no specialized equipment. The evaluator cares little how an optical piece can be improved. The test is purely a yes-no decision: Is the optical train good enough to transmit the image or is it not? The evaluation encompasses the *entire* optical path, even those elements not customarily included in the telescope, from the top of the atmosphere to the eye of the observer.

The star test evaluates telescopes in their final configuration, doing precisely what they were intended to do. The star test is not easily reduced to numbers, but it is very sensitive. A telescope that "passes" the star test need not be evaluated with a bench test. It has already met the most stringent criterion necessary to deliver beautiful images.

The star test is an examination of the image of a point source, most commonly a star, both in focus and on both sides of focus. The power of the star test is contained in this simple motion of the eyepiece to examine the expanded diffraction disk on both sides of focus. Not only is the expanded spot bigger and hence easier to see (the focused diffraction disks of most astronomical telescopes are tiny), it "unfolds" into a unique representation of the aberrations that caused it. In particular, an out-of-focus circular image appears similar at equal small distances inside and outside the focal point *but only if the optics are excellent.*[1]

The expanded disks will appear different if any aberration is degrading the system. The sensitivity of this test is phenomenal. My first mirror was a 200 mm f/6 reflector that regularly shows excellent images of the planets, yet still just barely passes the star test. It shows some inclination towards overcorrection, roughness, and a turned edge.

The telescope is automatically prepared to do the star test and the test is conducted with all optical elements in place. Many of the optical defects discussed in this book have nothing to do with errors on the glass, and would not even have been detected in the shop tests during fabrication. For example, the 200 mm reflector mentioned above is carefully held in a 9-point mirror support, and still shows some slight evidence that the mirror sags in its cell.

You will grow to rely on the star test as a check on alignment. A quick turn on the focuser is all that's needed to verify that misalignment is not disturbing your images. You'll come to depend on the appearance of outside-focus images to see what is happening in the upper atmosphere. When good seeing comes and goes, you can shift that evening's observing schedule to take advantage of superior tranquility.

## 1.2   Testing the Surfaces

You may rightly suspect that telescopes are not easy to make. The objective, or main optical element, of an astronomical telescope contains the most accurate macroscopic solid surfaces yet shaped by humans. Typical

---

[1]At this point, terminology should be defined to avoid subsequent confusion. In all further discussion, an image is said to be "out of focus" if it is defocused in *either* direction. "Inside focus" means that the eyepiece's focal plane is placed between the main optical element and focus; "outside focus" indicates that the eyepiece is withdrawn beyond focus. "In focus" and "focused" are used as synonyms, meaning that a pointlike object is focused to its minimum size.

tolerances are a thousand times smaller than the usual accuracies of a metal-cutting lathe.

As a means of comparison, let us imagine the surface of a common 200-mm (8-inch) telescope mirror expanded to 1 mile (1.6 km). If this mirror had the usual thickness ratio of small mirrors, it would be 880 feet thick (268 m). In common metal-shop practice, it is normal to machine such an 8-inch surface to a thousandth of an inch, or to a scaled accuracy of 8 inches. A wavelength of light expands from 0.000022 inches to 0.17 inches (4.4 mm) at this scale. The maximum optical error tolerable on such a surface would be only 0.55 mm, or about $2/100$ inches. Premium optics would be made to an accuracy of less than 0.01 inches (0.25 mm)—a playing-card thickness error on a disk a mile across and 300 yards high.

Clearly, testing such surface accuracy is not trivial. Common calipers, a measuring device of machinists, have a maximum accuracy of only about 10 micrometers ($\mu$m), or about 20 wavelengths of green light. Even if sufficiently accurate calipers were possible, one would have the additional problem of repeatedly placing them on the curved surface. The spread of measurements would greatly exceed the inherent accuracy of the measuring tool.

Obviously, some device or technique which can sense micro-deformations on the surface is needed. Light itself is the most appropriate tool. Less certain is the precise manner to use light to bring out these defects without demanding the same stringent measurements as gauging the surface profile by physical contact.

For example, it is not difficult to come up with completely useless ways to measure surfaces. One could place a point source of light (say, a pinhole) to one side of a mirror (see Fig. 1-1) and reflect it to a spot on a screen. By moving the mask around over the objective, we could see how the spot was forced to shift. In principle, this method would contain all the error information, but it is not the easiest way of proceeding. The spot is fuzzy, the system is difficult to align and focus, and the measurements are difficult to reduce because they are taken far from the optical axis. The position of the spot is dominated by the overall curvature of the surfaces and the motions of the mask, rather than the interesting deviations from the curvature. The way to perform an accurate and simply interpreted test eliminates first-order difficulties such as the innate curvature of the surface. It is best done along the optical axis either near the focus or the center of curvature of the lens or mirror.

Accurate tests are possible when the strengths of the testing geometry are exploited. The useless test in Fig. 1-1 becomes the very accurate caustic test when the image spot is moved near the center of curvature and the

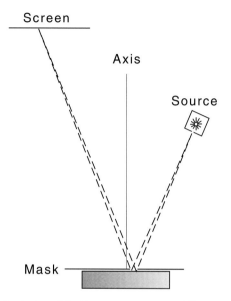

**Fig. 1-1.** *A poorly-designed testing arrangement. Alignment, focusing, and data reduction would be a nightmare even though the test contains all of the information required to infer the surface shape of the mirror.*

sensor is fitted with a knife edge or wire.

### 1.2.1   Sources of Errors

Accuracy of surface shape is a function of the stiffness of the material and the definition of just what surface accuracy means. For example, most machinist's gauge blocks and flat surface plates, the absolute standards by which they check their measuring tools, are rectangular chunks of steel. Steel is a fairly inflexible material, and machinists think of steel as capable of holding its shape. These blocks are more than accurate enough for the kind of precision demanded in machining as long as the temperature of the room does not vary too much. For optical use, however, the scale of precision is much smaller.

Microscopically, a block of steel expands under heating. Its linear dimensions depend on the ambient temperature. This change wouldn't ordinarily affect optical performance—after all, a sphere is still a sphere even if it has a slightly different radius. But as temperature varies, portions of the metal change faster and internal stresses build up. The surface slightly buckles as the temperature of the piece non-uniformly follows rapidly changing outside temperature.

Likewise, glass deforms under heating. Although it swells less than metal, the thermal conductivity of glass is lower and it has a problem getting rid of heat. Mirrors are typically coated on one side with metal, which complicates the way they radiate energy. The temperature of glass is a complex function of thermal radiation, convective air cooling, and conduction through the relatively few points at which the optical disk is supported.

Glass not only changes shape under heating, it deforms under pressure. A helpful way of viewing glass disks at the wavelength scale is to think of them as sheets of rubber. If you push on the top, the surface goes down. If you incorrectly support the bottom, the whole disk sags and the upper surface will deform. Thin pieces are harder to hold flat than thick pieces, large pieces more difficult than small ones. The cells that hold optics must not pinch or warp them.

No process is as stressful to optics as fabrication. Simple grinding even has a few pitfalls. Say that a mirror disk has a slight amount of cylindrical curvature on its rear side—it rocks on the backing instead of sitting flat. Under the pressure of grinding, it will deform away from its "backbone" and suffer astigmatic curvature when the pressure is relieved.

The fabrication stage at which most errors originate, however, is polishing. It takes place on polishing pitch, a material that no one fully understands. Some experienced opticians have learned the limits and general behavior of pitch, but even after years of experience, they are often surprised by its unstable nature.

Pitch is a highly viscous fluid used in a thin layer (3 to 6 mm) covering a disk used as a tool. This lapping surface (or "lap") is usually crosshatched with grooves that allow the fluid to spread and conform more readily to the polished surface. Pitch will behave more-or-less as a solid at fast speeds and as a liquid at slow speeds. For example, if you hit it with a hammer, it shatters. Lay a stick of pure pitch across the lip of a bowl, however, and eventually you'll find it has run to the bottom.

During polishing, powdered abrasive grains sink into the pitch surface where they are held as microscopic scrapers. Certain polishing agents are more effective than others, and cause more heat to be generated in the lap. The resistance to deformation in pitch varies strongly with temperature. Its characteristics on the outer portion of the disk will vary markedly from those of the inside because wet pitch on the periphery is exposed to the air and cools more rapidly by evaporation. If polishing is stretched too long, the pitch tool dries out, becomes overheated, and loses its shape. Bad polishing habits will result in excessive wear at the edge of the optical disk, giving it a run-down appearance under sensitive testing. Not varying the stroke when using a machine may cut shallow circular channels in the optics. In the case of fast aspherical optics, more polishing must be applied on the center of the disk. Clearly, many opportunities exist for errors to find their way to the optical surface.

### 1.2.2   Measures of Optical Quality

One way of gauging optical quality is to measure the peak-to-valley wavefront error. A wavefront is a line traced along the crest or trough of a wave. In regions far from focus, a wavefront is perpendicular to the direction of wave motion. Using a convenient example, a wavefront is the crest of a surfer's wave, parallel to the beach. The wave is moving toward the beach, at right angles to the crest.

A perfect converging wavefront is part of a sphere with its center at the focus. The light from a point source converges to the minimum spot size, called the "diffraction disk." After passing through an optical system with errors, a wavefront departs from the spherical shape, and the image spot will be larger and less intense.

Imagine two spheres with a common center at focus, somewhat like the layers of an onion. The outer layer touches the point that lags furthest behind the real wavefront and the inner one touches the point closest to the sphere's center. The different radii of these spheres defines the total wavefront error. (See Fig. 1-2.)

J.W. Strutt (Lord Rayleigh) stated an often quoted rule: If the total wavefront error—peak-to-valley—exceeds $1/4$ wavelength of yellow-green light (550 nm), then the optics begin to noticeably degrade. The reason that the image begins to fall apart is simple—a significant portion of the converging wavefront now has a phase mildly "disagreeing" with the majority. Rayleigh's rule is not a hard limit. Some people don't easily perceive diminished quality until total wavefront error exceeds $1/3$ wavelength. Others are more discriminating, detecting degradation at $1/8$ wavelength and below. Much of the sensitivity to optical faults depends on the type of observing, the type of error, and the sophistication of the observer (Ceravolo *et al.* 1992; Texereau 1984).

Below are some variations of the ways that different optical shops state the same $1/4$-wavelength quality:

- "$1/8$-*wavelength surface.*"   Say the primary mirror has a $1/8$-wavelength bump on it. The incident wavefront reflects from the peak of the bump while the adjacent portion of the wavefront is forced to travel to the base of the error. This section of the wavefront moves $1/8$ wavelength going in and $1/8$ wavelength coming out, leaving it $1/4$ wavelength behind the leading edge of the wave.

- "$\pm 1/16$-*wave surface.*"   If the same $1/8$-wavelength hill is not measured base-to-crest but measured from its average position, the error

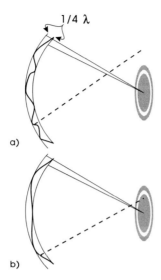

**Fig. 1-2.** *The difference between adequate and very good optics. Both of these wavefronts are contained within two shells ¼ wavelength apart, but the rougher one in a) scatters some light beyond the radius of the minimum-size diffraction spot. (Not to scale.)*

is spuriously divided by two yet again.

- *"¼₂₇-wave RMS on the surface."* This widely-used measure in the optics industry is known as *Maréchal's criterion* (Born and Wolf 1980, p. 469). A ¼ wavelength of spherical aberration (a large-scale departure from a sphere) approximately translates to a ¼₁₄-wavelength RMS Maréchal criterion (Maréchal 1947). Measuring it on the surface cuts it in half again.

- *"¼₃₁-wave RMS He-Ne laser light surface accuracy."* The red light of a helium-neon laser has a longer wavelength and the same error appears smaller. The easily calculated transition to visual wavelength has not been made.

Nearly every telescope user has a hazy memory of reading about the ¼-wavelength Rayleigh tolerance. The accuracies above apparently exceed the ¼-wavelength limit with room to spare, but they are different descriptions of the same ¼-wavelength tolerance.

These differing claims of surface accuracy are not inherently dishonest, as long as they are given in sufficient detail that one can pick apart their meanings. In fact, the $1/14$-wavelength RMS Maréchal tolerance is superior to the Rayleigh limit because it quantifies the fraction of the wavefront that is bent away from a perfect sphere. But these accuracies are seldom written with decoding instructions, and consumers are left to wonder what the claims mean, even if they know the distinctions.

Advertising claims by commercial firms have therefore been in a confusing state for some time. In recent years, a certain fraction of consumer telescope makers have sensibly avoided the whole question of assigning numbers to their optics. They merely state that their optics are diffraction-limited and let it go at that. Such a designation is better than the artificially inflated claims above. "Diffraction-limited" conventionally means that the $1/14$-wavelength RMS Maréchal limit has been met (Schroeder 1987).

Another factor often neglected in statements of optical quality is the slope of the error. If sharp channels, turned edges, or roughness appears on the optics, the overall wavefront error can often be contained within the expansive Rayleigh tolerance. The anomalous slope does not persist over the whole aperture. The sharply sloped fault still diverts light out of the central spot to pollute the rest of the image, but the optics are still "officially" perfect.

A. Danjon and A. Couder addressed this topic in their book *Lunettes et Télescopes* (Danjon and Couder 1935, pp. 518–522). They noticed that some instruments could slip by Rayleigh's limit yet possess enough surface roughness to scatter a hazy glow through lunar and planetary images. They stated that optics could not be judged as "good" until two conditions were simultaneously met:

1. Over the greatest part of the aperture, the wavefront has a mild slope and does not divert light rays outside the diffraction disk.

2. The Rayleigh $1/4$-wavelength tolerance is everywhere obeyed, and over most of the aperture, deviations should be appreciably less.

Condition #2 is just the Rayleigh limit, with a verbal warning having the same goal as limiting the RMS deviation. After stating these two conditions, Danjon and Couder point out that condition #1 on the slope of the mirror is typically more difficult to meet than the $1/4$-wavelength condition. Even though both wavefronts in Fig. 1-2 are within the Rayleigh tolerance, the wavefront in Fig. 1-2b would do the best imaging because it is more gently sloped.

Incidentally, for aberrations that smoothly change over the whole aperture (such as the error sketched in Fig. 1-2b), the maximum wavefront departure that leads to condition #1 is closer to $1/7$ wavelength. Thus, optics that truly satisfy both conditions are not only good, but excellent.

Another number, commonly used as a criterion of optical quality, is the *Strehl ratio* of the aperture (Born and Wolf 1980, p. 462; Mahajan 1982). The Strehl ratio is defined as the intensity of the image spot at its central brightest point divided by the same image intensity without aberration. The $1/4$-wavelength Rayleigh tolerance on spherical aberration causes a drop of the Strehl ratio to the value 0.8. The Strehl ratio is 1.00 with perfect optics. Maréchal's criterion on the RMS aberration came from noticing that it leads to the same decrease in the Strehl ratio.

The most complete, though expansive, way of indicating optical quality is to present the detailed *modulation transfer function* (or MTF), which is the ability of an optical system to preserve the contrast of bar patterns of various spacings. It will be the method used in this book. No optical difficulty can escape the MTF. Dusty optics, pits on the optical surface, spider diffraction, telescope vibration, microripple, aberrations, and obstructions of any sort reveal themselves in a lowered transfer function. MTF charts have the advantage of giving the spacing of detail that the optical problem attacks.

Other equally valid measures of optical quality could easily be defined. They will be discussed in more detail in Chapter 10.

## 1.3 The Star Test—A Brief Overview

Observers rightly regard an out-of-focus instrument as nothing more than a problem to be cured. A telescope is either in focus or is almost useless—at least for the job it was meant to perform. When used properly, a telescope must be focused as accurately as possible.

Implicit in the customary use of a telescope is the *fixed objective* assumption, which regards the image produced by the objective as the whole purpose of the telescope. The eyepiece is relegated to the secondary status of a mere accessory, a magnifier. It slides along the optical axis and has only one correct setting.

The star test uses the telescope in a new way. We must assume the eyepiece has a fixed position. From this viewpoint the eyepiece's field plane is seen as the whole purpose of the exercise. The eyepiece is regarded as *always* being in correct focus and examines whatever occupies its field plane. The field plane is usually constricted by a sharp-edged mask called a *field stop*. If you invert an eyepiece and look in the bottom, this stop is usually visible as a ring inside the base. The field stop is the crisp edge you see in an eyepiece. This edge has nothing to do—as it first seems—with the boundary of the objective.

Figure 1-3 shows an idealized eyepiece. We regard the eyepiece as fixed and the objective as mobile.

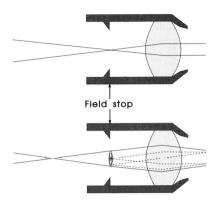

**Fig. 1-3.** *The use of the eyepiece for the star test. The top arrangement shows the usual proper setting of an eyepiece. The eyepiece on the bottom shows the star test's inspection of the defocused disk as an equally valid setting.*

If, as in the top of Fig. 1-3, the objective is located at precisely the right distance to put an image of a star on the eyepiece's field plane, the instrument is said to be *in focus*. The light coming from a point source leaves the rear of the eyepiece in a parallel bundle. Fig. 1-3, bottom, shows an *out-of-focus* instrument. Here the path of the rays depicted by solid lines exits the tube in a converging bundle that is not focused properly on the retina unless the eye's powers of accommodation are very large.

The "looking path" of two points on the out-of-focus disk is denoted by dotted lines. One imagines that the bundle of light is sliced neatly at the focal plane of the eyepiece and that the eyepiece images this slice perfectly. If the eyepiece is moved to and fro across the position of focus, each slice can be examined in turn, and the memory of all such slices forms a collective record of the behavior of light near the focus. We are allowed to use this viewpoint because the in-focus location of the eyepiece is no more special than an out-of-focus location.

### 1.3.1  Diffraction Rings

Almost everywhere, the complicated situation of a converging wavefront can be approximated by replacing the wavefront with little "arrows" moving perpendicular to it. These arrows are called *light rays* and the intensity of such a beam can be calculated as the cross-sectional area of the ray bundle. However, elementary geometry used on a converging light cone leads to an important breakdown in the ray approximation. If a certain amount of power is incident on an area of aperture, the intensity can be calculated as this power divided by the area.[2] Halfway to focus, the area of the cone has shrunk to $1/4$ of its value right against the aperture, but it still contains the same power—so the intensity has increased 4 times. Move halfway again, and intensity further increases 4 times to a factor of 16 greater than it was at the aperture. You can double it again and again until you get to focus. What happens there?

The ray description has the area of the cone go to zero as the light approaches focus. This area must be multiplied by the intensity to make the power the same as it was all along the path. Because the speed of light through air is uniform, the energy content of the beam neither increases nor decreases. The ray approximation says that if the optics are perfect, the intensity of an image point is infinite. Needless to say, infinite intensity is impossible.

During the two hundred years between the invention of the telescope and the final acceptance of the wave theory of light, people actually believed there was no limit on optical quality. If optics were made of exquisite quality, the central spot would shrink in size—or so opticians thought. They must have agonized when their optical masterpieces, on which they had worked so diligently, still showed that disk surrounded by a system of rings.

We now know that there is a fundamental limit to imaging. Diffraction softens the image in the region of focus. For a given telescope focal length, the central spot (called the *Airy disk*) decreases linearly in diameter for larger apertures. The formula for the radius of the Airy disk with aperture diameter $D$ and focal length $f$ is

$$r_{\text{Airy}} = \frac{1.22\lambda f}{D} \quad (\lambda \text{ is the wavelength}). \tag{1.1}$$

Thus, the diameter of the diffraction disk is $11\mu m$ (0.0004 inches) for a 150-mm (6-inch) f/8 and $5.5\mu m$ for a 300-mm (12-inch) f/4. Since 4 times the light was intercepted by the larger telescope and it was squeezed inside $1/4$ the area, the larger telescope has a central image intensity 16 times as bright. A focused diffraction image appears on the left side of Fig. 1-4—the whole square is $(20\lambda f)/D$ across.

To those accustomed to purely symbolic equations, the factor 1.22 in the expression for the Airy disk seems messy and inexact, but it is unavoidable. Its source is the circularity of the aperture. If we were to make a square objective of distance $x$ on a side, the brightest portion of the diffraction spot would be a little square with side dimension $(2\lambda f)/x$. Similarly, apertures

---

[2]Radiometrically, this quantity is not the "intensity" at all, but should be called the "radiant flux density." However, this term is conventional among physicists.

**focused**                                        **out-of-focus**

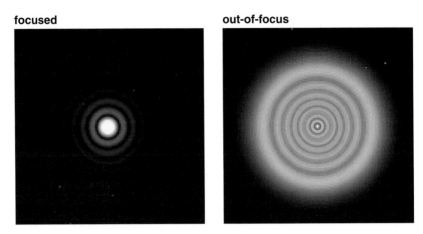

**Fig. 1-4.** *The theoretical diffraction image of a perfect telescope, both for the in-focus and one defocused case. The direction of eyepiece travel does not matter; the out-of-focus pattern looks the same on either side. The frame at the left is magnified 4 times that of the right.*

with aberrations and obstructions have their own unique diffraction spot sizes. The Airy disk is nothing special, save that it is the perfect diffraction disk of the circular window that so many real optical devices resemble.

Diffraction is an angular effect. The angular blurring of the image is not lessened by increasing the focal length of the telescope, or equivalently, the magnification. If one doubles the focal length, the Airy disk also doubles in size. Until this independence of fundamental image blurring on focal length was appreciated, telescopes were commonly specified by their focal length instead of their apertures. Nowadays, such terminology appears quaint.

The central spot is not the whole story. Thin, ghostly rings encircle the bright spot. With large instruments under ideal conditions, they are observable out to 3 or 4 rings, but stars in small telescopes show only one ring readily.

The out-of-focus pattern of Fig. 1-4 is channeled by some circular furrows. These are diffraction rings, too, although their location and magnitude are not a simple matter to calculate. The first conjecture would be that the dark lines were the previously hidden structure of the diffraction image that is now exposed because the expanding disk filled it with light. However, this reasonable guess is wrong. The images don't behave that way at all.

As the focuser is racked in or out, the grooves continue to appear at the center and move outward, like ripples spreading from a pebble dropped in a puddle. That central point successively dims to blackness and then lightens to become the brightest part of the disk. It does so each time it creates

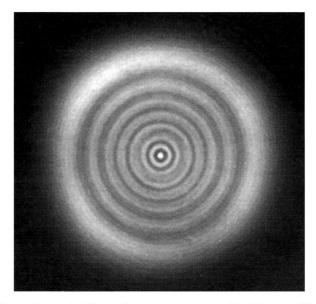

**Fig. 1-5.** *Photo of actual defocused situation calculated in Fig. 1-4. The picture was taken with a strongly stopped-down refractor.*

a new ring. The one seemingly unchanging feature of the expanding spot is the broad outer ring. It seems narrower as the focuser is turned, but it never goes away.

Notice another feature. The expanded disk is channeled, but its average brightness is more-or-less constant. The outer ring is somewhat brighter to average out that dark ring just inside of it. Still, except for the slightly brighter outer ring, the disk is remarkably flat. This principle is even more true for white-light diffraction images. Each contributing color exhibits a different number of rings in its expanded disk. The minima of one color sit on top of maxima of another color, and the net effect is largely to wash out any variation of the interior of the disk. Far out of focus, unobstructed telescopes display a flat disk with a clearly defined outer ring separated from the interior by a dark ring. Only a hint of grooved structuring exists inside.

Finally, one last characteristic is fundamental to the star test. The inside-focus disk is approximately identical to the outside-focus disk. No circularly symmetric aberration can appear the same on both sides of focus. If the patterns are similar, and if they are circular, the optics are nearly perfect.

Figure 1-5 shows an actual photograph of the defocused situation calculated in Fig. 1-4. The contrast of the pattern has been increased by using

one very pure red light from a helium-neon laser reflected in a small reflective sphere. A hole punched in metal and placed over a small refractor
created the aperture. The theoretical pattern reproduces the real behavior,
even showing the terracing of the outer parts of the disk.

## 1.4    The Reason for Star Testing

The appearance of a defocused image seen in Fig. 1-5 is rare. Aberrations or other optical difficulties conspire to destroy this perfection. By
moving the eyepiece inside and outside focus, you can detect and possibly identify the problems that disturb your telescope. Comparing images
seen at the same distances inside and outside focus is particularly powerful.
The differences between these patterns will betray one of the most common
optical errors, spherical aberration.

You will seldom see any one aberration unadorned by a mixture of other
optical effects. The diffraction pattern is hard to diagnose using the star
test without external information. Diagnosis is not the point, however.
You may decide after inspection that one of the difficulties described here
is dominating your system. You should regard identification of the problem
only as an interesting fact if the mistake is ground into the glass or use it
as a guide for telescope or site modification if the errors are correctable.

As you read this book, you will learn the appearance of the best image
possible, both in and out of focus. That appearance does not vary. It may
be modified by obstructions, but the effects of a secondary are predictable.

A good stellar image has a short list of identifying characteristics:

1.  The in-focus stellar image is circularly symmetric; it has a dim ring
    hugging the outer perimeter of the diffraction disk, and rings beyond
    that are vanishingly dark. (Bad optics have rings too, but they are
    bright and too many of them can be counted. They are often asym-
    metric.)

2.  The out-of-focus image is circularly symmetric; it is identical for all
    equal distances on either side of focus. (The images of aberrated
    apertures can be one or the other, but they are not both identical
    and round.)

3.  The out-of-focus image has a fairly flat distribution of intensity along
    the radial direction, except for a slightly brighter outer ring. It is
    divided by diffraction grooves, but they are of very low contrast. They
    are mostly washed out in white light (except for the inside of the outer
    ring and the outside of the secondary shadow, if any).

4.  If a central obstruction is used, its shadow reappears during defocus
    at equal distances on either side of focus.

You will also learn a systematic way of identifying optical errors and see image intensity patterns calculated for known amounts of aberration. Using this information, you may be able to estimate the size of your own telescope's aberrations and act on them if they are severe.

It is also useful to change viewpoints. Many useful concepts and procedures in modern physical optics can be used by observers to more fully understand their instruments. The first and greatest of these concepts is to view the telescope as a generalized filter. We can then use ideas developed for the electronics industry, with a few modifications changing the terminology to optics. The second concept is the idea that light is a wave. Diffraction causes fundamental limits to image quality. Using the viewpoints of wave optics and filtering theory,[3] we are forced to rely less on the questionable store of folk wisdom, mythology, and belief that has accumulated around telescope use.

---

[3]This way of looking at the process of imaging is called Fourier optics.

# Chapter 2

# An Abbreviated Star-Test Manual

## 2.1   Some Necessary Preliminaries

You will need a high magnification eyepiece to conduct the star test successfully. The exact power varies from telescope to telescope and depends on what is available, but it is about 10 per centimeter of aperture. For a 20 cm f/10 Schmidt-Cassegrain telescope, magnification should equal $20 \times 10 = 200$. Since the focal length of such an instrument is 2 meters, the eyepiece focal length should be around 10 mm. Shorter richest-field telescopes (RFTs) are not evaluated to the same degree of precision as planetary telescopes, so you can perhaps yield a bit on the eyepiece power. The same usually applies to huge instruments. In fact, you may be forced to compromise, because appropriate eyepieces for such telescopes are not commonly available.

You should set up your telescope so that it doesn't overlook nearby roadways or house roofs, because those structures hold the day's heat and slowly release it at night. Parts of the star test can be done peering through a small amount of turbulence, but it is best to avoid additional sources of aberration when possible. You should also allow your telescope enough time between setup and star test so that it can approach ambient temperature. The instrument need not be transported to a dark-sky site since the test target is a fairly bright star.

The test is immeasurably aided by a well-aligned instrument. If possible, collimate your telescope before testing it. One of the sections below teaches you how to recognize severe misalignment, but further testing will temporarily be halted if the telescope is not at least coarsely aligned (see Chapter 6).

It is unnecessary to wait for full darkness, but you must be able to find a star. The best star for 4–6 inch telescopes is about second magnitude, but larger instruments require correspondingly dimmer stars. Tiny refractors may demand a first magnitude star. Daytime tests can also be performed using the glitter of the Sun reflected in a smoothly spherical Christmas-tree ornament. Place it 60–300 meters away[1] with the intervening path over grass. Try to hang the bulb so that it is viewed against a smooth background.

If you wear eyeglasses, leave them on. This warning should only apply to those suffering from astigmatism, but refocusing a strong correction normally handled by glasses may force the eyepiece to add anomalous aberration. It's easy enough to prevent this extra source of error. Besides, you only need to inspect the center of the field of view.

The most effective form of the star test requires that you know how far you have defocused the image. This detail will be explained in Chapter 5, but the rest of the chapter will introduce you to most forms of optical problems.

Finally, before you begin to evaluate your instrument, decide what you realistically expect it to do. Does it have a low focal ratio for that type of instrument? A Newtonian telescope of f/5 or below is making a compromise of optical quality with physical size. It should not be judged to the same standards as a Newtonian mirror with focal ratio of f/8. Similarly, a richest-field achromatic refractor with focal ratio of f/5 should not be held to the same harsh tolerances as an obvious lunar-planetary refractor.

## 2.2   Optical Problems in Turn

The star test can be used with any telescope if you keep in mind only one of the principles discussed in the last chapter: *If the optics are perfect, the defocused images are fairly uniformly-illuminated disks. They appear the same at similar distances inside and outside of focus.*

The first procedure to try is called the "snap" test. Often, this crude evaluation is enough to judge a telescope as bad. Using high magnification, wiggle the focuser back and forth through best focus. Good telescopes will snap into crisp focus quickly. Bad telescopes will offer a range of equally acceptable focus positions, none very good. You will be uncertain about precisely where to stop your hand (Suiter 1990).

Don't condemn the instrument too quickly on the basis of poor performance on the snap test, however. This quick method has several practical difficulties. Often, the instrument is not rigidly mounted, and it's difficult to tell the condition of the image while your hand is shaking the telescope.

---

[1] See Chapter 5 for accurate limits of bulb size and placement. The larger distance is for large, fast instruments.

In addition, some observers have eyes that are capable of large focus accommodations. Eye focusing is not always under conscious control. As the focus is approached, the eye locks in and the internal focusing mechanism subverts the test.

The perfect circular aperture has only one appearance for the diffraction disk at each value of defocus. All modifications to this pattern represent various levels of optical problems. Such difficulties exist in three general categories:

1. Baseline characteristics of the optical system, such as

    (a) secondary mirror or diagonal obstruction of the optical path,

    (b) spider vanes in front of the mirror or mirror-clip blockages,

    (c) transmission variations (vignetting and imperfect coatings),

    (d) color variation in the refraction of the lenses.

2. Transient or repairable problems, such as

    (a) misalignment or abnormal tilts of the optical elements,

    (b) atmospheric turbulence effects,

    (c) artifacts caused by temperature differences near or within the telescope,

    (d) unusual strains in the optical elements (such as pinching or sagging of thin mirrors),

    (e) dust or dirt on the mirror or lenses.

3. Errors on the glass, such as

    (a) spherical aberration (a failure of the wavefront to conform to a sphere),

    (b) rough optical surfaces (causing light to be scattered from the central spot),

    (c) zones (light circular hills or trenches in the mirror, including turned-down edges of the glass disks),

    (d) chromatic aberration (uncorrected color errors),

    (e) astigmatism (non-uniform stretching of the image along an axis).

Some of these errors are discussed briefly below, and some are saved for the main body of the book. What you must keep in mind is that there is a proper ordering for consideration of optical errors. You have to learn to recognize the characteristic out-of-focus star patterns that are a consequence of your choice of optical system (category "1" above). For example, nothing will get rid of the obstruction in simple reflectors, so you must expect its shadow in the defocused star image.

Next, you must learn strategies that lead to minimum interference from the temporary or curable difficulties of category "2." You cannot make a valid check for slight astigmatism if your instrument is hopelessly out of alignment. If you take a warm telescope from the house to the cold outdoors, the images will dance and swirl. Your tube frequently ducts the heat off the mirror, causing the stretching characteristic of tube currents. Often, your optics are cruelly bound into their cells, and the warping caused by such stresses masks true optical errors ground into the glass. Finally, you must determine if the atmospheric seeing is good enough to do a valid test. While the star test is less sensitive to turbulence than the double-star resolution evaluation, it is best done under quiet skies.

Once you have determined that category "2" errors are sufficiently small, you can go on to look for errors in the shape of the glass. These errors are the most debilitating because nothing can be done about them, save refiguring the optics. Even here, the order is important. You should look for spherical aberration first because it is the most common error.

Finally, you should not defocus the image too far. If you do, you will find no errors. If you are testing a fast f/4 Newtonian, you will probably see most of these errors best with eyepiece motion less than $1/30$ inch (0.85 mm). If you are testing a slow f/10 Schmidt-Cassegrain, the same sequence of images is visible with eyepiece motions of $1/5$ inch (about 5 mm). These values are taken from Table 5-1.

### 2.2.1   Secondary Mirror Obstruction

The inside-focus pattern is the same as the outside-focus pattern even for obstructed instruments. Though the presence of a diagonal or secondary mirror degrades the optical quality a little, the appearance of the aberration-free image on either side of focus is the same for good optics. As an example, an otherwise-perfect aperture is shown in Fig. 2-1 as the obstruction is increased to 20% and 33%.

The most remarkable change from the unobstructed behavior is the coarseness of the pattern. We have traded the fine tracery of the unobstructed pattern for the unsubtle variations caused by the secondary. Only two wide bright rings are shown in the lit region outside the secondary's shadow in the 33% pattern. Fewer dips in intensity are seen across the disk.

The sole difference between these three rows is the size of the secondary. Why should a tiny obstruction—only $1/9$ of the surface area—have such a profound effect?

**unobstructed**

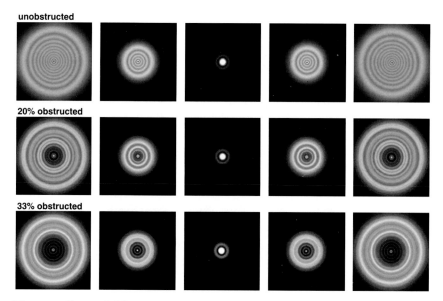

**20% obstructed**

**33% obstructed**

**Fig. 2-1. Central Obstruction.** *Images from three perfect telescopes are shown from inside focus (left) to outside focus (right). Typical behaviors of (top) refractors, (middle) long-focus Newtonians, (bottom) commercial Schmidt-Cassegrains.*

First of all, it doesn't really cause that big a difference. Those dips are extremely delicate and they are destroyed by nearly anything (as in mixing together colors in white light). Except for the minor brightenings and the shadow at the center, the disk is still fairly uniform, and it is still identical on opposite sides of focus.

For the purpose of diffraction calculations, we are allowed to pretend that the shadow is a miniature aperture, only out of phase with the larger opening (called Babinet's principle—Hecht 1987, p. 458). This tiny blockage has a much larger diffraction pattern, just as if the telescope were stopped down to the secondary's size. But remember, it is imbedded as a tiny correction to the larger pattern surrounding it. Thus, the small shadow's diffraction pattern is not visible as a distinct entity, but it causes enough coarse changes to destroy the lace-like variations seen in the out-of-focus disk of the unobstructed aperture (see Fig. 1-4 or 1-5).

The other feature of note in Fig. 2-1 is the little bright spot at the center of the out-of-focus shadows. Interestingly enough, the successful observation of such spots is part of the experimental confirmation of the wave theory of light. When Fresnel first presented his paper on the wave theory to the French Academy in 1818, one of the listeners was S.D. Poisson, a vehement opponent of the light-as-waves description (he was a proponent of the light-as-particles ray theory). He used Fresnel's new theory of diffraction to show that a bright spot should appear at some locations in the shadow of a circular obstacle. Poisson thought that such a ridiculous conclusion would settle the nonsense about light waves once and for all. Imagine his chagrin when this spot was found soon after. In fact, it had been discovered long before, and the report had escaped notice by optical theorists. This little bright patch is still called *Poisson's spot.*

The spot appearing here is a composite of the central spot expected from the full aperture and the inner negative aperture, but a Poisson spot is observable without even using an outer aperture just by carefully arranging a circular shadow in a beam of light diverging from a pinhole.

**focused OB=30%**                    **out-of-focus OB=30%**

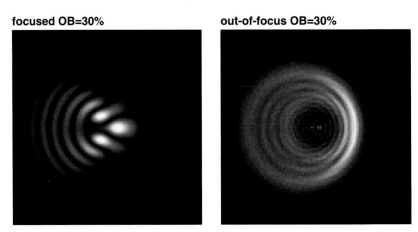

**Fig. 2-2. Misalignment.** *A severely misaligned reflector with a secondary obstruction of 30%. On the left is a focused image and on the right is the same image defocused. The magnification of the focused image is 6 times that of the defocused one.*

### 2.2.2   Misalignment

Misalignment can be exposed by star testing. In fact, before testing can be continued much further, the optics must be properly collimated. This procedure is described in more detail later, but Fig. 2-2 depicts a typical misaligned Newtonian telescope. The region of good imaging may be outside a high-magnification eyepiece's field stop in a misaligned telescope. Misalignment aberrations can be straightforwardly corrected, so you should not greet their appearance with a feeling of dread. Assuming nothing is wrong with the glass, such aberrations will vanish in the center of the field with proper alignment.

The focused image has a small amount of astigmatism but mostly shows the effects of coma. The word *coma* comes from Latin, meaning "hair" and is also the root word of the familiar astronomical term *comet.* Coma, when severe, stretches the image out into two wing structures.

### 2.2.3   Atmospheric Motion and Turbulence

Another troubling image aberration is caused by wavefront passage through the many atmospheric turbulence cells occupying the long cylinder of air in front of the instrument. This tube of air is always part of an earth-bound optical system. Refraction by air is very small, but it does exist. It changes with temperature and pressure.

Hot air is lighter than cold air, and the ability of air to refract light increases with density. Density differences also result in a fundamental instability of the atmosphere. Sunlight chiefly heats the ground, leaving little energy in any particular volume of air in its passage through the atmosphere. The hot ground warms the air above it, and the warmer air becomes less dense. The cool air above it falls, and the warm air rises to occupy the same volume as the cool air, making a temporary vortex. At some point, the decrease in pressure cools the rising warm air, and the falling cool air warms for the opposite reason. The two volumes of air have just changed places. The ground is now slightly cooler, and both volumes of air are slightly warmer. Perhaps the upper volume of air will become unstable with respect to a still higher volume of air.

Inefficiencies of the process make the difference in temperatures of the two layers less profound, and without further heating of the ground, the process will wind down like an old clock. Such motion is an invisible cyclical heat engine, transporting energy from the hot ground to the cool upper atmosphere. The energy of sunlight percolates upward by convection through a cauldron of air.

During the daytime, this heating continues. Convection cells persist and sometimes grow. Leavened by the efficient heat transport properties of water and taking advantage of the shade provided by clouds, convection structures can expand to colossal dimensions—beyond little wisps and dust devils, beyond even thermal currents exploited by soaring birds. They can grow to summer afternoon thunderstorms. At the margins of the major convective structures are fine-scale cells, and at the edges of those little cells, even finer scale cells, until the swirls disappear into seething turbulence at microscopic scales.

It is no surprise that solar observation is usually best conducted in the morning, before the ground has heated much. A daytime test using the image of the Sun in a reflective sphere is best done in the very early morning. Also, turbulence is strong anywhere near clouds, since clouds are a flag that indicates one of these gigantic heat engines is operating.

It is nighttime that mostly concerns us, however. Without sunlight to drive the process, convection must rely on residual ground warmth or currents in the atmosphere caused masses of air at different temperatures. At some time during a clear night, the ground cools by heat radiation to have a lower temperature than the air above it. Because cool air is denser than warm air, this result is more stable. The convective cells on clear nights are less spectacular. Through near-pinholes, such as the human eye, this effect is seen as a slight spreading or bunching of light—stellar "twinkling." Through larger apertures, such as a telescope, the effect seldom appears as changes in brightness. In small telescopes, the image jumps around; in larger instruments the image is fixed but blurred.

In the outside-focus star test image, such cells look like nothing so much as the dappling of sunlight on the bottom of a swimming pool. Driven by high altitude winds, they wash across the aperture.

**focused**        **out-of-focus**        **out-of-focus (later)**

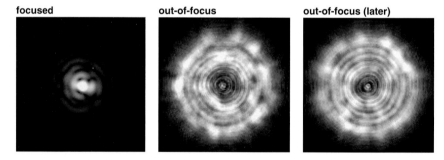

**Fig. 2-3. Air Turbulence.** *A frozen moment of a turbulent image is shown in a focused pattern (left) and a defocused pattern (center). A delay of only a moment can show the example pattern at right. The focused image is magnified 5 times that of the defocused images.*

Figure 2-3 shows a snapshot calculation of such a roughened diffraction disk. Look particularly at the focused image. The diffraction pattern varies so rapidly that such appearances aren't often directly observable. At least you can follow the changes in the outside-focus pattern as the cells sweep rapidly across the front of the telescope. The most visible change in the focused pattern is the angle at which splinters of light appear.

### 2.2.4   Tube Currents

Yet another atmospheric effect concerns the telescope user. Small telescopes are often carried from a warm house to the cold outdoors. These days, they are frequently transported to dark-sky sites in a warm automobile for some distance before reassembly. Even permanently mounted observatory instruments are seldom maintained at precisely the outside temperature at which they will be used. As a consequence, portions of the mounting—and most notably the mirror itself—must cool.

Glass has a high heat capacity and the accompanying low heat conductivity. In other words, glass optics have both a lot of heat to dump and the inclination to hold on to it a long time. Large, full-thickness mirrors take hours to cool.

Air convection is responsible for a large fraction of the energy transport. In the presence of gravity, the air warmed by higher temperature surfaces in the tube is displaced by falling cool air. In an open-tubed reflector that is tilted at an angle, the result is a tube current, as seen in Fig. 2-4. Other cooling effects are visible in windowed reflectors and even refractors, but they may not take precisely this form.

**inside focus**   **focused**   **outside focus**

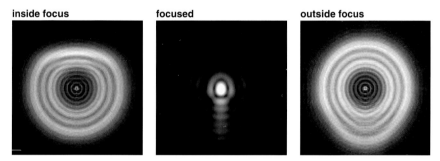

**Fig. 2-4. Tube Current.** *A common tube current appearance is the squeezed or herniated lobe on one side of the disk, and a flattened look on the other. Magnification of the focused image has been increased 6 times.*

The heated air exits the telescope as it would a chimney. It generally hugs the upper side of the tube as it is ducted out. As light passes more quickly through the less-dense warm air, the wavefront there curls up like a page being turned. At certain angles, the in-focus image resembles the Moon setting over a quiet sea. After the telescope cools, these effects go away.

### 2.2.5   Pinched or Deformed Optics

Particularly common with overly-tight reflector cells or thin mirrors bending under their own weight is the aberration that has the appearance of Fig. 2-5. Details of the deformation will change the precise out-of-focus pattern. This deformation depends on which clip is tight, how many support points hold up the mirror, and whether the optics are supported on the edge or on the bottom. It will change with different telescope elevations.

In focus, the particular deformation modeled here results in a three-sided spike pattern.

### 2.2.6  Spherical Aberration

If abrasive is placed between two disks of glass and they are rubbed together with the orientation and stroke length completely random, what can be expected? At the end of thousands of such rubbing motions, part of two spheres must result—one convex and the other concave.

Thus, spheres (or more accurately, spherical bowls) are easy to make, at least compared with other three-dimensional surfaces. Unfortunately, spheres do not image properly. If a hemispherical reflector or a spherical lens is imagined, it is not difficult to see why.

Let's say light rays are incident on such surfaces as in Fig. 2-6. As the impact point deviates from a center-on-center direct hit, the focus wanders from a single point. Clearly, this aberration is an ever-present danger.

The mechanisms that evolved to correct this problem are fascinating because they point out the essential differences between refractive and reflective astronomical optics. They are almost two separate lines of development.

In the case of refractors, the spherical lens was retained and refined. In refractors, optical surfaces can be placed close together without getting in each other's way. More elaborate optical systems can be designed by invoking trade-offs between the curvature and separation of closely-spaced elements. The first optical designer to attack aberrations systematically was Joseph Fraunhofer. His masterpiece instrument, the great Dorpat achromatic refractor, was corrected not only for spherical and chromatic aberration, but off-axis coma besides. This instrument became the pattern for telescopes of the 1800s in much the same manner as Hadley's telescope had been the fundamental design of the 1700s. Fraunhofer accomplished this task with spherical surfaces (with a small amount of retouching) and clever design. Variations of Fraunhofer's airspaced 2-element doublet refractors are sold today and still give outstanding images.

Reflecting telescopes took another path. If you place a lens very near a mirror, light traverses it twice, which may or may not be useful. Rear-surface mirror telescopes have been designed (indeed, one was suggested by Newton himself in *Opticks*, p. 105), but they are usually specialty instruments that are difficult to construct. All-spherical reflectors are not impossible, but they had to wait for sophisticated mixed lens/mirror systems (such as the Maksutov telescope). Makers of reflectors turned to aspherical optics quite early.

**focused** **out-of-focus**

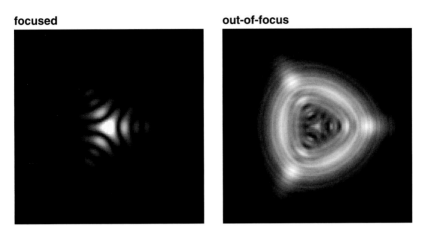

**Fig. 2-5. Deformed Optics.** *The three-lobed pattern that results from too-tight mirror clips or a thin mirror that is inadequately supported. Left: focused pattern. Right: one appearance of the slightly defocused disk. Focused pattern is expanded 2.5 times.*

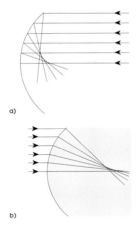

**Fig. 2-6.** *Spherical aberration in reflectors* (a) *and refractors* (b).

The aspherical surface for a one-mirror astronomical telescope is a parabola that is spun on its axis like a top. This three-dimensional surface is called a "paraboloid." Unfortunately, the paraboloidal surface does not happen randomly. The maker must take the more-or-less statistical process that forms a sphere and control it (with pressure, special strokes, or small tools) to deform the surface to a paraboloid. Two-mirror systems have been devised that demand everything from hyperboloids to oblate spheroids.

Aspherizing takes good bench testing and understanding of materials and methods. As might be suspected, some telescope makers are more conscientious with such operations than others. Pitch, which is used for polishing and shaping the surface, is one of the most cantankerous materials used in any process. Fabrication can go badly when pitch is used without respect.

In my experience of testing approximately 100 nominal paraboloids, about half of the commercial mirrors have been marginally undercorrected. They have a surface somewhere between a sphere and paraboloid, barely within tolerance or slightly outside of it. A quarter of the mirrors have been severely undercorrected, and about a quarter were figured within acceptable limits. Most of the undercorrected mirrors were of the short-focus variety, between f/4 and f/6. Nearly all of the f/6 to f/8 paraboloids were adequately figured. I have seen few commercial Newtonian mirrors that were overcorrected—although many amateur-made mirrors seem to be.

For experienced opticians, paraboloidal mirrors are not all that difficult to make. Because Newtonian telescope mirrors tend to be undercorrected, the makers must be spending as little time as possible on each mirror. This practice can perhaps be explained (if not justified) by the current low prices of consumer mirrors. The makers are attempting to figure mirrors to the near edge of the tolerance, minimizing time and costs. The inevitable statistical spread means that many such mirrors will be unacceptable.

Undercorrection is shown in Fig. 2-7. Inside focus, much of the light is bunched up into the outside ring. Beyond focus, it has been pushed to a fuzzy patch in the center or to the outside of the secondary shadow. This is the signature of undercorrection. Memorize these patterns. If you have an opportunity to test Newtonians, you will see undercorrection repeatedly, and it is common enough in other types of telescopes. Spherical aberration is perhaps the only unadulterated glass error that you will ever see. The rest are usually mixed together.

Some people may misread the overall tone of these comments as a condemnation of Newtonian reflectors. Nothing of the sort is intended. The two best telescopes I have ever seen—and that includes refractors—have been exquisite Newtonians. The crisp star images of a well-made and well-aligned paraboloid are a beautiful sight. It is a shame that more of them do not perform as well as they can.

### 2.2.7  Rough Surfaces

Another common aberration afflicting telescopes is surface roughness. It results from using rapid polishing materials and maintaining insuffic-

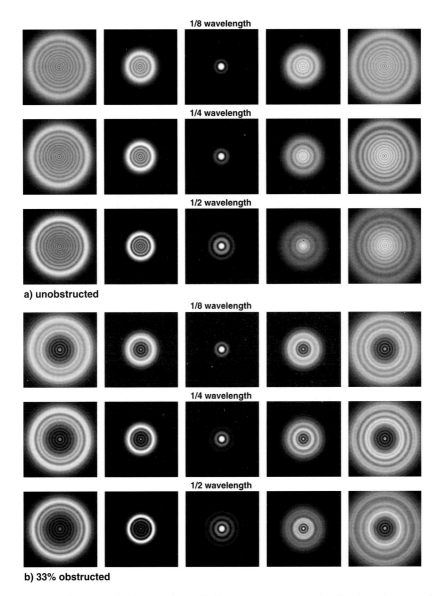

**Fig. 2-7. Spherical Aberration.** *Undercorrection appearing in* a) *unobstructed apertures, and* b) *33% obstructed apertures. Inside focus (toward left): much of the light is collected in a strong outer ring, leaving a dim center. Middle: The focused image steadily worsens as aberration increases. Outside focus (toward right): the outer side of the image fades away and the missing light is found near the center. (Focused-image magnification is 4 times that of the defocused frames.)*

ient contact between the pitch polishing lap and the optical surface being
worked. The polishing operation is a strange and delicate process. Transient conditions on the surface of the lap can modify the contact between
the tool and the optics. If the surface is polished by hand, one can feel the
tool grab and kick almost like a living thing. Manual workers know immediately that something is wrong, and they can rewet the lap with polishing
compound and press until contact is once again established.

As a simple matter of economics, optics aren't worked much by hand.
A \$300 telescope mirror probably requires between 2 and 4 hours of the
optician's time. Such work must be prosecuted rapidly with machines or
the cost of telescope mirrors would quickly escalate out of the reach of
consumers. When a lap begins to seize, the machine neither notices nor
cares. It has power enough to roll over the lap's squeaking complaints.
If the optician has not worked out a standing procedure to avoid such
difficulties, one possible consequence could be rough surfaces.

**focused**                  **out-of-focus**                  **smooth**

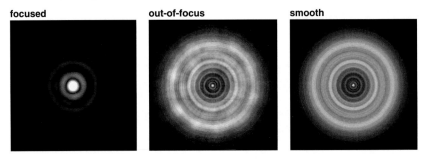

**Fig. 2-8. Roughness.** *A small amount of surface roughness. Left: the focused
image. Middle: defocused rough surface image. Right: a smooth defocused image
for comparison.*

Figure 2-8 is an example of the behavior of light in the diffraction pattern from an excessively rough surface. Of course, only one such appearance
is illustrated. The pattern depends on such details as the scale of the roughness as well as its graininess and periodicity. These patterns, if the page is
placed at sufficient distance, exhibit a weak spiky effect. These spikes can
be distinguished from the roughness induced in the atmosphere by their
motionless aspect. Atmospheric turbulence shifts and changes. As a result,
spikes shoot out from one side of the image and then another. Rough surfaces, however, are coldly rigid. Nevertheless, the sky isn't usually steady
enough to test for this problem on an actual star; most often this is an error
best left to an earthbound artificial source.

### 2.2.8 Zonal Aberrations

Part of what makes a successful optical surface is the effect of statistical averaging. One of the most paradoxical features of optical work is that the best surfaces are the result of superficially sloppy practice. Behind the variations, however, are carefully delineated boundaries.

Machines are less random. The operator must make adjustments to add a pseudo-random component to the stroke. If insufficient artificial variations are imposed on the machine, it will tend to dig circular furrows or wavy deformations, called zonal defects, in the optical surface. Zones can also be the result of employing small polishers on a larger optical surface. Use of small polishers without sufficient blending can cause zones in both handmade and machine-fabricated optics. See Fig. 2-9.

**inside focus**          **outside focus**          **normal**

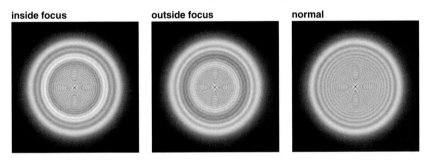

**Fig. 2-9. Zonal Defect.** *Zonal aberration on an unobstructed aperture caused by a trench at 60% of the radius of the disk. Far inside of focus, the zone appears as a bright ring on the uniform disk, and outside it becomes a dark ring. On the right is an unaberrated pattern.*

Zonal defects are common in small optics at the center. They appear as an indentation or a bump (the photograph in Fig. A-3 of Appendix A is an example). Zones at the center are less harmful than zones appearing at other radii. In obstructed reflectors they are confined largely to the shadow of the diagonal and rendered harmless. Even if they show, defects at the center occupy only a small part of the surface area.

### 2.2.9 Turned Edges

Turned-down edge is a defect where the edge does not end abruptly but curls over gradually. This special case of zonal aberration results in a surprisingly large amount of damage to the image because the edge of the aperture has a large fraction of the total surface area. It deflects more light.

Turned edge comes either from polishing pitch that is too soft or from applying incorrect pressure when the optical surface is extended over the edge of the polishing tool (Texereau 1984). It is extremely difficult to remove once generated, and the fear of it causes telescope makers to over-compensate with an extremely hard grade of pitch. Some add adulterants that change the pitch's readiness to flow. Stiff or waxy pitch often worsens the problems with rough surfaces, though, so the net effect is a trade between two noxious aberrations.

In an otherwise perfect reflector, turned-down edge appears as a softening of the ring structure inside focus and a corresponding hardening of the ring structure outside of focus. To avoid confusion, look for this effect through a strongly colored filter. Figure 2-10 shows two 25% apertures, one normal and the other with a turned edge. The light misdirected from a turned-down edge appears as a hazy glow in the vicinity of the image on the inside of focus (remove the filter if you look for this halo).

On both sides of focus, a narrow turned-down edge displays a fairly flat distribution of light in the disk.

**normal**               **TE inside focus**            **TE outside focus**

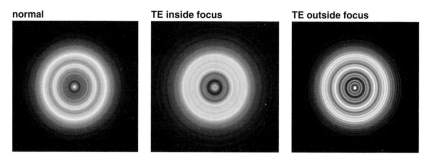

**Fig. 2-10. Turned-Down Edge.** *Turned edge in a 25% obstructed aperture. A normal 25% aperture appears at the left. The inside-focus disk shows loss of contrast and a diffuse glow surrounding it. The outside-focus disk seems less affected in terms of light distribution, but the contrast is increased in the rings.*

### 2.2.10   Astigmatism

Pure astigmatism can occur even in perfect telescopes (particularly refractors) if the system is not aligned properly. The cure is simple, and the aberration disappears quickly upon the telescope's collimation. It also occurs in Newtonian telescopes that have curved secondary mirrors. Because of the 45° tilt of the supposedly flat mirror, a bulging or concave diagonal will be expressed as astigmatism in the image.

Astigmatism in the glass itself is caused by three fabrication errors. It can result from pressing the disk against a cylindrical surface—for example, the rear surface of the disk may not be flat. Another cause is too rapid cooling of the glass disk when it was poured, freezing unrelieved stresses into the disk. This error is scarcely ever seen in deliberately made optical disks, but is common enough in portholes or other undocumented glass. And last, failing to rotate the optical disk with respect to the tool grinds a cylinder into the disk directly.

In all cases, out-of-focus astigmatic images will show two oval patterns at 90° to one another (see Fig. 2-11). If astigmatism is severe, certain focus positions will give stellar images that look like straight lines.

**inside focus**                    **focused**                    **outside focus**

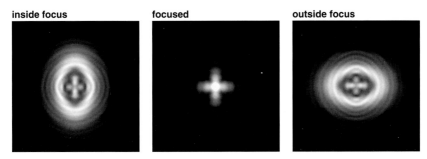

**Fig. 2-11. Astigmatism.** *Appearance of astigmatism immediately on either side of focus. Middle: at best focus, the pattern is a cross. Out of focus, the profile is stretched into an oval, with the direction of stretch changing a quarter turn on opposite sides of focus.*

At best focus, astigmatism will show the indicated crossed pattern. Small amounts display a thickening of the first diffraction ring along the cross directions.

## 2.3   Concluding Remarks

This chapter is meant only as a brief tour of the enormous landscape that can be found in the star test. Do not confuse this nodding acquaintance with real expertise. The star test's vastness and complexity are astounding. You will continue learning new features of the star test many years into the future.

The size of the preceding sections is one measure of the importance given to them as optical problems. If one topic can be recommended for study, it is spherical aberration—i.e., simple correction error. Become an expert in its detection. You will see this error again and again.

# Chapter 3

# Telescopes Are Filters

The telescope is a device that reproduces an image of reality. It does not write on paper like a copy machine, but its images are just as unreal. It creates its reproduction on a tiny image plane only a few centimeters from the tip of the observer's nose. The scrutiny is done using a powerful magnifying lens called an eyepiece. Only through the multiplicity of imaged values (location, color, brightness) and the selective visual processing power of the human brain does this reproduction get interpreted as reality.

Similarly, the visual image projected onto the retina is only representative of reality. Those with keen vision are able to derive more information about the external world than people with weak vision, but each individual tends to give equal value to that perception, regardless of its absolute quality. We tend to ignore errors.

Before going farther, look at Fig. 3-1. Think of a filter as a process that degrades information contained in an image or signal. Filters are not only objects such as the colored disks of glass you might attach to the eyepiece. They are anything which removes information from the image, even relatively subtle factors such as the limitation on aperture and the wavelength of light viewed. This concept, which I call the "wobbly stack," represents a partial list of the filters between the observer of an image and reality. Some of the filtrations depicted are not independent. For example, eyepiece aberrations may, by good fortune or design, partially cancel the main instrument's aberrations.

The effects of each of these filters can be lessened, but not all may be removed. For example, one can avoid atmospheric turbulence by going into space. One can lessen aberration errors by building near-perfect optics. One can even avoid the mushy errors of the eye-brain system by using the more predictable filtration of photography. So why wouldn't it be possible to put an absolutely perfect image of Jupiter onto a sheet of

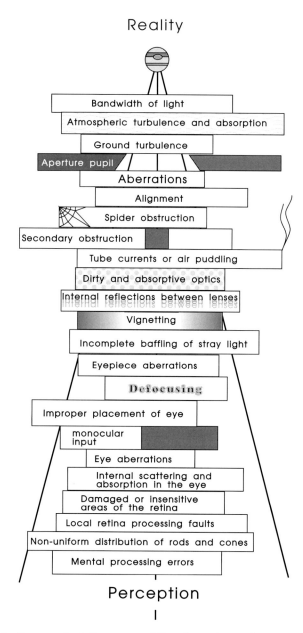

**Fig. 3-1.** *A diagram depicting some of the aberrations, obstructions, misalignments and processing errors that can degrade an image: the "wobbly stack."*

photographic film?

The most important form of filtration cannot be removed or diminished—a filtering caused by the *aperture*, or the finite extent of the window through which the telescope looks. Let's imagine that we have some sort of super-film that records everything that is projected on it. Further imagine that the instrument has absolutely perfect optics. We suppose that if a photograph of Jupiter taken with such a system is inspected with a microscope, we have a perfect image of everything at the distance of Jupiter—volcanoes on Io, tiny ice crystals in the atmosphere, the smallest cloud-belt whorls, etc. If we can do it for a full-sized telescope, we can do it for a little one. It might even be easier to make perfect small optics than large ones. If the optics are tiny, what then?

We have reached a fundamental limit. Small lenses don't image as well as large ones. The sharpness of the image of every optical system is limited by the presence of the aperture. If we squeeze a representation of the universe through a tiny hole, we should expect this image to be a bit scuffed by the passage. Passage of light through larger apertures results in less damage.

## 3.1 Perceptions of Reality

Figure 3-1 shows many limitations that we can do nothing about. Although other receptors are often used, most people interpret eyeball vision as the best representation of reality. Thus, we all send the signal through an unavoidable filtration system that happens to be attached to our heads. Some might argue that this filtering is always present and can be viewed as a sort of baseline. True, we are probably accustomed to our own vision, but we are most familiar with its performance under bright lights, using two eyes. In a telescope, with low illumination and monocular vision, many of the errors that would otherwise be incidental are worsened until they cause significant and unexpected information loss.

The only things that can be done about such unavoidable errors is to be aware of them and use strategies to lessen their effects. For example, the most commonly used corrective measure for the awkward distribution of low-light sensors on the retina is not to look directly at dim objects, i.e., to use averted vision. The unbalance caused by monocular viewing can be eliminated with binoculars.

The filters covered in this book concentrate on the center of the stack, from the atmosphere down to the image inspected by the eyepiece. This is not to say that these are the worst sources of error, but they are filters most associated with the telescope, its environment, and its use. They are the forms of filtering that we are most able to affect by corrective actions.

Eyepieces are neglected here. Although changing the eyepiece changes the optical system, it is not usually the worst source of optical difficulty. If a high magnification is used, the errors of the primary optics will dominate unless the eyepiece is entirely defective or it is used for the unusually steep light cone of a low focal ratio telescope. Also, a poor eyepiece can be identified by trying it in several instruments.

Aberrations that may seem less important are covered because they are generally caused by construction details peculiar to the particular instrument or repeated poor habits of use. For example, if you store your telescope in a hot shed and only use it in the early evening, you will be plagued by tube currents. Telescopes that are misaligned seldom become better aligned the next time they are used. Optics don't heal by themselves.

Clearly, the most desirable image would be a one-to-one mapping of points on the real object to points on the image. Telescopes already violate this principle by compressing much of the three-dimensional universe to a two-dimensional plane or slightly curved surface. Only for nearby objects are the images stretched out into a three-dimensional image space. Thus, a gas cloud 500 light-years away is imaged on top of a giant star visible 200 light-years beyond it. People are accustomed to this effect and tend to ignore it. Only where we have independent knowledge of the three-dimensional placement of the objects does this compression becomes objectionable. Many people are familiar with a similar perspective compression effect when they use binoculars at a sports event. If they are far enough from the action, the field seems flattened to a playing area a few steps deep.

For most purposes, the filtration caused by squeezing the image onto a sheet is not harmful. In fact, this and other forms of filtering can be quite useful. Astronomical telescopes are not troubled with the vanishingly small depth of field so bothersome in microscopy, where only part of the object is clear at any one focus.

Another positive use of filters is the way emission nebulae pop out from skyglow using narrow-band nebular filters. Although such filters diminish the interesting signal slightly, they profoundly reduce the superimposed noise of skyglow. The observer is happy to take the somewhat weaker true image as a trade for eliminating artificial light.

## 3.2   A Comparison to Audio

Because generalized filtering is a difficult concept at first, let's use an example where the filtration ideas appear in our common vocabulary—the commercial sound system (see comparisons in Table 3-1). Because electronics are a more recent invention than telescopes, and the terminology for audio was invented by engineers brought up on signal-processing mathematics, many modern words used for sound systems tend to have filtering concepts built right in. Many people are familiar with audio hardware or have a superficial understanding of the words. Comparisons, or at least some strained analogies, can be made to similar patterns in telescope filtration. In the audio descriptions, 20,000 cycles/second or 20,000 Hz equals 20 kilohertz, abbreviated as "kHz."

Table 3-1
Generalized telescope and associated equipment filtrations that behave in an analogous manner to another reproduction device, the high-fidelity sound system.

| FILTRATION (telescope/eye/camera) | FILTRATION (sound system) |
| --- | --- |
| aperture diameter | size of speakers |
| colored filters | equalizer filters |
| image processing | signal processing |
| scattered light | audio noise |
| spatial response | frequency response |

### 3.2.1  Aperture Diameter/Size of Speakers

A typical stereo system has a cascaded set of sound reproduction devices called speakers, more technically named *transducers.* They convert electrical energy to the air compressional waves of sound. A typical stereo has subdivided speakers into at least two ranges, "woofers" and "tweeters." Low-frequency woofers are quite large, while high-frequency tweeters tend to be very tiny.

Low-frequency speakers, having to cycle a large quantity of air, occasionally move large distances and have enormous diameters. High-frequency speakers cannot be visually perceived to move at all and seem to work well in small sizes. Most people figure the reason the frequency range is broken up into multiple transducers is because no single speaker can cover the range, which is mostly true. However, we can easily imagine, if not build, a single speaker that would reproduce the entire frequency range with equal facility. Why would we still expect speakers to be divided?

Flat speakers (and optics) transfer energy in an angular range according to how many wavelengths fit across the aperture. The speed of sound is about 330 meters/second, or about a mile every 5 seconds. A sound at 880 Hz, or 880 cycles/second, would have a wavelength of $^{330}/_{880}$, or $^3/_8$ meter. If we had a speaker of this size, about 15 inches, it would put out most of the 880 Hz energy in a 120° cone. In other words, twice the 60° angle of an equilateral triangle, 1 wavelength across the speaker at the base, 1 wavelength on each side. This size is effective for stereo imaging, because sound can spread widely into a room. So we're done designing a speaker, right?

Consider our imaginary, one-size-fits-all single speaker for a moment. It works fine at 880 Hz, but we can hear to frequencies about 20 times higher, to around 17,600 Hz. Young people might hear higher pitched sounds, older ones lower. Now the wavelength at 17.6 kHz is 15.9 mm (about 5/8 inch). The emergent cone of energy from this same speaker is twice the narrow angle in a long, skinny triangle 20 wavelengths at the base and 1 wavelength high—less than 6°. At high frequencies, the angular spread of our single speaker is so narrow that we need to carefully aim such a source to hear it directly. Even worse, the mix of frequencies depends on whether we are directly in front of the speaker or sitting to the side, because each frequency has its own cone. The "sweet spot" of best stereo effect would be hard to find. High-pitched music from such a speaker may only be detectable in one ear at a time and may vary with motion of the head. Sound engineers still design multi-speaker systems of different sizes because no single speaker would emit sound into the optimum angle at all frequencies. They also design speakers in other shapes for this reason. Flat is sometimes not the best form for a speaker.

What is annoying in a sound system is desirable in a telescope, however. A typical telescopic aperture is 200 mm, or 360,000 wavelengths across. We still use the crude estimate of the angle of the energy cone similar to the speaker above—twice the narrow angle of a skinny triangle one wavelength high and $3.6 \times 10^5$ wavelengths across the base. This cone is less than 1.2 arcseconds across. Thus, most of the energy of a star detected by a 200-mm visual telescope can be found in an angle confined to less than 1.2 arcseconds.

One can also see from these resolution arguments why the location of a subwoofer (a very low frequency speaker) makes no difference. At a typical frequency of a subwoofer—say, 33 Hz—the wavelength is 330/33, or 10 meters. Any subwoofer smaller than a railroad car cannot even pretend to be able to direct the sound in any particular direction. Subwoofer location matters little because it radiates sound in all directions. The listener also isn't capable of hearing it in a unique location; the sound has such low frequency that normal two-eared perception is subverted by acoustic transmission directly through the head.

Similarly, radio telescopes have to be huge to offer any resolution. A 20-cm (8-inch) telescope has an aperture of only about one wavelength of the 21-cm line often observed by radio astronomers. If one were foolish enough to build a single-element, 8-inch radio telescope, a point image of 21-cm radiation would occupy a broad, fuzzy 120° angle.

### 3.2.2   Colored Filters/Equalizer Filters

Equalizer filters are often added to sound systems to compensate for the room damping or reverberation. The rough equivalent in a telescope is to add color filters to the optical system. The color filters perform a similar shift or emphasis in the frequency spectrum.

It is no whim or accident that the sonic signature of an individual room is called the room's *coloration*. Sound spaces with unusually high amounts of upholstery or curtain absorption are called "warm," meaning that they absorb high frequencies much more strongly than low ones. Red and orange colors are also called "warm." The cure for a warm sonic space is to boost high frequencies. Similarly, when we use a blue filter on Mars, we can see high dust clouds more easily because they reflect more of the blue sunlight than the ruddy Martian surface.

The brain itself acts as a compensating filter for the external world. Since the time of Edison, listeners have repeatedly declared their contemporary audio technology to be perfect, even when it was scratchy and indistinct. Our light perceptions are equally questionable. The brain will automatically adjust nearly any color balance it sees to the color balance it experiences beneath the Sun.

A good example is illumination under artificial lighting. Look into a fluorescent-lit room from the outdoors. Your color balance is held fixed by the brighter natural sunlight, so the room light you see inside is greenish. Mercury vapor lighting is composed (mostly) of two pure colors, a green line and a blue-violet one. Even under these extraordinary conditions, the eye manages to fool us most of the time. Only when the eye is confronted with just one color does it give up. Even then, I suspect if you gave the eye-brain system enough time, it would eventually adjust to perceive any single color as a kind of washed-out gray.

### 3.2.3   Image Processing/Signal Processing

So many techniques to process audio signals and images exist that they all cannot be included here. Let's look at an example—oversampling.

Sixteen-bit numbers are imprinted on a Compact Disc (CD) at the rate of 44.1 kHz, and they are read off the medium at the same rate. The values are then delivered to a digital-to-analog converter (DAC), which takes the numbers and "undoes" them back into a voltage that one hopes is a reasonable simulation of the original recorded signal.

One would think that 44.1 kHz would be more than fast enough to reproduce sound of less than half that frequency, but it turns out that this is only barely sufficient. If the original signal is 11 kHz, a sampling rate of 44 kHz

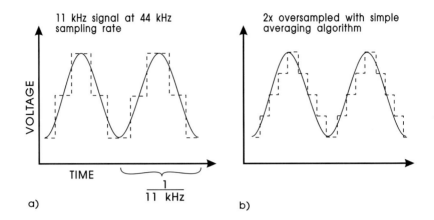

**Fig. 3-2.** *Sampling of digital audio signals.*

yields only four values per wave (see Fig. 3-2a). The DAC is attempting to produce the dashed stair-step pattern, which does not simulate the original sinusoidal tone very well. The stair-step is rich in higher frequencies, called harmonics, of 22 kHz and higher. More exotic combinations of waveforms could actually create artifacts that would spill into audible frequencies.

One could use electronic analog filters to reject DAC frequencies 20 kHz and higher, but it takes extremely sophisticated (i.e., expensive) electronics to produce a precipitous cutoff beyond a certain frequency. Inexpensive analog lowpass filters attenuate sound at a rate of, for example, 12 dB/octave, or a factor of 16 with each doubling of frequency. In other words, a perfect amplifier feeding one of these lowpass filters with an intensity of 1 at 11 kHz has an intensity of $1/16$ at 22 kHz and $1/256$ at 44 kHz. Unfortunately, some of the attenuation leaks into audible frequencies. The response curve is unacceptable for high-fidelity sound reproduction.

The solution often used is to digitally "oversample" the signal. A DAC that operates at 88.2 kHz is used, and the signal is sampled at twice the usual rate. Using a digital filter with an interpolation algorithm (algorithm is a fancy word for *recipe*), one can achieve something like the dotted line of Fig. 3-2b. The analog lowpass smoothing can then be readily applied with a cutoff frequency of 44 kHz instead of the more objectionable 22 kHz. Of course, actual CD players probably use much more sophisticated filters and algorithms than this one. This scheme has been presented only to give you a feel for the processing (Strong and Plitnick 1992, p. 440).

The simple act of choosing a higher-powered eyepiece is itself a form of oversampling (see Fig. 3-3). Here, you are giving up the outer portions of

**a) single-sampled**          **b) double-sampled**

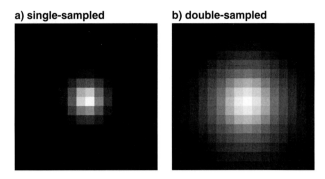

**Fig. 3-3.** *Using higher magnification is a form of oversampling. Here, the object seen at higher power is spread over four times the area of the retina, allowing more receptors to participate in averaging the image.*

the image area in favor of expanding the signal over more retinal receptors. Areas of the image can be identified that have a fairly constant signal strength and coloration, but if they are smaller than a retinal receptor, that intensity will be mixed together with a nearby area.

The retina, like any other light sensor, is noisy. One mechanism the visual system uses to suppress noise is to consider receptors in batches. A detail that shows on only one receptor may be interpreted as noise and ignored unless it is very bright or contrasty. Going to higher magnification allows you to expand small areas until they cover more individual receptors. The average over many noisy detectors is a less noisy number, so lower contrast details can be seen. This procedure works on low contrast details even when the magnification expands the blurring of the telescope beyond the best resolution of the eye, which makes it a true form of oversampling. The eye has a maximum resolution of about 1 arcminute, but the image continues to improve until magnification drives the radius of the Airy disk beyond 4 to 8 arcminutes.

### 3.2.4  Scattered Light/Audio Noise

Every sound system is troubled by noise. In some cases, this noise can be objectionable (as in scratchy old phonograph disks) and in other cases the noise can be imperceptible (as in modern digital systems). The absolute level of the noise is less important than its *signal-to-noise ratio*, or SNR. When the music is soft, a constant low level of noise can become unacceptable because it now sounds relatively strong compared with the interesting signal. However, the same level of noise goes undetected when the music is loud.

One obtains a better appreciation of the relative effects of noise by compressing the signal-to-noise ratio logarithmically to the *decibel* scale,

$$\text{SNR} = 10 \log_{10}(I_s/I_n), \tag{3.1}$$

where $I_s$ is the power of the signal and $I_n$ is the power of the noise. For the strongest signals in a typical CD, the digital SNR is somewhere above 96 dB. For a high quality analog cassette tape, a similar number might be around 55 dB (Strong and Plitnick 1992, p. 441). Of course, the lowering of quality caused by passage through the rest of the sound reproduction system lowers these SNRs a good deal. Noise begins to become objectionable when it is 20 dB below the interesting signal and offensive when it is 10 dB below what one is trying to perceive. When SNR reaches 0 dB, or conditions where noise and signal have equal intensities, people have a difficult time recognizing spoken single words, only catching about 70% of them (Kinsler *et al.* 1982, p. 284).

The analogue to noise in optical systems is scattered light. Say that the surfaces of your optics are dirty, or they are rough on the wavelength scale. Some light diffracts from the tiny irregularities and is scattered beyond the image of the object. If you are trying to observe a very dim object right next to a bright object, the smearing of the light, even though it is a very tiny fraction of the bright object's light, can be strong enough to render the dim object unobservable. The "noise floor" has risen enough to be objectionable. Contrast is appreciably reduced.

We can calculate the scattering from a single round piece of dust, $1/1,000$ of the diameter of the aperture across (for a 200-mm telescope, the speck of dust would be a 0.2 mm disk). One millionth of the energy incident on the aperture would hit the rear side of the speck and be absorbed or reflected. However, we would see a fairly normal Airy disk that has *two-millionths* of the energy missing (van de Hulst 1981). The other millionth part of the energy has been scattered throughout the field of view. If we assume that we are looking at a large extended object and that none of the scattered light has been lost outside the region of interest, then the signal-to-noise ratio is as low as $10 \log_{10}(1,000,000) = 60$ dB, still far below the noise level of good magnetic tape. At 1,000 specks, we would find that our SNR could be well on the way to becoming noticeable at 30 dB. Thirty decibels is approximately 7.5 magnitudes. Thus, if we were looking at a first magnitude star, we would see the scattered light in a fuzzy glow with a total brightness of 8.5 magnitude.

Scattered light only damages the image in specialized observing situations. Noise that is 24 dB down is only about as bright as the second ring of a perfect diffraction pattern. Such light would only be troubling if it covered something dim, a situation that is seldom the case in dark-field observation. Scattering is a worse problem in solar and lunar observation, or in the perception of very low contrast detail on planets.

### 3.2.5 Spatial Frequency/Audio Frequency Responses

A good sound system is supposed to perform sound reproduction between the frequencies of 20 and 20,000 Hz (20 kHz). A frequency of 20 Hz is a rumble you almost feel instead of hear; 20,000 Hz is a fingernails-on-blackboard squeak. Outside these limits, it was once thought, humans do not hear well enough to make reproducing tones in recorded music worthwhile. More recently, audiologists have discovered that part of the information required to make what we hear seem real is contained somewhat outside these limits. Nevertheless, high fidelity sound reproduction is conventionally contained between 20 Hz and 20 kHz. Tones lower in frequency than 20 Hz are called *infrasound*, and tones higher in frequency than 20 kHz are called *ultrasound*. The analogy to "infrared" and "ultraviolet" is obvious.

Think about what the 20–20,000 Hz limits mean. As long as a tone has a frequency between these limits, the audio electronics will reproduce it without too much loss or unusual gain. Once frequencies go into the infrasound or ultrasound range, the electronics are allowed to fail badly and the sound is degraded or vanishes. In other words, even if a higher frequency tone were put in the front end of the audio electronics, little or nothing is reproduced at the speaker end.

A similar effect can be seen in telescopes, but in optical systems the most interesting effect does not take place in the domain of optical frequencies, or "colors." It occurs for angle.

When a telescope is pointed at a white picket fence not too far distant, the gaps can be viewed crisply against a darker background. If, instead, you tape a small piece of paper with alternating white and dark bars on the same fence and look at it through the telescope, you are less likely to see the bars reproduced well. At some fine scale determined by moving the telescope closer or farther away, you will see the bars dissolve into a gray blur. The instrument is no longer reproducing the reality that may be verified by moving closer to the object. You know that the telescope is looking at bars, but it is no longer transmitting them as distinct stripes. Here, the effect is very close to the inability of audio electronics to reproduce too high a frequency, only in this case a portion of the object cycled between dark and light and back to dark again as different angles were considered.

What is the analogy to frequency here? In the case of an audio tone, the standard units of frequency are cycles/second or hertz (named after 19th-century physicist Heinrich Hertz). In the case of astronomical images, the units are cycles/arcsecond. The resemblance to frequency is so unmistakable that the quantity used to describe the transmission of detail in an image is called *spatial frequency*. Spatial frequency has generalized units of cycles/angle, but it has also been stated in cycles/distance in the focal plane. This quantity is commonly used in stating the spatial response of a camera lens—something like "200 lines/mm"—although it customarily appears by itself without the more correct "in the focal plane" trailer.

One might wonder if a low frequency cutoff exists in optical systems analogous to the 20 Hz cutoff of audio systems. You might think that none exists because dark and white bars are easier to see at low frequency. An effective cutoff is given by the limitations of the field, however. Once fewer than one bar shows in the lowest magnification eyepiece, the bars cannot really be said to resolve. Put another way, the illumination variation probably cannot be distinguished from the inherent vignetting of the system. A visual telescope of focal ratio f/8 has a maximum spatial frequency of 226 lines/mm at the focal plane. If that focal plane has a width of 25 mm inside the eyepiece, the lowest spatial frequency is certainly greater than 1 line/50 mm, or 0.02 lines/mm. The ratio of these two numbers is 1131. Thus, the telescope has about the same 3 orders-of-magnitude bandwidth of the typical 20–20,000 Hz audio system.

## 3.3   The Modulation Transfer Function (MTF)

Many of the audio-to-visual comparisons above are interesting but have no practical application. Spatial frequency response of optics is a core issue, however, and there is a very important reason it is used. This response is the most objective measure of the quality of an optical system.

Spatial frequency response is generally written using the filtering concept of a transfer function. If the target displays a sinusoidal modulation—changing gradually from bright to dark—and we view the optical system as a black box filter, then it exits with a lesser variation. Perhaps the exit signal varies only from light gray to dark gray.

The spatial frequency target is not a light and dark bar pattern as in the picket fence example above but a smoothly varying pattern such as that shown in Fig. 3-4a. Strictly, such a pattern should extend infinitely to either side, but practical use limits it to a few bars. The common 3- or 4-bar resolution chart is not a valid target field in the sense of either being infinite or sinusoidal, but it is such an easy target to use that it commonly serves to estimate optical quality anyway. One other requirement is that the illumination of the bar pattern is completely incoherent, usually a very easy requirement to fill.

If $C$ stands for contrast and $\nu$ is the spatial frequency, the way we will define the modulation transfer function (MTF) is

$$C_{\text{after}}(\nu) = \text{MTF}(\nu)\,C_{\text{before}}(\nu), \qquad (3.2)$$

where $\text{MTF}(\nu)$ is always less than 1.

Let's look at this simple equation and see what it means. If one has a target pattern with a certain value of contrast, the transfer function of the optical system always acts on that contrast to lessen it. Readers familiar with filtering concepts know that, in general, the transfer function can change the phase of the signal (suggesting that the most general transfer function is complex). Here, we will be concerned only with its amplitude, the modulation transfer function. The contrast (both before and after) is measured from the intensity levels at the darkest place on a dark bar and the brightest location on the light bar.

$$C(\nu) = \frac{I_{\text{bright}} - I_{\text{dark}}}{I_{\text{bright}} + I_{\text{dark}}}, \qquad (3.3)$$

where the intensities are measured as in Fig. 3-4. Note that if the "before" pattern has a dark intensity of zero, the modulation transfer function becomes the image contrast itself (Hecht 1987, p. 507).

The MTF is all-encompassing and powerful. Even optical difficulties not originating in wavefront errors but in obstruction and non-uniform transmission find a way of being expressed in the modulation transfer function.

What form does it take? One would think that in perfect optical systems, the value of the MTF would be 1 for all spatial frequencies. No such optical system exists although a large planar mirror comes very close. Consulting Fig. 3-1 depicting the "wobbly stack" of filters, we can ask which filters are active even under ideal conditions. Clearly the atmosphere can be neglected—assume that the telescope is under perfect skies, or in space. The eye and its processing errors also will be ignored. Assume alignment and cleanliness are perfect and that the vignetting can be ignored. This process can be continued until the stack is made as short as possible.

What is left? Remember, even a perfect optical system has these two filters: 1) the wave nature of the light used to make the image, and 2) the limited aperture. This irreducible minimum is enough to force the MTF to a value less than unity and determine where it goes to zero. The perfect circular aperture's MTF is depicted in Fig. 3-5.

Admittedly, this curve doesn't much resemble the flat curve of the typical audio system, because it is plotted on a linear scale and extends somewhat beyond the spatial frequency bandwidth. The logarithmic decibel scale used for music tends to compress the spectrum to a wide, flat-topped

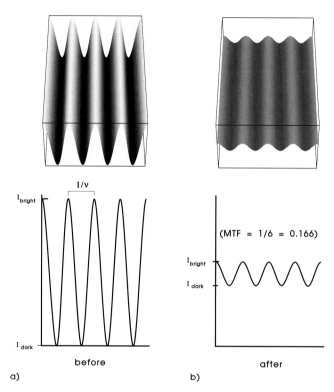

**Fig. 3-4.** *Target intensity of modulated brightness: a) before filtering, b) after filtering. Note: the energy of the image is still the same, but in b) it is less modulated. The target is not actually corrugated—this is just a way of indicating surface brightness.*

appearance ($0.5 = -3$ dB, $0.25 = -6$ dB, etc.). If this plot were of an audio system, the bottom axis would go from 0 to well beyond 20,000 Hz. In fact, easily audible sounds would occupy the lowest $1/10$ of the spectrum. Similarly, much interesting detail in sky objects is at low spatial frequencies where the transfer function is high. This plot emphasizes the highest frequencies where the transfer is likeliest to fall down.

The maximum spatial frequency (on the far right, 1.0 on the chart) is

$$S_{\max} = \frac{1}{\theta_{\min}} = \frac{D}{\lambda} \quad \text{[cycles/angle]} \tag{3.4}$$

with $\theta_{\min}$ representing a separation angle slightly narrower than the $1.22\lambda/D$ angle associated with the radius of the diffraction disk, also known as the Rayleigh resolution criterion. Here, a bar separation equal to the radius of the diffraction disk would occur at $1/1.22 = 0.82$ of the maximum spatial frequency (marked with bar).

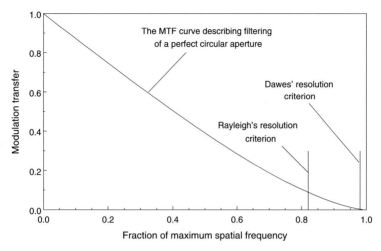

**Fig. 3-5.** *The best-case unobstructed circular MTF. Incoherent lighting of the target is assumed.*

If we wish to use the notation that is more associated with cameras, the maximum spatial frequency at the focal plane (where $F$ is the focal ratio) is

$$S'_{\max} = \frac{1}{F\lambda} \ [\text{cycles/length}]. \tag{3.5}$$

For example, if the aperture has a diameter of 200 mm and a focal length of 1200 mm and the wavelength considered is $550 \times 10^{-6}$ mm, then $S'_{\max}$ is 303 cycles/mm or lines/mm. $S_{\max}$ in angle notation for a 200 mm aperture would be 364,000 cycles/radian or 1.76 cycles/arcsecond.

## 3.4 The MTF in Use

Astronomy authors claim that an aperture obstructed by about 30% is about as bad as an unobstructed aperture with $1/4$ wavelength of spherical aberration. How do they know this? Seemingly, they are comparing two widely different phenomena. Are the images equally degraded?

Everyone who has experience with evaluating images knows that these writers couldn't have derived that 30% number from experience. Differences between optical images are subtle, and this number is too precise. There are many ways to compute this quantity, such as specifying the amount of energy in the central disk. For our purpose here, we calculate the energies contained inside the diffraction spot of an unobstructed aperture with $1/4$ wavelength of spherical aberration and several obstructed apertures that are otherwise perfect. We choose the obstruction that most closely matches the energy loss of spherical aberration. The answer is an aperture about 32% obstructed.[1]

However, we must examine the frequency responses of these two situations to see where the blanket statement of equivalence breaks down. The corresponding MTFs are plotted in Fig. 3-6. We see that they are roughly the same for spatial frequencies about half of the Rayleigh criterion. For 200-mm telescopes, these two optical situations show periodic planetary detail having spacings of roughly 1 to 2 arcseconds equally well.

The response at higher and lower spatial frequencies are different, however. At the high end, the obstructed aperture delivers better contrast than $1/4$ wavelength of spherical aberration. Surprisingly, it even performs better than a perfect aperture.

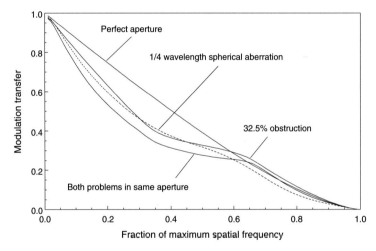

**Fig. 3-6.** *Comparing the filtration of simple spherical aberration and central obstruction.*

At the low end, the obstructed aperture has a higher MTF for spatial frequencies until bar separations are more than eight times the Rayleigh criterion. For a 200-mm aperture, details separated between 2 and 5 arcseconds are shown better by the obstructed aperture. On coarse details separated more than 5 arcseconds the two contrasts are pretty much the same, but still slightly less than the perfect aperture.

Thus, for low-power, deep-sky viewing, $1/4$ wavelength of spherical aberration is slightly worse than the obstruction. For double-star separation at or slightly beyond the Rayleigh criterion, the obstruction wins again. Only

[1]See Table 10-1.

for intermediate spatial frequencies is the frequency response about the same or inferior in the obstructed instrument.

The obstruction may be adjusted until the transfer functions are a little closer (the shadow diameter would be nearly 35% of the full aperture), but all-inclusive comparisons should not be made without caution.

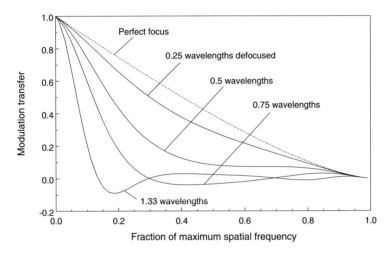

**Fig. 3-7.** *MTFs associated with various amounts of defocusing.*

## 3.4.1   MTF Associated with Defocusing

The simplest way to degrade the image is by defocusing it. Figure 3-7 shows the way MTF droops with increased defocus. At $1/4$ wavelength defocus, performance begins to suffer noticeably; by $3/4$ wavelength it is unacceptable.

These transfer functions have an extremely interesting property. At higher values of defocusing, the transfer function becomes negative for some spatial frequencies. If this behavior is traced back through the contrast equations above, it is seen to result in a switch of bright and dark image intensities. The sinusoidal bar targets look like negatives of themselves.[2]

Does this mean that at certain focus positions the star will look dark and the night sky light? Of course not. The image of a truly point-like star is composed of all spatial frequencies. The contrast is transferred with the correct sign at plenty of other spatial frequencies. This bizarre effect

---

[2]The MTF can't be negative under its strictest definition, but here it is allowed to carry the sign of the full optical transfer function when the phase is near 0 or $\pi$. See Appendix B for more details.

does not affect normal images in this manner—it usually just contributes to the overall appearance of blur. However, if two or three cloud bands on Jupiter have the right separation, a slightly defocused telescope can result in a spurious band appearing between them.

Just because it's rare does not mean that an arrangement can't be made to allow observation of this effect. In Fig. 3-8 contrast reversal is readily seen. This picture was taken with a severely defocused camera lens pointed at a radial bar target. These bars aren't sinusoidal but they are periodic. As the pattern passes through a completely unresolved gray area, it emerges on the other side with the opposite intensity. Only near the edge does it fail to act this way (Goodman 1968, p. 126).

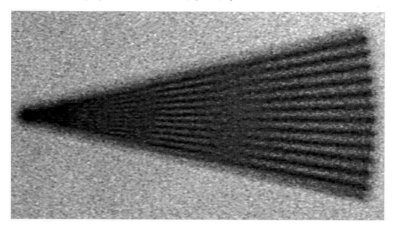

**Fig. 3-8.** *Defocused radial bar target. Look from the narrow end at glancing incidence to the paper. Some of the bars reverse dark-to-light.*

### 3.4.2   Stacking of MTFs

As long as the optical difficulties are independent of one another, the total MTF of the system is just the individual MTFs multiplied together according to the following recipe:

$$\text{MTF}_{\text{total}} = \text{MTF}_{\text{perfect}} \left( \frac{\text{MTF}_1}{\text{MTF}_{\text{perfect}}} \right) \left( \frac{\text{MTF}_2}{\text{MTF}_{\text{perfect}}} \right) \cdots \left( \frac{\text{MTF}_n}{\text{MTF}_{\text{perfect}}} \right) \tag{3.6}$$

Each quantity in brackets is known as the *degradation factor* of the optical error denoted by 1, 2, etc. The numerator of each degradation factor is the MTF as it would have been measured if the aperture suffered from that optical problem alone.

Of course, no two optical difficulties are truly independent, even if they seem to be unrelated at first glance. From Fig. 3-6 we may reason that spherical aberration on the surface has nothing to do with a secondary suspended above it. But the secondary casts a shadow on the mirror and thus changes the contribution of the aberration to the wavefront. The middle spatial frequencies of the "Both" curve of Fig. 3-6 is not as bad as expected from this degradation equation.

A particularly fortunate result of this lack of independence is the effect on a zonal defect at the center of a mirror. If the diagonal is sufficiently large, it will completely shade the error and you will not be able to detect the aberration.

Some optical devices, particularly those without interchangeable eyepieces, have optics designed as a unit. Aberrations inherent in the objective are canceled by oppositely directed aberrations in the eyepiece or other tailpiece optics. When separated, they perform poorly or not at all (common in military surplus equipment). When trying to use the degradation equation for such optics, the evaluator must be careful to circumscribe the whole system—not just part of it.

For most astronomical telescopes, the unknown nature of what will be attached at the back (whether it is a camera or an eyepiece) demands that the objective alone do good imaging. An unwritten protocol in the design of astronomical telescopes demands that the designer encapsulate the maximum number of desirable features at the focus of both the eyepiece and the objective.

Methods exist to measure the MTF curve for a set of optics, but later chapters will not emphasize them, since they involve a great deal of extra equipment (Baker 1992, Murata 1965). This book concentrates on the theoretical description of ideal cases. Pay close attention to the MTF curves in the pages that follow. Even though these curves may appear uninteresting and similar to each other, they encompass all optical problems. If you learn to interpret them, you will better understand the way your optics are degraded.

# Chapter 4

# Diffraction

For people learning diffraction the first time, the various viewpoints presented in this chapter may be overwhelming and the main conclusions can be lost in the detail. Several elements are crucial for this discussion, however, so let's look at them at the beginning:

1. Diffraction is caused by the wave nature of light. Because light cannot be localized, images are necessarily fuzzy. The quantum mechanical concept of the photon as a particle does not help fix its position.

2. Diffraction is a consequence of a limited aperture. It is an *angular* blurring that is independent of the focusing power of the instrument.

3. Diffraction is not just a phenomenon observable in the rings. The spread of the central spot is caused by diffraction.

4. Quasi-static light and dark regions exist because diffraction can be modeled as a standing wave, with the aperture providing the boundaries.

5. A limit exists to optical quality that is difficult to exceed.

Once readers have a working knowledge of diffraction, the star test is more easily understood. Diffraction itself is not often explained well, and many people believe a kind of folklore about what it is and what causes it. Authors either sidestep diffraction entirely, or they take the too-easy refuge of mathematics. The scarcity of introductory instructions is unfortunate, because the concepts underlying diffraction are not all that difficult to understand. More importantly, some of these ideas are the most beautiful and fundamental in physics. Diffraction touches on notions as varied as the limits of what is knowable and concept of the particle.

Diffraction is much more than the process that generates rings around a stellar image. While it is true that diffraction makes these rings, it is possible to shade the edges of the aperture to make such ringing arbitrarily small. Diffraction, though, still blurs the central spot. Images without rings still display diffraction. Literally, diffraction means a "breaking up" of a wavefront, which is disturbed by passage of the wave near an obscuring body.

Say that we were in a universe where light consisted of infinitely tiny particles that could be traced from the star, through the telescope, and finally to the eye. Diffraction would not exist in such a world. Either the particles continue undisturbed beyond the obscuring body, or they hit and are stopped. Close approach would make no difference. The region outside the illuminated cone near focus, where you wouldn't normally expect light, is called the *geometric shadow*.

When optical designers ray trace optics, they are using the "light-as-particles" assumption that light will go only where geometry allows. The concept of light moving in particles is called "ray optics." In ray tracing the system, they are assuming that light will go through the optics as if it were a tiny elastic sphere, smacking into optical surfaces, deflected according to empirical rules of refraction and reflection. Surprisingly, this ballistic model will predict the course of light fairly well. To first order, it does a fine job.

Unfortunately, the behavior of light has other characteristics not explained by modeling light as a particle. Light seems to be able to turn corners. By itself, this feature is not too surprising. Any enterprising 17th century physicist could have postulated, for example, that a particle of light has some finite size. As it brushes near a surface, it could be pushed back into the lit region. But experiments done near straight edges showed that light was deflected into the shadows of the obscuration. Instead of banging its shoulders into the obscuring body and being thrown into the lit region, the light ray seemed to be grabbing the edge of the aperture and swinging around. Strangely, some of the shadow also seemed to bleed into the lit region.

Some angles of deflection are preferred. Moving away from the position of best focus, the illumination dims as expected. But here's the strange behavior—it then starts to brighten again. With higher and higher angles, the illumination goes through many such oscillations, which cause the familiar diffraction rings around stars. A theory postulating light as particles has no way of understanding such behavior, except by supposing a defect in the optics. At focus, one doesn't expect light to be anywhere except at a dazzling point in the center.

The eventual explanation came by saying that light did not resemble particles as much as waves. Many of these effects can be observed in a

In quantum mechanics, a way one can describe the position of a photon before it has been detected is to give its probability density, i.e., the likelihood of encountering the photon at a particular location. A particle's probability density is related to its wave function. Where the wave function is strong, the probability density is high. But the density is only measurable by running many photons through the optics.

Perhaps the best way of explaining this principle is to imagine the following experiment. Say we had the aperture of Fig. 4-2a, and a single photon was coming from the left. Photographic film is at the focus. The photon strikes the emulsion at location A, triggering a response in a single grain of the photosensitive material. If we were to stop here and develop the film, we would already have contradictory evidence. On one hand, the darkened grain isn't located precisely at the location of geometric focus, which is where the dotted line intersects the film. But the emulsion was only struck at that one point, leaving us with the impression that a particle was detected. "Maybe the alignment is off," we might say, and carefully run the experiment again. Now it hits at B.

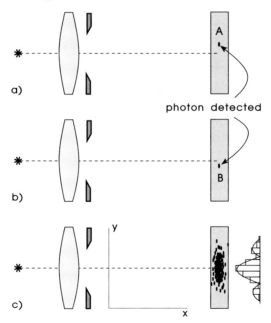

**Fig. 4-2.** a) *One hit at A; b) another hit at B; c) many hits with histogram.*

At this point sensible photographers would recognize that they will run out of film before they get any closer to the truth. For the next trial, we leave the film in long enough to gather many photon hits. We divide the area into miniature areas called *picture elements*, or *pixels*, then count all the hits within each pixel and plot them to the right as in Fig. 4-2c. Now we see a trend—the diffraction pattern is beginning to show. But we already know that such behavior is explained by a wave.

So, we return to the original question, is light best described by particles or waves? On one hand, it is clearly observed that something impacts the photographic emulsion at individual locations. You can dim the intensity of the light until the grain darkening rate is arbitrarily slow. That seems to indicate tiny particles. On the other hand, lots of such individual particles are statistically distributed in the pattern expected for a wave.

We took it as an article of faith that light has no intelligence or motives. Here we seem to find that photons apparently can remember where other photons have already been detected. Record-keeping and communications are two more powers that are difficult to ascribe to light particles.

We have encountered so-called *"wave-particle duality,"* one of the seeming paradoxes of quantum physics. The whole idea of particles (whether they be photons, electron, quarks, or whatever) whizzing around is an example of one of those concrete real-world ideas that doesn't apply at the quantum level. We cannot impose our kind of macroscopic reality on the microscopic situation. We would like particles to be neatly spherical, to be colored with different hues, and all to have a bright, rectangular highlight where a window reflects on the upper left side. But the quantum world doesn't present us with such comforting pictures. The important thing to remember is that we cannot measure whether a photon is a particle or a wave *at the same time.*

The only way we can determine the existence of a photon is to pin it against a photodetector. We can think of it as a wave as long as we don't try to locate it. When we do, its probability density collapses from an infinity of locations defined by the wave function to a single point. We can look at the tiny grain of the photograph and say "it *was* there" as long as we realize that the verb is in the past tense. The only way to be sure a photon exists is to destroy it.

The first physicist to put this in mathematical form was Werner Heisenberg, who expressed what is known as the uncertainty—or better, "indeterminacy"—principle. Far from being a discouraging limit to what we can know, this principle tells us new things about the dynamics of particle motion. One can even use the indeterminacy principle to derive an approximate expression for the radius of the diffraction disk.

What is unknown about this situation is where the photon (that is, the "ray") entered the aperture. We know where it ended up and where it started, but we are uncertain about the intervening path. The Heisenberg indeterminacy principle is stated roughly as follows: The uncertainty in the momentum of a particle in a certain direction times the uncertainty of its position is approximately a very small constant, or

$$\Delta p_y \, \Delta y \approx h \qquad (4.1)$$

where $\Delta p_y$ is the fuzziness in momentum in the $y$ direction, $\Delta y$ is the fuzziness in position $y$, and $h$ is that small number, called Planck's constant. We can rewrite this approximation to find the spread of the detection angle after many counts:

$$\frac{\Delta p_y}{p_y} \approx \frac{h}{p_y \Delta y} \approx \theta_{\text{diffraction}}. \qquad (4.2)$$

The expression for the momentum of a photon is the energy divided by the speed of light, or $E/c$. The photon's energy is $E = h\nu$. The constant $c$ is the speed of light, $\nu$ is the frequency of the light, and $\lambda$ is the wavelength; $c = \nu\lambda$ describes the way these quantities interrelate. The uncertainty in position $\Delta y$ is just the diameter of the aperture $D$. Thus, the uncertainty in angle becomes

$$\theta_{\text{diffraction}} \approx \frac{hc}{\nu h D} = \frac{\lambda}{D}. \qquad (4.3)$$

This result is close to the $1.22\lambda/D$ expression for the angular radius of the Airy disk.[1]

## 4.2 The Consequence of Filtering

We have already seen in Chapter 3 how the telescope has a limited spatial frequency response analogous to the 20–20,000 Hz frequency response of audio equipment. What is the implication of that filtering? Can knowledge about the limitation on spatial frequencies be used to derive interesting facts about diffraction?

The two-dimensional circular surface of an aperture injects some non-instructive mathematical complications into the problem, so it will be easier to turn once again to the simpler situation of audio electronics. In this case, we are interested only in variations in time or frequency.

The audio analogue of a star or a point optical source is an electronic pop. It could also be caused by a scratch or fault on an old vinyl LP disk. If you've ever tried to listen to a distant radio station through an intervening storm, you are probably familiar with the staccato crackle as a lightning strike takes place. One thing that you probably did not notice, however, is that every one of those pops sounds identical, varying only in amplitude.

[1]Equation 4.1 is simplified. Those who are interested in this topic can find more in any elementary quantum mechanics text, e.g. Park 1974.

This fact seems innocent enough, but it gives us an insight into sound reproduction. Every little crackle sounds precisely the same through one audio system.  If you listened to another audio system having a greatly different configuration—say a cheap, hand-held transistor radio compared with your stereo—it may have a different tonality. Yet each pop produced by that other radio is the same as well.

The correct interpretation of this uniform behavior is that you aren't listening to details of the electrical activity in the storm or the source. You're hearing some sort of signature of the reproduction device itself. The crackling noise is merely its best attempt at reproducing an abrupt jump.

At the beginning of the 19th century, physicist Joseph Fourier discovered that complicated, even discontinuous, functions could be simulated to arbitrarily high precision by the sum of a series of sine and cosine functions of higher and higher frequency. A "pop" could be described by this infinite series:

$$a(t) = 1 + 2\big(\cos(t) + \cos(2t) + \cos(3t) + \cdots\big), \qquad (4.4)$$

where $a(t)$ is the amplitude as a function of time. The sharp crack we actually hear is the intensity $I = a^2(t)$.

Being a filter, the audio system doesn't transfer frequencies to an arbitrarily high value; it starts failing at about 20,000 Hz. Thus, we're going to have to truncate this series somewhere. Figure 4-3 shows the effect on the intensity if we lop off the series at 10 cosine terms. The sharp spike of the crackle has been reduced to quite a different function.

This response function resembles a diffraction pattern, complete with rings. In fact, it is identical to the diffraction pattern of a slit or rectangular aperture. Diffraction is a result of the optical system's failure to transmit arbitrarily high spatial frequencies, just as the ringing of Fig. 4-3 is an effect of the limited audio bandwidth.  A point-like star acts like a sharp audio impulse. A star's diffraction pattern is similar to an impulse response function. It is called a *point-spread function* because most stars are far away and occupy insensibly small angles. Not only do rings appear in Fig. 4-3, but also the infinitely sharp spike has broadened into a narrow peak of measurable width.

Astute readers probably realize that the symmetry of the pattern means the response curve oscillates long before the pop on the record actually happens but that such an oscillation isn't possible.  The name of this limitation is *causality,* or the requirement that cause precede effect. Causality is a central issue of special relativity, but it even has implications here. The symmetry of Fig. 4-3 is an artifact of the simple-minded way this process was modeled.  The phase shifts of the individual cosine terms in the equation above were ignored.  We implicitly assumed that

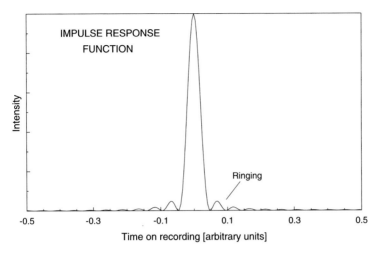

**Fig. 4-3.** *The intensity of an audio crackle is simulated as a truncation of the series in Eq. 4.4.*

all signals go through the system at the same speed with the same phase. An actual system delays every frequency a little and adjusts the phases in such a way that no signal could be detected before it happened. The pattern would become asymmetrical with most of the ringing coming after the sharpest spike. Each audio system has its own characteristic slurring of this pattern.

Fortunately, optical diffraction patterns aren't calculated from time-based frequencies and don't have to obey causality. They can be nicely symmetrical. After all, spatial frequency is only a convenient analogy to true frequency. You are free to look at either side of an optical pattern, but you can't go back in time.

## 4.3  Waves Are Reborn

The next and most important way we will look at diffraction is a very old theory originally proposed by Christian Huygens (1629–1695) to explain why light is observed in the shadow region.

The term *wave propagation* is used without much attention to its origins. Propagation is a word originally associated with botany, where it meant to make new plants from cuttings. Its meanings include the multiplication, reproduction, or dissemination of plants and animals. It has come to mean the spread of ideas or even misinformation (hence, "propaganda"). But the concept of reproduction is inherent to propagation and gives a clue as to what Huygens suggested.

Huygens could explain light appearing in shadows by assuming that every point on a wavefront was emitting its own spherically diverging wavelet. The next instant of the wave would be given by the sum of all of these tiny wavelets. Only in the direction the wavefront was traveling would the wavelets not cancel each other. In other directions, a sideways-moving wavelet would cancel another point's wavelet that was out of phase with it. Similarly, if a hedge tries to grow sideways, it finds that a leaf on another branch has already taken the sunlight. The only direction that growth is free is upward and outward.

An instant later, each new point of the wavefront would emit yet another spherically diverging wavelet. Similarly, in the hedge, inner leaves wither and are replaced by outer leaves. Thus, we could describe wave progression as a rebirth at each new wavefront, a "propagation" in the old botanical sense.

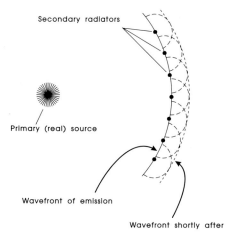

**Fig. 4-4.** *Free-field divergence of a spherical wave.*

The situation of Fig. 4-4 does not require a consideration of propagation, but in Fig. 4-5 we see a reason for it. When the wave propagating from a distant source encounters an aperture, a sudden disturbance occurs in the beautiful symmetry. Points inside the aperture emit wavelets up, down, or out, but no corresponding sources over in the shadow of the aperture provide canceling interference from that direction. In the center of the aperture, the wave propagates much as it did in the free-field, but off at the edge, some of the energy leaks over into the geometric shadow. The little points emitting wavelets are called *elemental radiators* or *secondary sources*. These radiators aren't envisioned as truly hanging like beads at the aperture. They are only an infinite number of mathematical points.

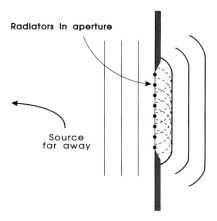

**Fig. 4-5.** *Diffraction of a plane wave at an aperture.*

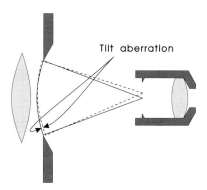

**Fig. 4-6.** *A lens, aperture, and eyepiece showing tilt aberration.*

### 4.3.1 Diffraction and Focusing

Diffraction in astronomical telescopes is caused by the restriction of light to an entrance aperture. Focusing is a convenience imposed on the optical system. This is implied in Fig. 4-6, where the aperture and the focusing power have been divided into two independent functions. One function is the windowing of light by an iris or a rectangular cover—the diffracting aperture. Diffraction occurs whether the light is focused or not; it happens even in pinhole cameras.

All optical work is done on the nondiffractive focusing parts of the optical system. Thus, the optician's task is not to make an existing problem worse by adding additional aberrations to a lens or mirror. An optician cannot correct the window through which the telescope is looking.

The following discussion assumes that the focusing is already done when the wavefront encounters the aperture. This convention does not change the general principles involved.

### 4.3.2    Fresnel Zones

At focus, all of the radiators should oscillate with the same phase. Every point of a perfect aperture appears to be cycling together with every other point. A sensor at such a focus is awash in light. However, at a slight angle with the optical axis (as in Fig. 4-6), the sensor sees some of the points oscillating a little behind the other points. They aren't really doing anything different, but part of the aperture is farther away. Because time passes as the light goes the extra distance, those radiators are perceived at the offset point's location to be lagging behind the rest. Partial wave cancellation results in the total intensity of the light being less at this lateral distance from focus.

If the sensor is far enough off axis, some distant portions of the aperture are seen to be once again in phase. Actually, they are a full wavelength behind the near portions of the aperture, but since the oscillation is sinusoidal, we can't tell the difference. The sources of those waves are atomic transitions that occur quickly, but the burst of light can be a single wave packet many meters and millions of wavelengths long. In the course of a few wavelengths, we really can't see any difference from one wave crest to another.

Different delays are indicated in Fig. 4-7 by *Fresnel zones*,[2] dark and light regions on the aperture. Zero phase occurs only at the interface between two zones. Elemental radiators that are ahead in phase are denoted as "+" regions. Points that are behind in phase are called "−" regions. The dark or light color is only an identifier of each region; it denotes a phase change of a half wavelength. It does not represent the actual appearance, nor does it represent the illumination. In reality, these regions gradually fade into each other. The actual phase varies smoothly, but these regions jerk from one sign to the other.

The detection position in Fig. 4-7 is indicated by a tiny dot, which is in the focal plane of an eyepiece. Furthermore, the pattern on the aperture indicates the Fresnel zones as seen from that dot, rather than from our outside perspective.

This pattern changes rapidly. In only $9.2 \times 10^{-16}$ seconds, the pattern is reversed from positive to negative (remember, the waves are flying into the

---

[2]Named after physicist Augustin J. Fresnel, 1788–1827.

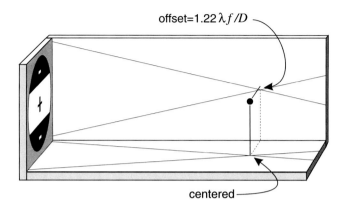

offset=1.22 λƒ/D

centered

**Fig. 4-7.** *Fresnel zones as seen from a point offset from a star. Notice the projections of the light cone on the bottom and far wall of the telescope. This offset is $1.22 f\lambda/D$ to the right of the focused image. The positive and negative areas cancel so that this offset is the first dark ring.*

aperture). If we follow the motion of the bars incrementally over small time scales, they are rushing down. If the detector is on the lower side of focus, they rush upward. The actual received wave at any given location is the average over time of the summed phase values of all these tiny radiators.

The Fresnel zone description of phases on the aperture should not be confused with the appearance of the image. Each location on the image has its own set of Fresnel zones. The Fresnel zone patterns are not observable directly since they refer to the wave field and we are capable of measuring only intensity at the sensor. This Fresnel zone picture is a convenient model, nothing else. Nevertheless, it succeeds in demonstrating many of the phenomena of diffraction and is the basis of the more accurate calculations described in Appendix B.

At risk of being too simple-minded, let's think of that aperture as being a large disk of construction paper. To determine the net wave intensity, we cut out all the like-colored areas of the disk and throw them into two separate piles, one positive and the other negative. We then weigh each pile and come up with two values, say 5 grams negative and 4 grams positive. Four grams cancel each other, leaving us with 1 extra gram of negative weight—call that value the "wave sum." Thus, the average wave sum is $-1g/9g = -1/9$. To calculate a number proportional to the intensity of the light, which is always a positive quantity, we need to square this sum to yield an intensity of $1/81$.

The intensity is weak, so our offset must be somewhere between the rings. Figure 4-7 is actually at a balance point. It is precisely between the

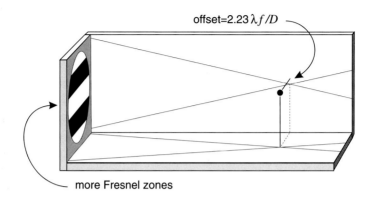

**Fig. 4-8.** *Second minimum of diffraction pattern at $2.23f\lambda/D$.*

rings, and so the dark area should cancel the light area, depending on the quality of the drawing and our skill with the imaginary scissors. Figure 4-8 shows the next dark ring, which occurs at a distance farther from the axis. Here the tilt is worse, so more zones show, and two more bars are visible. Between the offsets of Fig. 4-7 and Fig. 4-8 is the first diffraction ring, where the positive and negative sections do the worst job of canceling each other. Five bars show there, but the two outside bars are very thin.

The important thing to learn from Fresnel patterns is that the wave sum is inefficient everywhere except precisely at perfect focus. Think about the construction paper again. At focus the aperture everywhere has the same sign—nothing cancels. The wave sum is 9g/9g, and the intensity is 1. On even the brightest portion of the first ring, you would get an uncanceled wave sum of about 1.2g/9g and a light intensity only about $1/57$ the brightest value. The farther you go sideways, the worse the situation gets. At some point you realize that all you're cutting out are almost equal narrow ribbons of construction paper.

### 4.3.3   Fresnel Zones with Defocus

The wavefront changes character when the eyepiece is defocused. Figure 4-9 shows the induced aberration at the aperture if the eyepiece is drawn back. The resulting Fresnel zones are circular, as in Fig. 4-10. With the passage of half a wavelength, the pattern reverses, producing a negative spot in the center. However, the square of the wave sum is the same, so the intensity has the same positive value. For sensor locations beyond focus, the passing of time would show a collapsing pattern with new zones appearing at the

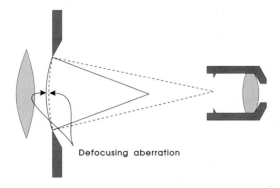

Defocusing aberration

**Fig. 4-9.** *Defocusing aberration. The secondary sources are vibrating on the solid arc, yet the eyepiece's focal plane is at the center of the dashed arc. The aberration resembles a smoothly pushed-in deformation. The center of the aperture appears delayed relative to the outer portions.*

pulled back
and centered

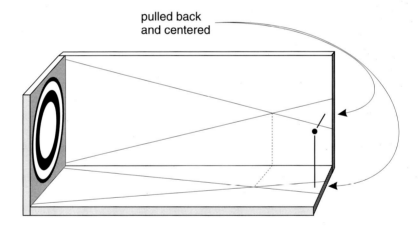

**Fig. 4-10.** *Fresnel zones at a defocusing aberration of 1.7 wavelengths.*

edge of the aperture. These new zones move inward to disappear at the center. For locations inside focus, we'd see identical snapshot patterns, but new zones would appear exploding from the center and moving out.

Even though the pattern is collapsing and we could have picked any snapshot, the wavefront phase is chosen so that the central spot is biggest. The total amount of defocusing aberration in Fig. 4-10 is about 1.7 wavelengths. This value may be determined by counting colors from the center and moving out; the edge is about 3.4 half-wavelength zones out.

We deliberately choose the wavefront phase so that the area of the central positive zone is exactly equal to the areas of all other zones ringing it. The wave sum should be zero when the number of zones is 2, 4, 6, etc. More elaborate theories predict the on-axis image intensity goes to zero when the defocusing aberration is 1, 2, 3... wavelengths, just as predicted by this simple Fresnel zone model.

Moving upwards, as in Fig. 4-11, shows the effect of mixing tilt and defocusing aberrations. Figure 4-12 is the same image pattern with an arrow pointing out the sensor location on the image. The edge of geometric shadow is shown as a light ring.

The strong, outer ring seen in most defocused patterns corresponds to the location where the central Fresnel spot begins sliding off the aperture. (In fact, it is half gone at the beginning of geometric shadow.) Thus, the slightly brighter edge ring in defocused images represents the last flourish of the central Fresnel zone before it disappears and darkness closes in. Notice how the brightest parts of the disks do not fill the circle of geometric shadow and how some of the light has escaped the disk to occupy the shadow. If that pattern were described by ray optics, the disk would be an absolutely featureless circle with perfect darkness outside the radius of geometric shadow.

This image shows another intriguing behavior. Soft rings terrace the pattern, even in the shadow zone. As the sensor is offset further, fresh Fresnel zones come into view, each causing a wiggle in the intensity.

## 4.4   Nodes and Antinodes

Certain locations in the volume around the brightest image point appear to be dark compared with their immediate surroundings. Figures 4-7 and 4-8 showed two such points on the first and second dark rings. In defocusing, on-axis darkness is found when the number of Fresnel zones is an even number. These locations appear to be quiet while the tumult rages around them. They are nulls, more commonly called *nodes*. The opposite of a node is an *antinode,* where the wave action is strongest and the brightness is at a local maximum. A good example of antinodes are the peaks of the diffraction rings, as well as the highest point on the central image spot itself.

Everyone has seen nodes, even though many aren't aware of it. If you look carefully at a guitar string, you can see the simplest type of vibration in Fig. 4-13a. There are two nodes at the bridge and fret, and a single antinode at the center. This situation is called a *standing wave.* Of course, the presence of the two nodes at the edges of the string is hardly a surprise. These positions are mechanically constrained and can hardly be expected to move much.

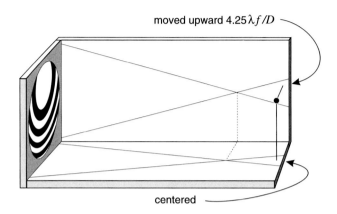

moved upward 4.25 λ*f* /D

centered

**Fig. 4-11.** *An off-center bull's-eye Fresnel zone pattern showing two aberrations (defocus and tilt) mixed together.*

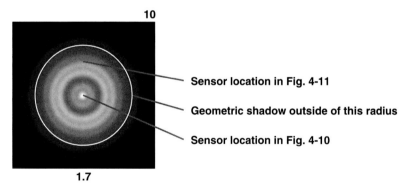

10

**Sensor location in Fig. 4-11**

**Geometric shadow outside of this radius**

**Sensor location in Fig. 4-10**

1.7

**Fig. 4-12.** *The indicated location is where the intensity is calculated as the Fresnel zone sum of Fig. 4-11. The bright ring indicates the boundary of geometric shadow.*

But nodes can hang freely in space, seemingly held by no physical restraints. If you pluck the guitar string as in Fig. 4-13b, you will see the pattern of Fig. 4-13c shortly after you release the string. After more time passes, it will decay to the situation in a). When you plucked the string, the stroke contained a multitude of frequencies (remember Fourier and the impulse response function). The strongest frequencies are the "fundamental" in a) and the "first harmonic" in c). No modes of vibration exist other than multiples of the fundamental frequency.

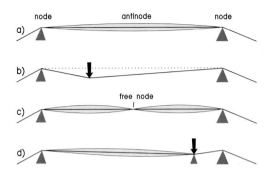

**Fig. 4-13.** *Nodes and antinodes of a guitar string.*

Situations a) and c) are an octave apart. What if you want a tone somewhere in between? You can't find it with a fixed distance separating the fret and bridge. To obtain an intermediate tone you must depress the string at another fret (Fig. 4-13d), which implies a new fundamental and new harmonic sequence.

Now, if nodes and antinodes were only found in stringed instruments, they would hardly be useful for a discussion of diffraction. Standing waves are everywhere, however. For example, they are visible on the surfaces of rapidly vibrating liquids. These standing waves are sometimes seen in a coffee cup or other container shaking on the same tabletop as an appliance or tool with a fast electric motor. The surface appears almost stationary, even though you know intellectually that the speed of water waves is much faster than the almost leisurely drift of the waves. An equivalent to the bridge and fret in this case is the edge of the container, and the standing wave appears in the two-dimensional surface of the fluid. If the container is round, the most likely vibration is radially symmetric. If it is square, you see a sort of checkerboard figure.

A three-dimensional case can occasionally be found in an old microwave oven. Microwave cooking patterns are typically stirred by a hidden metal fan placed over the exit portal of the microwave transmitter. These fans can fail, and the only noticeable change is that cooking becomes very uneven. A stationary standing wave pattern is set up that overheats at the antinodes and leaves the food almost raw at the nodes.

Even with a working fan, holes and bright regions can interfere with even cooking. For this reason, the food must be moved at least once during cooking. Everyone has experienced the tiny hot spots that scorch overheated popcorn in microwave ovens. These antinodal regions are roughly 1–2 cm across.

What are the bridge and frets here? The microwave oven is a metal cavity whose walls are nodes because electrical conductors cannot have electric fields deep within them. Since any form of electromagnetic radiation has both electric and magnetic fields propagating in tandem, the metal cavity reflects microwaves efficiently. Even in the window, you are looking through a metal mesh that behaves as a solid metal wall to microwaves. The food is always elevated on a low tray because it won't heat right against a node.

Here's the connection to telescope optics. A telescope aperture is oscillating at a given unchanging frequency (like the microwave transmitter). Bright places in the image are the equivalent of hot spots in the oven. Dark places are similar to cold spots that leave food uncooked.

We can thus interpret the behavior of the diffraction structure near focus as a standing wave. A slice through the focal region of an image that suffers from a small amount of spherical aberration is depicted in Fig. 4-14. This figure shows how the light collapses to focus and expands again beyond it, with the region closer to the objective on the left above the label −2 and the region farther from the objective above the label 2. It is printed at very low contrast to emphasize the low-level structure. The nodes and antinodes are easy to identify. Because the aperture is a rigid geometrical structure, there are locations where the wave doesn't fit correctly and places where the vibration is favored.

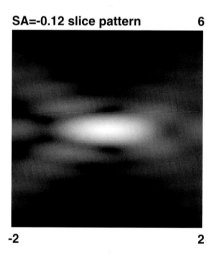

**Fig. 4-14.** *Longitudinal slice near focus of an aperture suffering from slight spherical aberration.*

This situation is very much like a brook trickling over a rocky streambed. Over one particular pebble, the surface of the water is elevated a small amount. In other places the surface seems undisturbed. The overall look is deceptively frozen, and we forget that in only a few moments all the water has moved downstream to be replaced by fresh water occupying the same configuration.

Similarly, we interpret the standing wave of the image as some sort of fixed artifact, but energy is rushing through the instrument at the speed of light. The nodal points that can be seen as dark rings in the focused image and corrugations in the defocused image are induced by the geometry of the situation. They are more like the pebble than the water. Aberrations disturb the geometry and in doing so affect the standing waves.

## 4.5    Other Aberrations—The Pupil Function

The tilt and defocusing aberrations are correctable errors. True, you can't see much if the image is defocused, but you can regain a crisp image with only a turn of a knob. Tilt error merely requires you to redirect your gaze to the center of the stellar image. The observer can't get rid of the smearing of the image caused by diffraction, but if the magnification is small enough, that spread is acceptably small.

Up to now, the discussion has been mostly about perfect apertures. What happens when some imperfection causes the wavefront to buckle as it passes through the aperture? Our little secondary sources, or radiators, are no longer on the surface of a sphere. They are confined to some sort of surface shape for which no unique focus position can be found. Asymmetries form in the node patterns (as in Fig. 4-14).

The best focus position no longer sees these radiators at a single phase. The wave sum can never equal the whole area of the aperture. Of course, for most of the realistic aberrations considered in this book, the errors at best focus will never get so large as to demand more than one coarse Fresnel zone to show it. Not until aberration amounts to $1/2$ wavelength peak-to-valley will more than one Fresnel zone appear on the aperture at best focus. A more accurate way of doing the wave sum will show that the peak intensity is always less than unity for aberrated apertures.

These Fresnel zones are a good educational device, but they don't allow sufficient gradation to permit detailed examination of what is happening with radiators at the aperture. For that, we need to introduce the *pupil function*. For now, we can define the pupil function as a surface containing information about both the phase and the transmission of the aberration. It is defined more precisely in Appendix B.

The aberration distortion of the wavefront for simple defocusing appears in Fig. 4-15. The aperture is shown below the wavefront. Fresnel zones are contours of such a surface. The transmission portion of the pupil function looks like a flat tabletop because this aperture has uniform transmission to the edge. Most of the pupil functions appearing later will have similar on-off transmission behavior. The aberration function is shown most often because it is generally the most interesting component of the complete pupil function.

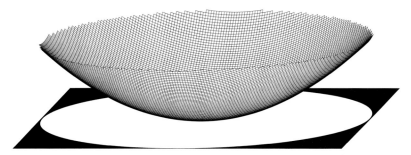

**Fig. 4-15.** *The aberration function of defocusing, with the aperture indicated in black below the wavefront surface. The direction of focus is up.*

Figure 4-15 shows the defocusing aberration function outside focus. The aberration function inside focus is a low mound. For a perfect aperture, the aberration function would be a flat plate. All of the optical difficulties appearing in this book will have an associated pupil function. Far from being just a conceptual device, the pupil function contains the essence of image formation in the telescope. Mathematical operations on the pupil function lead to the diffraction pattern and the modulation transfer function.

# Chapter 5

# Conducting the Star Test

Astronomers have long used the star test as a comforting touch with reality. A quick turn of the focuser is often enough to confirm that the telescope is aligned, cooled off, and ready for operation. Making such a determination requires no reference to numbers, but occasionally you'll want to use the star test to estimate the strength of aberrations on the glass. You must then know exactly how far to defocus the telescope in terms of quantities that can be compared with wavefront deformations.

Also, convenient use of the star test often has nothing to do with "stars." In some cases, atmospheric turbulence, apparent stellar motion, or waiting for a clear night makes using true stars too difficult. To conduct daytime or earthbound tests, you can no longer rely on the great distances and small angular extent of actual stars. When using an artificial source, you must figure the minimum distance at which it can be placed and the maximum size of the pinhole. If you are sloppy about these points, you could unfairly decide that a good telescope is bad.

This chapter deals primarily with the following three topics:

1. Translating defocusing aberration to the more familiar but less general topic of eyepiece movement.

2. Sizing, making, and placing artificial sources.

3. Setting up and doing an "official" star test, as opposed to the usual check of the operating conditions of the telescope.

Important results of this chapter are listed in tables. For completeness, the derivations are sketched either here or in the Appendix. Those who are interested can see where some of the concepts in this chapter originated, but performing an effective star test requires no more than careful use of the tables.

## 5.1   Defocusing and Sensitivity

Figures appearing in this book avoid any reference to how far you must turn the focuser forward or backward to obtain a certain amount of defocus. Instead, any defocus amount refers to *defocusing aberration* measured in wavelengths on the aperture pupil (see end of Chapter 4). Why use defocus in such a peculiar manner, when the straightforward method of eyepiece motion can be easily understood by everyone?

The answer is simple; telescopes are too different from one another. The exact amount the focuser must travel to show a given pattern varies with the focal ratio of the telescope. Telescopes with equivalent aberrations and obstructions will show identical patterns, but they all do so for different eyepiece motions. If you specify focuser motion, you must also give the focal ratio. The result is a muddy picture of a truly simple concept.

Defocusing aberration, as measured on the wavefront, is a sort of universal coordinate system that classifies identical behavior in many different telescopes. In an effort to reduce the multiplicity of patterns, defocusing aberration is used as a generic variable. It has features that transcend telescope type. More importantly, it is easy to go the other way and calculate how far you must move the eyepiece to yield a given defocus aberration.

### 5.1.1   Focuser Motion Related to Defocusing Aberration

The defocusing aberration was mentioned briefly at the end of Chapter 4, but no derivation of it was made. It is a simple expression that describes the differences in the sagittae of two different wavefront spheres.[1] The difference between two eyepiece positions for a given number of wavelengths of defocusing aberration is derived in Appendix E. The result is

$$f - f' = \Delta f = 8F^2 \Delta n \lambda, \tag{5.1}$$

where $F$ is the focal ratio, $\lambda$ is the wavelength, and $\Delta n$ is the change in defocusing aberration in wavelengths.

If $n$ is allowed to go from $+1/4$ to $-1/4$, this quantity becomes $\Delta f = 4\lambda F^2$. This is an expression for the *depth of focus*, or the maximum range for improperly setting the focuser. Since the diameter of the diffraction image is $2.44\lambda F$, the image spot is much longer than it is wide. In fact, the length-to-width ratio

$$\frac{\text{length}}{\text{width}} = \frac{4F^2\lambda}{2.44\lambda F} = 1.64F \tag{5.2}$$

---

[1]The *sagitta* is the amount by which the sphere protrudes through the aperture. Because the radii to the edges of this partial sphere look like stretched bowstrings, it was natural to name this quantity *sagitta*, or *arrow*. (See Figure in Appendix E.)

is nearly 25 for an f/15 instrument.

The length of this sausage-shaped region is very helpful. It permits small amounts of error in the setting of focus in accessory instruments (such as cameras). It makes less difference in adjusting visual focus because focus is usually fine-tuned by the eye itself. Only those observers who have had cataract surgery or who have little flexibility in their eyes may be forced to rely exclusively on the focusing action of the telescope.

Sidgwick gave another formula for depth of focus: $\Delta f = 4(1.22\lambda F^2)$. This factor is 1.22 larger than the one derived here (Sidgwick 1955, p. 425). The seeming discrepancy comes from the methods used to derive the expressions. Neither formula is meant to be a crisp limit, only the point where the image begins to degrade noticeably. Both expressions are proportional to the focal ratio squared. Thus, an f/5 telescope has only a quarter of the focusing tolerance of an f/10 telescope.

Tables 5-1a and 5-1b list eyepiece motions for varying focal ratios and defocusing aberrations. For example, if we defocus the image of an f/6 Newtonian by 8 wavelengths, we can see from the tables that we must change the focus by 0.050 inches (or 1.27 mm). In the convention used here, one must focus *outward* when the defocus aberration is given as a positive number and focus *inward* if defocus aberration is given as negative.

Much can be learned by carefully examining these tables. They show that defocus distances are vanishingly small for fast focal ratios. The first tabulated column is labeled by 0.5 wavelength of defocusing aberration, or about the depth of focus mentioned above. Yet to achieve focusing within $\pm 1/4$ wavelength at f/4 (or $\Delta n = 0.5$), one must hold focus to within 0.0014 inches, or 0.035 mm. Clearly, if our eyes weren't somewhat internally adjustable, we would struggle to focus fast instruments. Slow motion helical or motorized focusers would seem to be justified for these low focal ratio telescopes.

At the other end of the chart are extremely long focal ratios like f/22, which would describe two-mirror Kutter schiefspieglers. To induce 12 wavelengths of defocusing aberration in such instruments, we would have to move the eyepiece over an inch. It is apparent that on such slow instruments, we will scrutinize only small defocusing aberrations before running out of focuser travel. Long focal length telescopes, however, are usually lunar-planetary instruments. They are deliberately tested to higher standards, so small amounts of defocus are the most interesting. A focal ratio of 50 is included because you might mask down your instrument to see a supposedly perfect image.

On fast instruments, the star-test image will probably be evaluated at high values of defocus, beyond even 12 wavelengths. This is not too much of a problem because the test is still sensitive to the relatively severe

Table 5-1a
Defocus distances for different
focal ratios and defocusing aberrations
(distances in inches)
Wavelength is $2.165 \times 10^{-5}$ in

| Focal ratio | Defocusing Aberration (wavelengths) | | | | |
| | 0.5 | 1 | 4 | 8 | 12 |
| --- | --- | --- | --- | --- | --- |
| 4 | 0.0014 | 0.0028 | 0.011 | 0.022 | 0.033 |
| 4.5 | 0.0018 | 0.0035 | 0.014 | 0.028 | 0.042 |
| 5 | 0.0022 | 0.0043 | 0.017 | 0.035 | 0.052 |
| 6 | 0.0031 | 0.0062 | 0.025 | 0.050 | 0.075 |
| 7 | 0.0042 | 0.0085 | 0.034 | 0.068 | 0.102 |
| 8 | 0.0055 | 0.011 | 0.044 | 0.089 | 0.133 |
| 9 | 0.0070 | 0.014 | 0.056 | 0.112 | 0.168 |
| 10 | 0.0087 | 0.017 | 0.069 | 0.139 | 0.208 |
| 11 | 0.010 | 0.021 | 0.084 | 0.168 | 0.252 |
| 12 | 0.012 | 0.025 | 0.100 | 0.200 | 0.299 |
| 15 | 0.019 | 0.039 | 0.156 | 0.312 | 0.468 |
| 22 | 0.042 | 0.084 | 0.335 | 0.671 | 1.006 |
| 50 | 0.217 | 0.433 | 1.732 | 3.465 | 5.197 |

Table 5-1b
Defocus distances for different
focal ratios and defocusing aberrations
(distances in millimeters)
Wavelength is 550 nm

| Focal ratio | Defocusing Aberration (wavelengths) | | | | |
| | 0.5 | 1 | 4 | 8 | 12 |
| --- | --- | --- | --- | --- | --- |
| 4 | 0.035 | 0.070 | 0.282 | 0.563 | 0.845 |
| 4.5 | 0.045 | 0.089 | 0.356 | 0.713 | 1.069 |
| 5 | 0.055 | 0.110 | 0.440 | 0.880 | 1.320 |
| 6 | 0.079 | 0.158 | 0.634 | 1.267 | 1.901 |
| 7 | 0.108 | 0.216 | 0.862 | 1.725 | 2.587 |
| 8 | 0.141 | 0.282 | 1.126 | 2.253 | 3.379 |
| 9 | 0.178 | 0.356 | 1.426 | 2.851 | 4.277 |
| 10 | 0.220 | 0.440 | 1.760 | 3.520 | 5.280 |
| 11 | 0.266 | 0.532 | 2.130 | 4.259 | 6.389 |
| 12 | 0.317 | 0.634 | 2.534 | 5.069 | 7.603 |
| 15 | 0.495 | 0.990 | 3.960 | 7.920 | 11.880 |
| 22 | 1.065 | 2.130 | 8.518 | 17.037 | 25.555 |
| 50 | 5.500 | 11.000 | 44.000 | 88.000 | 132.000 |

aberrations that pester these instruments.

The best way of using Tables 5-1a and 5-1b is to look up the values corresponding to your focal ratio and write them down somewhere. It might even be convenient to calibrate your focuser knob. Rack it a full turn and see how much it advances focus. This procedure is easy on Newtonians and refractors. You just measure the change in the amount of protrusion in the focuser tube. For example, if one turn of the knob yields $3/4$ inch (19.05 mm) of focuser travel, a $30°$ twist gives about $1/16$ inch (1.6 mm).

This motion is equivalent to 10 wavelengths defocusing aberration for a telescope working at f/6.

On Cassegrain-type catadioptrics, it is less obvious how to tell which direction focus is tracking or how far it moves. These instruments usually achieve focus not by physically transporting the eyepiece, but by internally moving the primary mirror toward the secondary. First, focus the telescope with an eyepiece sitting firmly in its socket. Then, loosen the eyepiece and draw it 10 mm or so outside of the socket. Now, tighten the set screw. Find focus once again, being aware of the direction and angle that you have turned the focuser knob (it may help to stick a temporary pointer on the end of the knob). You have found the direction and amount of an effective 10 mm *inward* focus change. On my Schmidt-Cassegrain, this motion was counterclockwise.

### 5.1.2 Sensitivity of the Star Test

In the equations governing diffraction (Appendix B), defocus is added as a uniformly interfering term to the summation. The point where errors show themselves with highest sensitivity is right at focus because no defocusing term has been added to dilute the image. However, the focused image has two problems:

1. You can't tell where on the surface the error originated.

2. The way the error is expressed is in the *intensity* of the diffraction rings.

A good example is the degradation caused by a secondary mirror. Light has been kicked from the center of the focused image into the rings, but you can't tell why by peering at the focused image. Furthermore, the human eye is not skilled in determining absolute intensities of the rings. Yet, by drawing the eyepiece a little out of focus, you see the shadow of the diagonal begin to appear. The shadow more-or-less follows its origins, and aberrations behave similarly. As you defocus the instrument, the light partially unmixes and you can at least guess at the difficulty causing the trouble.

Unfortunately, if you defocus any image far enough, it will look the same regardless of the extent of the error—a flat, uniform disk of light with obstructions clearly delineated. Even the spider shows itself if you defocus too far. The star test loses sensitivity with increased defocus. The light becomes completely unmixed.

Our goal is to find an intermediate focus where the light has become slightly less entangled but is still mixed enough to show optical errors.

In my opinion, most optical errors are best shown at less than 8 to 12 wavelengths defocusing aberration (a prominent exception is the presence of zones, which often are best seen when defocused further).

What is the upper limit of sensitivity under ideal conditions? A photograph in Fig. 1-5 depicts the actual defocused diffraction pattern of a nearly perfect circular aperture. In the theoretical pattern of Fig. 1-4, the defocus was adjusted until the theory closely matched the photograph. Variations of only $1/50$ wavelength were enough to destroy the match. Even then, the photograph betrays slight differences caused by microscopic projections at the edge of the aperture stop, which had been made from punched metal. Under laboratory conditions, using monochromatic light, the star test can detect wavefront distortions of $1/50$ wavelength peak-to-valley, an outstandingly sensitive measure.

Welford (1960) stated that the star test was accurate to $1/20$ wavelength for broad deformations of the wavefront and $1/60$ wavelength for sharp variations. Welford's estimate matches the observations here. Later on, in Chapter 11 on zonal defects, it is noted that the star test is sensitive to sharp zones even in the presence of gross defocusing. Again, observation concurs with Welford's result.

Field conditions will lessen this sensitivity considerably. Even so, the star test is more than adequate. Using light of more than one color and testing under less than optimal conditions, the slight spherical aberration of telescopes having total wavefront error of less than $1/10$ wavelength is still quite easy to detect.

## 5.2   Artificial Sources

The star test is often performed in the field on a real star. However, for critical testing, you will find that an artificial source of light is convenient and less variable. Artificial sources are preferred for a number of reasons:

1. You can, to some extent, control the brightness.

2. With bright sources, the color can be readily altered and adjusted using filters.

3. The close-in nature of the test allows less of the turbulent atmosphere to intervene.

4. Since the source is fixed with reference to the telescope, it requires no tracking. If required, you can clamp the telescope down rigidly.

The beautifully steady pattern that results from use of an artificial source will spoil you. There are some disadvantages, however:

1. The use of an artificial star usually demands a nearly horizontal telescope position. This places maximum demands on the optical mounting cells. Unusual astigmatism, misalignment, or warping may derive solely from the vertical position of the cell.

2. Some of the recommended source placement distances listed in Table 5-2 demand that you look through horizontal spans of 1600 feet (about 0.5 km) although most entries in the table are much less.

3. You need to make a point-like source of light. You must know the diameter of the pinhole to ensure that it is smaller than the resolution of your instrument. Unlike real stars, the source is not always guaranteed to be small.

### 5.2.1 Distance of Artificial Sources

A paraboloidal reflector is the perfect single mirror for light originating at astronomical distances. However, if the source is at a distance of only twice the focal length, a sphere is the perfect surface. At an intermediate distance, the ideal mirror is a prolate spheroid. Thus, three different forms do the best imaging at three different distances. A telescope could perform adequately when star tested with a nearby source yet fail when directed at the distant sky. Even worse, a fine telescope could be unfairly misjudged by failing the test on a source that is much too close. How much is the test disturbed if the source is placed nearby?

The largest effect of using an artificial source close at hand is to induce spherical aberration in the system. In other words, when a perfect astronomical telescope is forced to peer myopically at a nearby source, it shows spherical overcorrection that is not found when directed skyward. W.T. Welford says the star test should be conducted with an artificial star placed more than 20 focal lengths away, but he also warns his readers to do accurate ray tracing of the optical system before it is used at questionably close source distances (Welford 1987). We can see below that Welford's suggestion of 20 times the focal length is a very good one for normal apertures and focal ratios, but it fails rather badly for fast mirrors.

In the May, 1991, issue of *Sky & Telescope,* Roger Sinnott traced rays through paraboloidal mirrors and saw how close the source could be placed before unacceptable spherical overcorrection was noticed. This empirically-derived formula, rewritten for the notation used here, is

$$N \text{ [ft]} = 28 \left( \frac{D}{F} \right)^2 \text{ [D in inches]} \tag{5.3}$$

where $F$ is the focal ratio and $D$, the aperture diameter. This equation is rewritten to calculate the multiplier of the focal length:

$$\text{Mult} = \left(\frac{336}{FD}\right)\left(\frac{D}{F}\right)^2 = 336\frac{D}{F^3} \text{ [D in inches]}. \tag{5.4}$$

The formula can be put in any unit system by pulling out the unit of wavelength:

$$\text{Mult} = (336)(2.17 \times 10^{-5})\frac{D}{F^3\lambda} = \frac{1}{137}\frac{D}{F^3\lambda}. \tag{5.5}$$

By comparing a parabola and an ellipse that are tangent at the center and touching at the edge of the mirror and doubling the greatest difference, a similar result can be derived analytically. This results in the slightly different formula

$$\text{Mult} = \frac{1}{128}\frac{D}{F^3\lambda}. \tag{5.6}$$

The difference is insignificant, and it probably occurs because Sinnott's program automatically accounts for the different angle of exit from a mirror's surface while the analytic calculation ignores this angle. Table 5-2 uses Sinnott's result because it leads to smaller separations. Even though it is numerically derived, it probably is more accurate for the low focal ratios of greatest interest. An example calculation: a 6-inch f/4 paraboloid has $1/4$ wavelength of spherical overcorrection when directed toward a source placed at 63 feet (multiple of focal length: 31.5). The distances in this table induce approximately $1/4$ wavelength of spherical aberration in a Newtonian reflector (Sinnott 1991).

Since the distances appearing in this table are only on the edge of optical respectability, readers are advised to *double* them for use in the star test. Wavelength enters in the denominator of Equations 5.5 or 5.6, meaning that a perfect mirror will appear less than $1/8$ wavelength overcorrected with the source placed at such a distance.

Don't fret if you are forced to position the source a few steps closer than you would like. In my years of telescope testing experience, few instruments possessed less than $1/8$ wavelength total error on the wavefront. (Sadly, almost the same can be said for $1/4$ wavelength.)

Distances greater than Welford's empirical rule take place only for low focal ratios or large apertures. Most elaborate optical systems, such as refractors, are made in slower configurations. Twenty times the focal length will probably test these systems adequately. Indeed, the telescope with the highest chance of breaking Welford's rule will probably be the Newtonian reflector for which this table is calculated.

Table 5-2
Telescope-to-pinhole distances resulting in
$1/4$ wavelength overcorrection error in paraboloids
(multiples of focal length)

| | | Focal Ratio | | | | | |
|---|---|---|---|---|---|---|---|
| | | 4 | 5 | 6 | 8 | 10 | 15 |
| D(in) | D(mm) | | | | | | |
| 2.4 | 61 | 13 | 10* | 10* | 10* | 10* | 10* |
| 3 | 76 | 16 | 10* | 10* | 10* | 10* | 10* |
| 4.25 | 108 | 22 | 11 | 10* | 10* | 10* | 10* |
| 6 | 152 | 32 | 16 | 10* | 10* | 10* | 10* |
| 8 | 203 | 42 | 22 | 12 | 10* | 10* | 10* |
| 10 | 254 | 53 | 27 | 16 | 10* | 10* | 10* |
| 12.5 | 318 | 66 | 34 | 19 | 10* | 10* | 10* |
| 14 | 356 | 74 | 38 | 22 | 10* | 10* | 10* |
| 16 | 406 | 84 | 43 | 25 | 11 | 10* | 10* |
| 17.5 | 445 | 92 | 47 | 27 | 11 | 10* | 10* |
| 20 | 508 | 105 | 54 | 31 | 13 | 10* | 10* |
| 24 | 610 | 126 | 65 | 37 | 16 | 10* | 10* |

Values that will be less than 20 times the focal length (after doubling) are suppressed in the table and marked with asterisks. Such close source distances will stretch the focus outward more than $1/20$ of the normal focal length of the instrument. As the focuser tube seldom allows such motions without running out of travel or seriously vignetting the telescope, such close source distances are not recommended if they can be avoided.

In fact, a good policy before testing is to remove the eyepiece after focusing on the artificial source. Place your eye at the approximate focal plane and verify that the whole optical system is still in view (you may need to use a flashlight to illuminate the inside of the tube). If not, you've got to move the source farther away and try again.

One trouble zone occurs in this table. In fast and extremely large mirrors, the tolerable distance increases explosively. For a 24-inch f/4 mirror, the source should be placed (after doubling) at a distance of at least 2016 feet (0.61 km). These huge instruments are comparatively rare, and more importantly, they are seldom tested for quality much beyond the diffraction limit. Large telescopes are used for light gathering power, so using the $1/4$-wavelength distances in Table 5-2, undoubled, is better than not doing the test at all.

If you are testing more ordinary instruments, twice the distance in the table is easily achieved. For the more common 12.5-inch f/5, the source distance has contracted to a manageable 354 feet (0.11 km).

Even though Table 5-2 strictly applies only to Newtonian reflectors, we shall use it as a general guide for the star test. These numbers, I believe, will be approximately valid for fixed optical systems in general.

Unfortunately, this table does not work where the focusing mechanism of the telescope itself damages the optical correction. This situation is common for general-purpose Schmidt-Cassegrain telescopes that change the mirror-secondary separation to achieve focus. Happily, the source separation that leads to rays being diverted outside the Airy disk has been estimated by Rutten and van Venrooij. For a 200-mm (8-inch) f/10 having surface shapes approximating those available in commercial units, the separation is approximately 48 meters, or 24 focal lengths (Rutten and van Venrooij 1988, p. 87). In the discussion on the Danjon and Couder conditions in Ch. 1, it was pointed out that simple spherical aberration shifts rays outside the diffraction disk at about $1/7$ wavelength. Thus, a separation of 20 focal lengths would be adequate for an accuracy of at least $1/4$ wavelength, and about 40 focal lengths will test to far beyond the diffraction limit.

One additional instruction for the reader: If you cannot measure the source distance because of intervening impediments, try to err on the long side. You cannot place the source too far away. If your system seems to have a smooth overcorrection error, put the source at a greater distance (maybe even returning to a true star) and test again before you conclude that the error is on the glass.

### 5.2.2   Diameter of Artificial Sources

We must carefully select a pinhole size in the artificial source so that it is smaller than the resolution of the instrument. On the other hand, it must be large enough to allow sufficient illumination to fill a defocused image with light. To calculate such a diameter, we extend the Airy disk radius to the distance of the pinhole. If that radius is chosen as the *diameter* of the source pinhole, we ensure that the source is no more than half of the angular extent of a point image.

This calculation is done for distances twice those in Table 5-2. The results are listed in Tables 5-3a and 5-3b. A quick glance at these tables shows some pinholes that will be extremely difficult to make or measure. It is certainly no easy task to make accurate sizes of pinholes only 0.07 mm (or about 0.003 inches) across. But these pinholes refer to unusual telescopes— a 3-inch f/5, for example. Twenty times the focal length of a 3-inch f/5 is only 300 inches (7.6 m). It is relatively simple to use a pinhole 4 times as large (0.28 mm) and place it 4 times as far away (100 ft). The artificial source is still only a backyard away.

The pinhole can be punched in aluminum foil. To check the pinhole's size, expand it in a slide projector. Use a projection lens of known focal length and place the projector a measured distance from the screen. For

Table 5-3a
Maximum diameters in millimeters
for artificial sources

| D(in) | D(mm) | Focal Ratio | | | | | |
|---|---|---|---|---|---|---|---|
| | | 4 | 5 | 6 | 8 | 10 | 15 |
| 2.4 | 61 | 0.07 | 0.07 | 0.08 | 0.11 | 0.13 | 0.20 |
| 3 | 76 | 0.09 | 0.07 | 0.08 | 0.11 | 0.13 | 0.20 |
| 4.25 | 108 | 0.12 | 0.08 | 0.08 | 0.11 | 0.13 | 0.20 |
| 6 | 152 | 0.17 | 0.11 | 0.08 | 0.11 | 0.13 | 0.20 |
| 8 | 203 | 0.23 | 0.14 | 0.10 | 0.11 | 0.13 | 0.20 |
| 10 | 254 | 0.28 | 0.18 | 0.13 | 0.11 | 0.13 | 0.20 |
| 12.5 | 318 | 0.35 | 0.23 | 0.16 | 0.11 | 0.13 | 0.20 |
| 14 | 356 | 0.40 | 0.25 | 0.18 | 0.11 | 0.13 | 0.20 |
| 16 | 406 | 0.45 | 0.29 | 0.20 | 0.11 | 0.13 | 0.20 |
| 17.5 | 445 | 0.49 | 0.32 | 0.22 | 0.12 | 0.13 | 0.20 |
| 20 | 508 | 0.56 | 0.36 | 0.25 | 0.14 | 0.13 | 0.20 |
| 24 | 610 | 0.68 | 0.43 | 0.30 | 0.17 | 0.13 | 0.20 |

Table 5-3b
Maximum diameters in inches
for artificial sources

| D(in) | D(mm) | Focal Ratio | | | | | |
|---|---|---|---|---|---|---|---|
| | | 4 | 5 | 6 | 8 | 10 | 15 |
| 2.4 | 61 | 0.003 | 0.003 | 0.003 | 0.004 | 0.005 | 0.008 |
| 3 | 76 | 0.003 | 0.003 | 0.003 | 0.004 | 0.005 | 0.008 |
| 4.25 | 108 | 0.005 | 0.003 | 0.003 | 0.004 | 0.005 | 0.008 |
| 6 | 152 | 0.007 | 0.004 | 0.003 | 0.004 | 0.005 | 0.008 |
| 8 | 203 | 0.009 | 0.006 | 0.004 | 0.004 | 0.005 | 0.008 |
| 10 | 254 | 0.011 | 0.007 | 0.005 | 0.004 | 0.005 | 0.008 |
| 12.5 | 318 | 0.014 | 0.009 | 0.006 | 0.004 | 0.005 | 0.008 |
| 14 | 356 | 0.016 | 0.010 | 0.007 | 0.004 | 0.005 | 0.008 |
| 16 | 406 | 0.018 | 0.011 | 0.008 | 0.004 | 0.005 | 0.008 |
| 17.5 | 445 | 0.019 | 0.012 | 0.009 | 0.005 | 0.005 | 0.008 |
| 20 | 508 | 0.022 | 0.014 | 0.010 | 0.006 | 0.005 | 0.008 |
| 24 | 610 | 0.027 | 0.017 | 0.012 | 0.007 | 0.005 | 0.008 |

example, if a 75-mm projection lens is used and the projection distance is 5 meters, the magnification is about $5000/75 = 66$ power. The 0.28 mm pinhole is expanded to 18.5 mm by projection (somewhere around 3/4 inch). A check of approximate roundness finishes the inspection. Be careful that you don't leave the foil illuminated longer than a few seconds in the projection gate. It's like an oven in there, and a great deal of energy is being dumped into the metal. If you allow too much heat into the aluminum, your slide mount may burst into flames.

You can effectively shrink a large pinhole down to a tiny one using another technique. If you have access to a good high-magnification microscope objective, you can image a large pinhole onto a small replica of itself. Here, place the large pinhole where the microscope's eyepiece normally sits (4 – 6 inches from the threaded end of the objective). Shine light through the

pinhole and then through the microscope objective, in a reverse direction
to the way that microscopes customarily process light. The microscope
objective is pointed at the distant telescope and the source appears to be
floating a few millimeters in front of the objective. For example, if a 1-mm
pinhole is placed 100 mm behind a 5-mm focal length microscope objective, the source appears to be diminished to about 0.05 mm. You can also
use high-magnification oculars for this purpose (also used backwards), but
microscope objectives are best.

### 5.2.3   Using a Reflective Sphere Instead of a Pinhole

Even if you have success with the painstaking manufacture of the tiny
source itself, you must then attach it to a lamp or flashlight and focus
some light through the tiny opening. Making a true pinhole source can be
laborious, but there are easier ways of fabricating a source that works every
bit as well.

Since the star test is a supposedly easy technique for evaluating finished
telescope optics, readers probably do not want to be given elaborate and
difficult plans for constructing auxiliary equipment. Optical devices cannot
often be reproduced without having access to the same lenses and other
minor gadgets.

Yet the problem of adequate point-source construction must be solved
somehow. Astronomy popularizer John Dobson figures his mirrors using the
star test. Glints and reflections viewed at great distances serve as the point
source. He even claims to have performed the final test of one telescope
using the reflection in a bird's eye.

Using the glitter of the Sun in small spherical reflectors is an excellent
way of achieving the requisite small size and dazzling intensity. Dobson very
likely uses a variation of the device described below when a well-placed and
patient bird is not available.[2]

Conveniently, every year huge numbers of ideal spherical reflectors are
made in the form of blown-glass tree ornaments. These balls are silvered
on the interior and commonly available in sizes of 2.5 to 7.5 cm (1 to 3
inches). If we calculate the size of a bright light source reflected in such a
decoration, we can use these devices to make tiny virtual-image pinholes of
accurately known size. The derivation of the expression for the glitter size
involves some straightforward but non-instructive trigonometry, so it has
been placed in Appendix F.

One important thing to notice from the derivation appearing in the

---

[2]I do not recommend the star test as the sole method of testing during fabrication.
It is best used as an independent check of workshop tests. The star test can be quite
confusing when two or more types of surface deformation are contributing to the errors.

Appendix is that you don't have to do a trigonometric calculation every time you plan to use one of these spheres. You merely estimate that the glitter image will be less than about $1/300$ the diameter of the sphere for an average solar reflection. If the light is reflected back toward the Sun (i.e., a nearly centered reflection appears in the sphere), the half-degree solar disk shrinks to about $1/450$ of the sphere.

This $\approx 1/300$-diameter approximation has certain consequences when viewed in the context of Table 5-3. We see a range of needed pinhole diameters from 0.003 inches to 0.027 inches. Three hundred times these diameters are reflective spheres from about 1 inch (25 mm) to 9 inches (23 cm) diameter. The last sphere was calculated for a 61-cm (24-inch) f/4 reflector seen at a distance of 615 meters (0.38 miles). It is in a very unusual corner of Table 5-3. In fact, the largest source point that will probably be required by most readers is for a 17.5-inch f/4.5 reflector. It is about 0.016 inches (0.4 mm), which is the glitter size of the Sun in a 5-inch (125-mm) sphere.

Table 5-4 gives approximate maximum dimensions of virtual pinholes for various sizes of reflective sphere where the source of light subtends $1/2°$ (approximately the solar diameter).

Table 5-4
Approximate virtual pinhole
maximum dimensions
(light source is the Sun)

| sphere (in) | "pinhole" (in) | sphere (mm) | "pinhole" (mm) |
|---|---|---|---|
| 0.5 | 0.002 | 12.5 | 0.04 |
| 1.0 | 0.003 | 25 | 0.08 |
| 2.0 | 0.007 | 50 | 0.17 |
| 3.0 | 0.010 | 75 | 0.25 |
| 4.0 | 0.013 | 100 | 0.33 |
| 5.0 | 0.017 | 125 | 0.42 |
| 6.0 | 0.020 | 150 | 0.50 |
| 7.0 | 0.023 | 175 | 0.58 |
| 8.0 | 0.027 | 200 | 0.67 |
| 9.0 | 0.030 | 225 | 0.75 |
| 10.0 | 0.033 | 250 | 0.83 |

Few ornament bulbs are as large as 5 inches across. However, you can use a smaller glitter point. The reason so much care is taken with source size is because you're going to have to place that sphere 300 meters (about $1/5$ mile) from your 17.5-inch reflector. That's a long way, and you want bright images.

The sphere also need not be whole. A convex adhesive mirror, commonly available in automobile parts stores, is used for increasing the field angle of flat rear-view mirrors. If you draw a circle that is the diameter of the sphere you want, you can take it to the store and estimate which of these inexpensive reflectors most closely matches the circle.

Partial sphere reflectors must be aligned so that the reflection is visible in the direction of your instrument, but this task is easy and it will last long enough that you can do an unhurried test.

One last note: Other authors have recommended the use of black spheres because they obscure the reflection of the surroundings while still reflecting the Sun. Glossy black spheres diminish all light that strikes them. You could get an equivalent effect by using a neutral density 1.0 to 2.0 filter at the eyepiece (dimming not just the sphere, but the whole field of view). Using a glossy black surface may be a good policy during inspection of the dazzling image close to focus, but it is not productive when defocusing farther. If you must diminish the intensity, go ahead and do so with an eyepiece filter, but start with the brightest image possible. Alternatively, it is often convenient to have two spheres in close proximity, one smaller than the other (such as a shiny ball bearing next to the tree ornament). A check for small amounts of astigmatism, for example, is best done by rocking the focus very slightly on either side of the most compact image. The large sphere's image is often too bright and the smaller sphere serves well as a point source for small defocus.

### 5.2.4   Setting Up a Nighttime Artificial Source

You can arrange the same light reflection at night by providing your own illumination. Light no longer comes from a constant angle of the Sun, so care is required in arranging a lamp. Attach a flashlight on a photographic tripod or other adjustable support and direct it towards your sphere. The flashlight performs best when stopped down to about 1 cm and placed about 1 meter away. This procedure will approximate the $1/2°$ angular diameter of the Sun, so the tables above will work the same. You may achieve a tighter beam if you stop the flashlight down off-axis, so that the filament of the lamp is not directly visible. Use a flat sheet of aluminum foil to make the mask. The exit portal need not be perfectly round. The flashlight should be placed as near to the line of sight as possible.

You might also wish to color balance the light more closely to the output of real stars. Coloring the source lamp is particularly useful when testing refractors. Most incandescent filaments have a black body color temperature of around $2500°C$, or as red as Betelgeuse. The spectrum should be filtered either with a pale blue (Wratten 80A) eyepiece filter or by filtering the output of the flashlight with a similar light blue filter (Berry 1992). An ideal filter corrects indoor lighting (i.e., "tungsten" light bulbs) for outdoor slide film. For most testing, though, you will prefer a single color, and the reddish tinge of the flashlight is welcome. In fact, you may prefer to test in gold-colored spheres, which are also available as tree ornaments.

Choose a site without stray sources of light. A daytime test can be conducted nearly anywhere because the Sun is the brightest light source, but a nighttime test can be compromised by the presence of street lights nearby. Your flashlight is still likely to be the most prominent source reflected in the sphere. After all, it's close and is directed right at the sphere. However, nearby interfering street lights provide secondary glitter points, and other glints may make interpretation difficult—particularly at very small defocus aberrations.

Excluding stray sources of light is easy. For example, you could construct an "accordion" box to shade the sphere from all but lights in the direction of the telescope. This is a little cardboard box blackened on the inside and having a black poster board accordion-folded at the back. This folding acts as a non-glossy beam dump. Most often, though, all that is really required is a carefully-placed hood. Easier yet is to go where there aren't any spurious lights. Your usual observing site supposedly is a fairly dark locale. Just take the test equipment along.

You have one luxury that daytime testers do not have: you can move the source closer to the sphere until the pinhole begins to exceed the Airy disk. In fact, this process is made easier if you form a square hole in the flashlight mask. Stop and draw the flashlight back a small distance when this squareness appears.

## 5.3  Performing the Test

Because people wanting to test telescopes don't usually have access to towers or convenient topography to elevate the sphere, they must test through ground turbulence. Daytime testing is probably best done during the early morning and over a grassy field, but different locations and times have their own behavior. Often, a quiet time of non-turbulent behavior can be found to briefly persist near sunset. Go ahead and try the test anytime and anywhere; you may be pleasantly surprised. Also, try to place the Sun at your back to shade the eyepiece and ensure an approximately round reflection in the sphere.

You can mount your sphere in a stiff piece of poster board, poking the hanger through a hole cut in the board. If you don't use the board and wish to hang the sphere on a bush or a tree, then be sure to paint, tape, or otherwise obscure the hanger region of the ornament. It has nonspherical curvature that may present a second interfering point of light. If you are using a curved rear-view mirror, be sure to obscure the edge if it is shiny. (See Fig. 5-1.)

**Fig. 5-1.** *Spheres are illuminated by a large spotlight to exaggerate the glitter reflection. A convex rear-view mirror is shown connected to the tripod head. The stray reflection points have yet to be obscured by tape.*

One might think that a black poster board would work best, but a uniform color of dark green also works well. The uniformity is more important than the color, although bright colors should not be used.

Most telescopes require moderate distances, but large Newtonians of low focal ratio demand long, clear testing fields. Long distances that meet other requirements are sometimes hard to find. You may be able to locate straight stretches of country road, perhaps straddling a convenient valley. Be sure to set up your testing range over grass on the upwind side of the road. You don't want the heat from asphalt to disturb the test. Also, avoid optical paths that cross over building roofs. Public parks are ideal, since they feature large expanses of grass and might even be relatively deserted early in the morning.

If your telescope has a thin mirror, be prepared for astigmatism. Think of the thin mirror as flexible. Upended, it sags. If your telescope has a heavy mirror (thick or thin), also anticipate some warping. This is particularly true if you aren't supporting the mirror gently in a sling, although it appears occasionally even then.

Such patterns will not resemble the neatly symmetrical diagrams appearing in the pinched optics chapter because only two supports are likely to squeeze. If you can't eliminate this effect by careful mounting, you will have to test at elevated angles on real stars.

You may find the alignment of the telescope is changed when the instrument is pointed at the horizon. Because optics are mounted loosely, try to set up a situation with a slight upward tilt of the optical axis. With luck, the optics will lean back to rest against their natural supports. Either choose a testing range with a natural upward slope or mount the source higher. At worst, you may need to do temporary fine-alignment for the test. One suspects that glass power-line insulators are so popular as curved reflectors only because they are conveniently mounted on towers.

Then try a "snap test." Rock the focuser on either side of the sharpest image and see how difficult it is to set the focus. In the most desirable situation, the focus seems to snap into place, and no matter where you halt, you are always convinced that the limiting factor in focusing is your inability to stop your hand from turning precisely at the crispest image. (Much of this depends on the focal ratio and how steadily the telescope is mounted.) The least-desirable situation is one where the focus looks about equally good over a range of focuser travel. You drift through the region of best focus, unable to decide. Your hand-eye coordination is far from being the limiting factor (Suiter 1990).

If your visual power of accommodation is strong, then you must provide a dominant field object to hold the eye's focus while you vary the focuser. A reticle on the field plane of the eyepiece provides such an object. If you have an illuminated reticle eyepiece of 12 mm or below for photographic guiding, you can use it (possibly with a good Barlow). If you don't have a guiding eyepiece, stretch a scrap of black electrical tape halfway across the field stop of a high magnification eyepiece (the stop is the hole on the underside). If you have placed the tape close to the best focus of the ocular, you will see half of the eyepiece's field occluded by a sharp-edged shadow.

Place the point source image close to a straight edge of the artificial pattern. Your eye will naturally focus on the large, high-contrast edge. Then you can vary the image focus at will while the focus of your eye is held as if it were in a vise. This psychological trick is common in darkroom enlarger focusing aids.

Look for individual aberrations following the instructions in the chapters that deal with them. In testing refractors for optical errors having nothing to do with color correction, you may find it helpful to use a deep yellow or green filter on the eyepiece. In fact, using a colored filter is a good policy for

all telescopes, whether reflector or refractor. Even though reflectors have
no overt color errors, the star test still suffers confusion from the finite
bandwidth of white light. For example, red light of wavelength 630 nm
may be 10 wavelengths out of focus, while deep blue light of wavelength
420 nm is 15 wavelengths out of focus. A colored filter reduces the range
of contributing wavelengths in the image.

Another helpful tool is a 33% obstruction mask for your telescope. This
provides a uniform obstruction for critical spherical aberration tests. A
mask is easily made to fit over a reflector's spider. Just draw a circle one-
third the diameter of your primary mirror on thin cardboard about the
thickness of a manila file folder. Cut it out and fold it into quarters. Then
cut a slice about 6 mm to 10 mm long near the vertex of the "V" in the
folded center. Open it back up, and smooth it out. The center cut becomes
a cross. Fit it over the protruding rear side of the spider. A mask is not
necessary on f/10 Schmidt-Cassegrains because their obstruction is about
33% anyway. A refractor mask can be cut out of paper. Suspend the
obstruction on a web of sewing thread taped to the dewcap. Of course, if
your obstruction is over $1/3$ the aperture already, this option is not open to
you. Such telescopes are usually specialty instruments anyway, for which
the extra obstruction is accepted to secure some other advantage.

As an example of how to use these tables from beginning to end, as well
as a road map of the procedures and pitfalls you may encounter in star
testing telescopes, the rest of the chapter describes the testing procedure
for four imaginary instruments.

### 5.3.1   8-Inch f/6 Newtonian Reflector

We find in Table 5-2 that the source distance for $1/8$-wavelength error is
$2 \times 12f$ or 24 times the focal length of 4 feet. Multiplication yields a source
distance of 96 feet (29 m). Table 5-3a or 5-3b says the source diameter is
about 0.10 millimeter, or about 0.004 inch.

This pinhole diameter—multiplied by 300—indicates a solar reflection
in a 30-mm sphere. Since this is reasonably close to the 1-inch (25-mm)
ornament bulb, we will use that. Don't do a lot of extra work matching
these parameters precisely. You don't need to measure a 29-m testing range
carefully. The sensitivity of the star test is not helped or hindered by this
sort of precision. Pace the distance off; thirty-five steps should be enough.
If the only available spherical reflector is 2.5 inches in diameter, you can
easily go twice as far to about 200 feet (60 m). *You* are in control, not the
test.

The range is set up over a grassy lawn. It is about 8 A.M. with the
sphere placed to the south-southwest. The Sun is over the tester's left

shoulder.

We note from Tables 5-1a and 5-1b that the focusing travel necessary to achieve a defocusing aberration of 12 wavelengths is 1.9 mm (0.075 inches). The focuser withdraws $3/4$ inch per rotation, so we will turn the focuser less than about $\pm 1/10$ of a turn for most aberration checks.

The first thing you notice when viewing the defocused image is the seeming appearance of severe misalignment. When you set the telescope up, you checked the coarse alignment, and it was fine. You replace the sighthole eyepiece. The mirror's dot is still on the center. What is happening?

Then you notice that the focuser is racked back 50 mm farther than usual. In fact, you had to dig in your eyepiece box to find the focus extender tube. You look in the sighthole again and this time see the problem. At this focus position, the edge of the diagonal mirror cuts off the outer portion of the mirror. The vignetting is a little worse on one side than the other, which explains the off-center diagonal shadow. The out-of-focus disk isn't really that far misaligned, it just isn't completely illuminated.

You walk out to the sphere, pick it up, and take it another 30 steps farther back. Returning to the telescope, you put in an eyepiece and focus; it is about an inch closer to the tube. Pulling the eyepiece out and putting the sighthole back in, you can now see the whole mirror reflected in the diagonal. Offhand, you realize that you could have used a bigger sphere at this new distance. You decide to give this one a try anyway; it seems bright enough.

This time you notice that the secondary shadow leans slightly to the left side of the defocused image. This appearance indicates real misalignment. You twist the appropriate screw on the primary mirror cell (see Chapter 6) and then check the image again. It's worse. Returning to the adjustment screw and undoing the previous adjustment, you give it a slight turn in the opposite direction.

Checking again, you see much better alignment. A few more minor adjustments and alignment is finished. Collimation will probably have to be redone before the telescope is used on elevated objects because the tube assembly is unusually strained for this horizontal angle. At this point, you look for pinching or astigmatism. You see no such effects, but then this mirror is small, full-thickness, and gently mounted.

Performing the snap test, you see that the image goes through focus rapidly. That's good news. You stare at the defocused image and try to detect a stationary pattern indicating surface roughness in the slight turbulence. You don't see any, but you will test for this condition later in the dark. It's difficult to detect roughness in any turbulence, even the slight amount troubling the instrument now. One good point is the smooth appearance of the diffraction minima; they would be coarse or broken if roughness were severe. You put a yellow filter on the eyepiece. It seems as if the filter isn't deep enough because many colors can still be seen (in fact, color error seems worse). You put on a green filter. Now the minima are more visible.

Roll the focus back and forth equal distances on either side of focus to look for spherical aberration. Recall that this is exhibited by a hollow center on one side of focus and a bright center that diminishes toward the edge on the other side. Some tendency in this direction is visible, but it is not severe. You put the standard 33% obstruction mask on the protruding bolt at the rear of the spider and very carefully find best focus. Then you see how far you have to move the focuser inward and outward for the shadow of the diagonal to appear equally at the center. The darkness appears almost instantaneously with inward focus, but it hangs up briefly with outward motion.

This is a subjective judgement, so you replace the green filter with a neutral density filter to change conditions somewhat and try it again. Using a red filter, you obtain a fresh estimate. You remove all filters and try once more. It seems as if the average ratio of these motions is as large as 1:2 or 1:3. It may mean you have a marginally undercorrected mirror (see Chapter 10).

Taking the mask off, you next defocus the instrument from far inside focus to far outside focus, all the while looking for dips or extra bright rings that would indicate zones. You see no tight circular structure.

The last test is for turned edge. The way you normally look for this is to put on a deep-colored filter (red is good) and inspect the visibility of diffraction minima inside of focus compared with outside of focus. If turned-down edge is the only aberration, the rings are strong and crisp on the outside and weak or washed out on the inside. However, the effects of turned edge are competing with the effect of undercorrection, which also tends to wash out the diffraction rings on the outside of focus. You peer through the filtered eyepiece and can't really decide this point. One aberration fogs another.

*Assessment:* This telescope should perform passably on the planets, but it could do better. It is right at the edge of specifications, so you shouldn't complain to the maker. The optics don't seem to be severely rough, but a test for roughness will have to wait for a dark field of view and less turbulence. The telescope was acquired for general-purpose use, a task it should perform well.

### 5.3.2   16-Inch f/4 Dobson-mounted Newtonian

This telescope will require a larger separation from the source. Table 5-2 indicates that a distance of 84 focal lengths will cause $1/4$ wavelength of spherical overcorrection, so you double it and go to 168 focal lengths; 16 inches $\times$ 4 $\times$ 168 = 10,752 inches, or 896 feet (273 m). The required pinhole size is 0.018 inches, or 0.45 mm. To use a reflection of the Sun will require a reflective sphere over 5 inches in diameter.

You cannot find a suitable sphere in the tree ornament box, so you go to the automobile parts store and examine the adhesive wide angle rear view mirrors. A small mirror found there would seem to be about 7 inches in diameter if it were a complete sphere. It's a little too large, but close enough. Remember, you have a factor of two in the pinhole diameter table before your source exceeds the Airy disk size.

You tape over the outer few millimeters of the mirror because of a secondary reflection in a shiny bezel. You use masking tape because the color really doesn't make any difference. Looking around for an adjustable mounting, you think of a cheap camera tripod with an adjustable ball head. A scrap of wood attached to that tripod head will hold the curved mirror.

Then the search for a test site begins. You finally find a long upslope to the north. It is crossed by a road, which could give some trouble with turbulence, but you're willing to take a chance. You set up the source tripod at 9 A.M. on the high end of the slope. Going a few steps in the direction of the telescope and dropping your head to the sight line, you make sure the Sun is centered in the curved mirror. Also, you check the tripod for spurious reflections and tape over any prominent gleams.

Go downslope about $2/10$ mile (or 0.3 km) and set up the 16-inch. A quick look in the 6-mm eyepiece confirms that the optical path is seriously disturbed by turbulence (it's too late in the morning). You give up and decide to attempt the test during a night session at your observing site. This way, the telescope is likely to be operating in a less turbulent environment.

About 9 P.M. the very next night, high cirrus clouds move in and ruin the view. You decide to test the mirror and hope, in the meantime, that the clouds go away. Driving along the gravel access road that leads to the site, you again place the sphere about 0.3 km away. This time, however, the tripod is carrying the flashlight, so the sphere is hung from a pasture fence. The flashlight has a 1-cm hole in the mask, and it is placed about 1 m from the partial sphere. You locate it just off the optical path between the sphere and the telescope, so you will obtain a small, round reflection.

Since the path is closer to level, the telescope might lose alignment as it is heeled over. Looking at the sphere, you find that indeed it has lost collimation. As you raise the telescope toward zenith, you shake it gently, and ease it back down. That cures the problem.

You then inspect the image for pinching and astigmatism. The image does tend to form a cross at focus, but it's not so bad that it will interfere with the important test for spherical aberration.

In the snap test, the image does not focus as rapidly as you would like. However, you can readily focus your eyes from 100 mm to infinity, and suspect that your accommodation makes the snap test unreliable. You replace the 6-mm eyepiece with a 12-mm illuminated reticle eyepiece on a high-quality Barlow lens and repeat the snap test, all the time being watchful that the crossed wires of the reticle stay sharply in focus. The focus is still indeterminate over a significant region. That's not good.

Attaching the 33% mask to the back of the spider, you check the correction. The shadow appears almost at once on the inside and remains big and dark until the telescope is grossly defocused. It doesn't emerge on the other side until you twist the focuser 6 to 10 times farther, after which it emerges from a bright core. Filters alter this situation only slightly. The mirror seems profoundly undercorrected.

You have a dark suspicion that the large sphere size is perhaps dazzling your vision. Returning to the source, you increase the distance separating the flashlight and the sphere to 2 m. Even with the darker image, the severe undercorrection still shows.

The rings aren't visible on either side—possibly because of roughness or turbulence. Rings don't appear with a green filter either. One test does not decide roughness, however, especially with as large an instrument as a 16-inch, so you reserve judgement about that point.

Undercorrection is so bad that you don't even look for turned edge or zonal aberration.

*Assessment:* The telescope fails. It needs to be refigured. If it were even a little worse than a marginal $^1/_4$ wavelength, it would be acceptable. After all, you don't often expect diffraction-limited optics at f/4. But this instrument is far beyond the limits of acceptability.

### 5.3.3   6-Inch f/12 Apochromatic Refractor

Because this telescope is expected to perform well under the most difficult circumstances, it will be tested in a comparatively harsh manner. Twenty times the focal length is 120 feet, or 37 meters. To avoid vignetting from the baffling and to avoid an erroneous estimate of spherical aberration, you will push this distance to 80 m. Interpolating Table 5-3, you see that a pinhole diameter of about 0.16 mm would be correct at 37 meters, but you're going twice that far, so you want one twice as large. Three hundred pinhole diameters of 0.32 mm yields 96 mm, or about 4 inches.

You only have a 50-mm tree ornament, but since you will be doing this test at night it's easy to move the 1-cm masked flashlight to about 60 cm from the sphere instead of the usual 1 m. The 60-cm distance means that the hole will subtend a little less than a 1° angle as viewed from the sphere. You back the flashlight mask with an 80A "tungsten" camera filter in order to achieve better color balance for the chromatic aberration tests.

Taking the telescope to your usual observing site, you hang the sphere about 250 feet from the telescope. The flashlight is pointed at the sphere from a couple of feet away on the near side. Because the fully assembled telescope is inconveniently high when directed toward the horizon, you place it between the seats of two sturdy "movie director's" folding chairs. You will sit on the ground.

You attempt to point the telescope by moving the rear chair. The telescope is directed at the feet of the tripod, so you elevate the front by slipping in a magazine. The sphere is now slightly too low.

It seems easier to move the target than the telescope, so you walk to the source and move the sphere higher. You rearrange the flashlight, verifying that the brightest reflection is back toward the telescope.

The image needs only a jiggle to center it. You slip in a higher magnification eyepiece. The first thing to examine is color correction. The disk has a slight magenta or reddish fringe inside focus and a green fringe outside focus. In focus, there is no apparent color haze. No red dot appears just outside of focus, but since you are testing an apochromat, none is anticipated. Rainbow smearing is not apparent in any direction, which indicates that decentering or wedge error is absent. A brighter image would be helpful, so you move the flashlight to about 30 cm from the sphere.

Now, the Airy disk is noticeably bloated, but no color haze is visible. You return to the flashlight and move it back.

Putting a green filter on the eyepiece, you look for astigmatism or stretching as an indicator of misalignment. None can be seen. Defocusing either way, no apparent difficulty with correction appears. The telescope snaps well. You defocus a long distance and look for zones. None are seen. Turned edge doesn't show, but this is a refractor. The lens cell obscures the far edge.

You are disturbed by the lack of contrast in the diffraction rings. This could indicate a problem with roughness. Then again, your eye just may be unaccustomed to the delicacy of the rings. You put in a deep-red filter, but that cuts out too much light, so you turn once again to the green filter.

The in-focus image seems to have several asymmetric thickenings in the rings, but that could be caused by slow-moving air currents between the image and you. You watch long enough to decide that the pattern is fixed.

Centering the 33% paper obstruction on the sewing-thread web, you search for small correction difficulties. You are unable to detect any difference.

*Assessment:* This telescope may suffer a slight medium-scale roughness, which would compromise the images on perfect nights. Such a small amount of aberration would have gone unnoticed in the other instruments. Nevertheless, it is worrisome in a lunar-planetary refractor. However, you decide to do the formal star test again and evaluate it a number of nights on planetary images. Roughness is a difficult aberration to unambiguously separate from turbulence, and you could have misdiagnosed it.

### 5.3.4   8-Inch f/10 Schmidt-Cassegrain Catadioptric

To test this Schmidt-Cassegrain, recall that the telescope diverts rays beyond the edge of the Airy disk at about 48 m (157 ft), or about 24 times the focal length. (Table 5-2 results in an incorrect distance because the internal focusing mechanism compromises the optical correction.) You decide to increase separation distance to at least 100 m (328 ft). A source at this range is 2.5 times the 20 focal lengths recommended after Table 5-2, so it requires 2.5 times the 0.134-mm pinhole size of Table 5-3, or 0.335 mm. The reflective sphere should thus be 100 mm in diameter. You don't have a 4-inch sphere, but you can find a convex mirror that would be 7 inches in diameter if it were a complete sphere.

The pinhole can expand a factor of 2 before it exceeds the Airy disk size. Seven inches, though, is a bit close to the limit. Then you recall that if you test with the Sun directly to your back, with the glitter point centered in the sphere, the divisor is closer to 450 than 300. This condition would permit a sphere at least 6 inches across, and 7 inches is not too much more.

You set up the test early one morning with the Sun low on the eastern horizon and the sighting range to the west. A quick look in the eyepiece confirms that the image is too bright. After hurrying inside to get a 2-inch tree ornament, you set the new sphere at a range of 70 meters and point the instrument again. A peculiar tube current elongates the secondary shadow on one side of focus, but it goes away after a few minutes.

First comes alignment, a relatively straightforward operation since it involves only adjusting one element. Slipping on a deep-yellow filter, you do the snap test, but you can't say for sure whether the instrument snaps adequately. Focus seems soft, but not seriously defective.

You detect a small amount of spherical aberration, but you can't tell if it is undercorrection or overcorrection. The telescope is refocused with the regular high magnification eyepiece and yellow filter, the set screw loosened, and the eyepiece withdrawn $1/5$ inch (5 mm). Checking Tables 5-1a and 5-1b, you see that this amount corresponds to about 12 wavelengths outside focus. The edge of the pattern is stronger than the inside, so the system is overcorrected.

Since a 33% obstruction is already in place, you look for the first appearance of the secondary shadow. It appears only about 1.5 times as far on the other side. Since the instrument is expected to appear slightly overcorrected anyway (with the close source position), this amount is very mild.

In looking for roughness, you find an unusual amount of turbulence even this early in the morning. You'll have to test again when it is quieter.

*Assessment:* The instrument shows signs of being excellent, but ground turbulence is too severe. Observation of the planet Saturn that night showed Cassini's division looking sharp and black between bouts of bad seeing. You will try the test again at night using a flashlight source.

# Chapter 6

# Misalignment

A straightforward way of greatly improving a telescope's image is to align the optics. One of the most ignored optical problems, misalignment is also one of the most curable. The improvements derived by aligning previously neglected instruments are always noticeable, and sometimes the enhancement is startling.

The star test cannot only be used to diagnose misalignment, it is also useful to achieve fine alignment. Once you become familiar with the star-test method of making that last small adjustment on the collimation, you will make it a standard procedure during every observing session. With practice, star-test alignment becomes easy.

## 6.1  Kinematic View of Alignment

An optical surface is a three-dimensional object of finite size. To locate such an object in space, one must first find some point (usually its geometric center) and move that point's three linear coordinates. Once its center is placed, two remaining orientation angles must be fixed to specify its position. Actually, mathematicians describe three such rotation angles, but symmetry usually allows one to be ignored. For alignment, this hidden angle is a final pointless rotation around the symmetrical optical axis.

The three coordinates of the center as well as these three angles make up the six degrees of freedom necessary to know the position and orientation of a solid object precisely. The mounting points are well designed if they are sufficient to fix the object's location but not to overconstrain it. Three-legged stools are stable on the roughest floors because their three-point design is both necessary and sufficient. Stiff four-legged stools usually rock because the design has too many supports. The fourth leg cannot be precisely made to occupy the plane of the floor. This difficulty also accounts for the reason that optics mounting cells are so often multiples of three points.

Alignment is usually separated into two independent tasks. First, the centers of all optical elements are placed on a single axis line and properly spaced. Second, the tilts of each optical element are oriented so that each becomes a circle of revolution around the axis. Thus, if one twirls the optical system around the axis, it looks the same. The placement of the center on-axis is called *centering*, and obtaining the correct tilt orientation is called *squaring-on* by some authors.[1]

## 6.2   Effects of Misalignment

If alignment isn't precise, any number of bad effects can result. Although we will calculate patterns only for misaligned Newtonian reflectors, the behavior depicted here qualitatively describes a wide variety of systems and is generally useful.

Off-axis, a Newtonian reflector exhibits a mixture of two pure aberrations, coma and astigmatism. In this case, astigmatism isn't ground into the glass permanently. It is caused by viewing the mirror at an oblique angle. Similarly, coma is induced merely by the tilt of the mirror.

As misalignment worsens, astigmatism overtakes coma to become the dominant aberration. Coma worsens linearly with collimation error, while astigmatism increases as the square of the distance to the optical axis. This behavior is illustrated in Fig. 6-1. For all practical cases of misalignment, the crossover point is always beyond the level of even coarse alignment. Coma is always stronger than induced astigmatism for Newtonian telescopes.

The bright parts of a comatic image develop wing-shaped appendages, and some of the light is smeared away from the optical axis. Coma effects are the same inside or outside focus. In each case, the aberration stretches the image away from the optical axis.

Misalignment of the image in Newtonians is easier to perceive outside of focus. The skewed optics no longer have a centered obstruction, and outside focus the off-center shadow of the diagonal adds to the stretching caused by coma. The offset shadow makes coma seem even worse. Inside focus, the off-center shadow leans in a manner that partially counterbalances the coma stretch. Alignment on either side of focus is possible, but the preferred method is to pull the eyepiece back.

Astronomical telescopes have such a constricted field of view that coma caused by the objective is generally not visible unless the optics are mis-

---

[1]Tilted-component telescopes don't follow such a simple sequence. They require a procedure matched to the particular instrument.

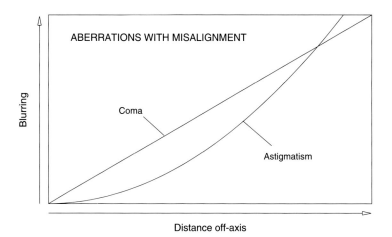

**Fig. 6-1.** *Astigmatism and coma aberration as misalignment becomes worse in Newtonian reflectors.*

aligned and the image is viewed at high magnification. Any off-axis smearing of the image in low-power eyepieces is primarily a fault of the ocular.

Unfortunately, coma and astigmatism in composite form are common errors in poorly collimated Newtonian reflectors and catadioptrics. Well-designed refractors and advanced reflectors use the multiplicity of surfaces to reduce or eliminate the coma error. Good refractors chiefly show misalignment through astigmatism.

Alignment is probably the single greatest contributor to the undeserved shabby reputation of Newtonian reflectors. These instruments are commonly made at very low focal ratios. Their owners don't realize their telescopes must be kept in razor-sharp alignment. A fast Newtonian usually spends its entire existence in a wretched state of collimation. Of course, if low magnifications are used, the zone of excellent alignment will usually be found somewhere within the field stop of the eyepiece. However, at high magnifications (where optical quality must be at its best), the focal-plane region of good quality can be at one edge of the field stop or possibly outside it entirely.

As an example, let's look closely at the common 10-inch (250-mm) f/4.5 Newtonian reflector. Schroeder (p. 96) says that f/4.5 paraboloids can tolerate misalignments of about 1.8 arcminutes. Superb images are thus confined to a region at the focal plane only 0.05 inches (1.2 mm) in diameter. This tolerance is a bit tight, however. "Decent" imaging would allow a misalignment of about 3 arcminutes, a circle on the focal plane of 0.08-inch (2 mm) diameter. The passable region is a circle $1/5$ the diameter of the full moon. This alignment is ruined with only about $^1/_{10}$ turn of a main mirror adjustment screw.

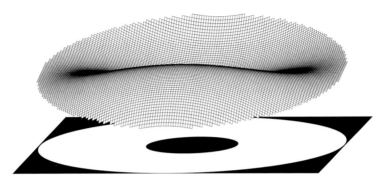

**Fig. 6-2.** *Aberration function of misaligned wavefront just after it has passed through the aperture.*

## 6.3    The Aberration Function of the Misaligned Newtonian

If focused near the smallest image blur circle, the aberration function of misalignment is similar to the complicated form that appears in Fig. 6-2. That figure scarcely does justice to the deformation. The phase surface is like a drumhead that has just taken an enormous off-center blow. One half-circle is deformed downward, and the other half-circle has a balancing bulge upward. Added to this form is a small amount of the saddle or potato-chip deformation characteristic of astigmatism. The aggregate result is a wonderfully interesting surface to investigate by calculations, but it is bad news if it describes the wavefront of a telescope.

The functional form of the coma aberration is

$$W_{\text{coma}}(\rho, \theta) = \frac{A_3^{\text{coma}}}{2}(3\rho^3 - 2\rho)\cos(\theta), \qquad (6.1)$$

where $\rho$ is the distance from the optical axis (normalized to reach 1 at the edge of the aperture), $A_3^{\text{coma}}$ is the total coma aberration, and $\theta$ is the angle from the axis of misalignment (Born and Wolf 1980). The slight amount of astigmatism mixed with this coma has the form appearing in Chapter 14, and the total deformation is $W_{\text{misalign}} = W_{\text{coma}} + W_{\text{astig}}$. The amounts of each aberration depend on the aperture and the focal ratio.

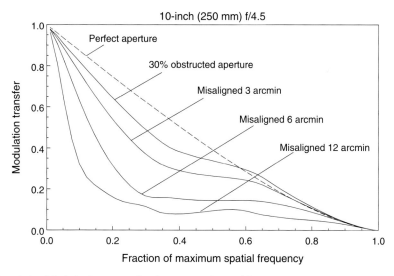

**Fig. 6-3.** *Modulation transfer function of steadily worsening Newtonian alignment (45° orientation of MTF target bars with respect to the direction of misalignment).*

## 6.4 Filtration of a Misaligned Newtonian

Since the phase surface is not axially symmetric, its MTF depends on which way the stripes of the MTF target are oriented. If we calculate the MTF at an average orientation, we can see how the behavior improves with better collimation. Five curves are depicted in Fig. 6-3. The first is the perfect circular aperture. The next is a 30% obstructed but otherwise perfect aperture. Third is the filtering caused by a shift of the focal plane sideways by the generous 3 arcminute tolerance. If this shift is doubled, the contrast sags considerably in the fourth curve. The last and bottom curve is the transfer expected from a severely misaligned mirror. Any alignment effort whatsoever results in better collimation than the last curve, but some Newtonian owners are so frightened of producing worse performance that they refuse to touch the adjustment screws.

The worst MTF curve dips quickly. The interesting behavior is found low on the spatial frequency axis. The initial drop indicates that the telescope is performing as well as a perfect aperture of about 1/4 the full diameter. Severe misalignment reduces the low spatial frequency contrast to that of a 2.5-inch telescope!

Even correcting the misalignment until the axis is tilted by twice the tolerance only improves the contrast so this mirror acts like one of half its aperture. This MTF curve is about the same as would occur for a 50% or

60% obstructed aperture. No one would stand for such huge obstructions, but many telescope owners casually accept misalignments of this magnitude.

The filtration of even a slightly misaligned telescope is enough to severely degrade the images. Be fearless in attempting to collimate your telescope. You can hardly do worse than an unaligned instrument, and the potential improvements obtained with only a small effort can be profound.

## 6.5   Aligning Three Telescopes

The alignment procedure for every commercial telescope cannot possibly be described because each maker has tiny variations in the manufacture of cells, mirror holders, and adjustment hardware. For this reason, we will examine the generic features of the process used in aligning only three common telescopes. In spite of this restriction, the descriptions which follow represent a large number of optical systems. You will not be given detailed instructions in the form of a recipe to be learned by rote ("then turn bolt A"). That job is best served by the instructions that came with the instrument. Instead, you will be taught procedures that can be applied to nearly every telescope.

Other collimation procedures use specialized methods or tools. Fussy readers are encouraged to pursue them. However, the instructions below produce reasonably straightforward collimation without cutting too much into valuable observing time. The justification and ordering of the steps will be the primary objective, with side comments concerning tricks and pitfalls.

1. *Establish the axis line.* The axis line is defined by two points, usually the center of the eyepiece and the center of the objective lens or mirror. It is customarily directed along the tube's center.

2. *Center the optical components on this axis line.* If the telescope has more elements than an objective and eyepiece, at least one non-trivial centering must take place. Sometimes, centering is set at the factory and is not adjustable by the telescope user.

3. *Establish the tilts of the elements.* Generally, the tilt adjustments must be made in a certain order from one of the two points that define the axis to the other point. Poor ordering makes alignment much more difficult.

4. *Repeat steps 1, 2, and 3 as an iterative procedure.* Because the adjustments are seldom completely independent, one alignment step can disturb previously correct settings. Coarse alignment is like raking leaves. The first pass doesn't gather every leaf; it takes a few swipes.

**5.** *Adjust only one element in fine alignment.* Fine alignment takes place on a real image. Normally, a tiny adjustment must be done on the element for which adjustment is most convenient.

Although it is not strictly necessary, you can save time and effort by using a helper to align. On all but the most compact telescopes, collimation is a job best done by two people, one at the eyepiece and one making adjustments.

### 6.5.1 The Newtonian Reflector

The presence of the diagonal mirror and the many confusing reflections make this adjustment the most difficult of the three discussed here.

Before the alignment begins, you have to make preparations. The first item needed is a centered sighting hole. This blank or lensless "eyepiece" has a small opening at the back instead of a lens element. The purpose of such a device is to allow you to unambiguously place your eye on the axis of the focuser tube. A less obvious purpose is to allow you to sight from a location right at the focal plane. It obscures the view unless the eye is placed close. Thus, the eye can be located not only at the center of the focuser tube but at the correct distance from the diagonal. You want to place this sighting hole near the location of the focal plane when the telescope is focused on distant objects.

An inexpensive source of these sighting holes are *clear* plastic 35-mm film cans with the bottoms cut out and a 3-mm hole drilled into the lid. Wind them with a few turns of tape so they will they fit snugly.

The second preparation is to place a marker dot at the geometric center of the mirror. Taking care not to touch the mirror's surface accidentally, lay a stiff ruler across the diameter. Along the ruler, you can determine the center very precisely, but at right angles to it, you can only estimate. At the center, draw a short (3 mm) line at a right angle to the straight edge. The center will be at some location along the direction of this stubby line. Do the same after a quarter turn of the mirror. Look closely at the center. What you should see is two short lines slightly offset as in Fig. 6-4. The true center is at the intersection of these two lines if they are extended until they meet. This is the place to put the dot.

Don't commit yourself to making a large dot at first. It's best to make a barely perceptible mark at this location and measure it both ways to verify it is the center. When you make a bigger mark, you will probably want to extend it out on one side to correct for the inevitable error. This dot can be something as simple as permanent black marker ink or as elaborate as white paint. (Some people claim a white dot is easier to see when you

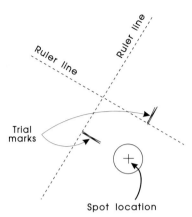

Ruler line

Ruler line

Trial
marks

Spot location

**Fig. 6-4.** *The procedure for finding and marking the true center of a circular disk.*

are attempting alignment in the dark with a flashlight.) Make the dot large enough to see easily (6 mm or $1/4$ inch). Do not worry about the dot or short lines interfering with optical quality. The marks are in the shadow of the diagonal mirror.

Steps 1 through 3 are best done in a brightly lit room illuminated by diffuse light. (Fluorescent light is ideal.) The inside of a telescope tube is not a well-lit place. During coarse adjustment, tape a sheet of white paper inside the tube across from the focuser. The paper will provide a lighter background to the outline of the diagonal holder than the normally darkened interior of the tube.

**Step 1: Establish the axis line.**

The axis line will be from the center of the eyepiece's field of view to the center of the mirror. This step would be trivially easy were it not dependent on the right angle break that happens at the diagonal. Once the diagonal is aligned, it will be simple to check, but it is impossible to verify now. We instead pay attention to one crucial fact, the need for the focuser to slide the eyepiece linearly along the optical axis, thus making sure that both your eyepiece and Barlow lens will be on this axis. A misaligned Barlow is a disaster for those who must wear eyeglasses, since the Barlow and medium-power eyepiece are used in preference to extremely short-focus eyepieces.

We will assume that the optical axis will be along the center of the tube and that the diagonal will be set precisely at $45°$. The problem of focuser motion reduces to making sure the focus tube is pointed at the tube's center line and that it doesn't lean toward either end of the tube. If you have an accurately round tube and the focuser fits snugly against it, you probably needn't worry, but such instruments are rare.

I can't give instructions for measuring the lean of the focuser because every situation is different. I can only point out some tricks for magnifying the lean direction. The first is to put something besides the eyepiece in the focuser. A good choice is a long tube the same diameter as an eyepiece. We will call it the "long eyepiece." If you extend such a tube on the outside of the focuser, it will become easily apparent if it leans toward either end of the tube. Make a right angle template out of a manila file folder or other thin cardboard sheet. Cut out enough of the corner so that it clears the focuser hardware, and lay it against the protruding tube. Any lean of the focuser along the telescope tube becomes immediately apparent.

Remove the diagonal, and extend the long eyepiece to the center of the telescope tube, or as near as you can get. See if the long eyepiece is pointed at a skewed position to either side of the telescope axis. This step is especially easy if your Newtonian has a spider. Just place a pointer or screw in the hole from which you removed the diagonal holder and look through the other end of the long eyepiece tube. Of course, center the spider first.

Once you've verified that your focuser fits squarely on the telescope and advances and retracts eyepieces more-or-less along the planned direction, you are ready to continue. If the fit is skewed, shim the focuser until it points squarely at the center of the tube.

### Step 2: Center the optical components along the axis line.

Since the axis will go through the center of the mirror and the center of the image plane wherever they might lie, "centering the components" means centering the diagonal along that line. Remember, diagonal placement is achieved without any reference to reflections. At this stage, the main mirror need not be inside the instrument. The diagonal could well be a block of cement. In fact, it is helpful to think of it as nonreflective. You must suppress any urge to center the reflections you see in the diagonal. That doesn't concern you now.

Consult Fig. 6-5. This diagram represents a perfectly aligned Newtonian. (Focal ratio has been exaggerated to make the anomalous behavior readily visible.) Note that the distance $d_{near}$ is greater than $d_{far}$. Alignment is perfect by definition, yet it seems as if the diagonal mirror is not centered. Already we seem to violate general condition 2.

Most importantly, the components must be *optically* centered, not physically centered. When you look through the little sighting hole replacing the

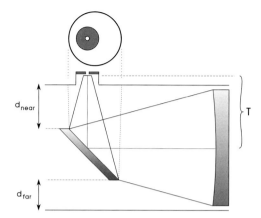

**Fig. 6-5.** *A perfectly aligned Newtonian telescope with focal ratio about 1.75. Displays centered and non-centered features.*

eyepiece, what do you see? The diagonal should appear as a perfect circle neatly centered at the bottom of the focuser tube. The offset is caused by perspective foreshortening of the far side of the diagonal. It is so much further away, that it actually appears smaller. You need to slide the diagonal sideways and down to center it on the converging cone of light. The view through the sighting hole is sketched in Fig. 6-6.

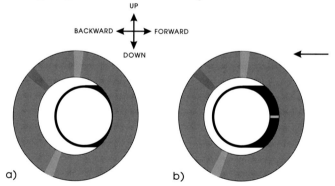

**Fig. 6-6.** *Centering of the diagonal at the bottom of the focuser tube. (This tube is depicted as the dark annulus at the outside with gray radial streaks in it.) a) An improperly placed diagonal. b) The correct position as a result of a backward slide of the diagonal holder. A light piece of paper is attached across the tube.*

The amount of forward offset is determined by trial-and-error. Move the diagonal forward and back until it *appears* centered. Please note that the word "appears" is emphasized in this statement. Because judgement may be difficult, you may be tempted to remove the sight hole and peer along the focuser tube at a grazing angle. Then you would incorrectly compare the front and back sides and incorrectly set the diagonal. The correct method is to view it from the center and move the diagonal until it only *looks* centered.

You may detect an error in the "up-down" direction of Fig. 6-6. That error is probably caused by an undetected tilt in the focuser or a side shift of the spider. Adjust for it either by shimming the focuser or by moving the spider before continuing. Figure 6-6b shows a properly centered diagonal.

The amount of offset of the diagonal away from the eyepiece is impossible to judge just by looking. It must be calculated and measured until the quantities $d_{near}$ and $d_{far}$ are correct. This offset can be straightforwardly calculated using analytic geometry. (Such a derivation appears in Appendix C.) Here is the answer and some easy approximations:

If $D$ is the diameter of the mirror, $L$ the diameter of the field of 100% illumination, $T$ the distance from the center of the tube to the focal plane, $f$ the focal length, and $s$ the sagitta of the mirror surface ($s \cong D^2/16f$), then the offset is

$$\text{Offset} = \frac{T + nL/2}{1 - n^2} - T \quad \text{where} \quad n = \frac{D - L}{2(f - s)}. \tag{6.2}$$

For a very small field of 100% illumination and a shallow mirror, this is approximately

$$\text{Offset} \cong \frac{T}{4F^2}, \tag{6.3}$$

where $F$ is the focal ratio.

Say you have two equal stacks of coins. If you remove one coin and place it on the other stack, the stacks differ in height by two coins. For the same reason $d_{near}$ is larger than $d_{far}$ by twice the offset. A number of estimates for $d_{near} - d_{far}$ are listed in Table 6-1. These typical offsets are generated by using Eq. 6.2 with reasonable estimates for $T$.

At long focal ratios, the offset is very small, so use of this table should only be critical in its lower left corner—for fast and big mirrors. For that reason, the approximation in Eq. 6.3 is more than adequate. Optimally, fast Newtonians should be designed with very small regions of full illumination at the focal plane (Peters and Pike 1977).

Most spiders can be adjusted to allow the diagonal to be offset deliberately merely by changing their mounting-screw adjustments. Do not worry if the vanes on opposite sides of the diagonal are not precisely lined up. This condition only modifies the spider diffraction pattern. The amount of light scattered by the spider is the same as before. In a way, the spider diffraction pattern with 8 less-bright spikes may be better than 4 strong ones in some observing circumstances.

Table 6-1
The difference between the two measurements from the tube
to the edge of the diagonal, $d_{near} - d_{far} = 2$ Offset
Field of 100% illumination is zero

| | | Focal Ratio | | | | | | |
|---|---|---|---|---|---|---|---|---|
| | | 4 | 4.5 | 5 | 6 | 7 | 8 | 10 |
| Diameter(in) | $T$ | | | 2 Offset (in) | | | | |
| 3 | 3.5 | 0.11 | 0.09 | 0.07 | 0.05 | 0.04 | 0.03 | 0.02 |
| 4.25 | 4.4 | 0.14 | 0.11 | 0.09 | 0.06 | 0.04 | 0.03 | 0.02 |
| 6 | 5.6 | 0.18 | 0.14 | 0.11 | 0.08 | 0.06 | 0.04 | 0.03 |
| 8 | 7.0 | 0.22 | 0.17 | 0.14 | 0.10 | 0.07 | 0.05 | 0.04 |
| 10 | 8.4 | 0.26 | 0.21 | 0.17 | 0.12 | 0.09 | 0.07 | 0.04 |
| 12.5 | 10.2 | 0.32 | 0.25 | 0.20 | 0.14 | 0.10 | 0.08 | 0.05 |
| 14.25 | 11.4 | 0.36 | 0.28 | 0.23 | 0.16 | 0.12 | 0.09 | 0.06 |
| 16 | 12.6 | 0.39 | 0.31 | 0.25 | 0.18 | 0.13 | 0.10 | 0.06 |
| 17.5 | 13.6 | 0.43 | 0.34 | 0.27 | 0.19 | 0.14 | 0.11 | 0.07 |
| 20 | 15.4 | 0.48 | 0.38 | 0.31 | 0.21 | 0.16 | 0.12 | 0.08 |
| 24 | 18.2 | 0.57 | 0.45 | 0.36 | 0.25 | 0.19 | 0.14 | 0.09 |

| | | Focal Ratio | | | | | | |
|---|---|---|---|---|---|---|---|---|
| | | 4 | 4.5 | 5 | 6 | 7 | 8 | 10 |
| Diameter(mm) | $T$ | | | 2 Offset (mm) | | | | |
| 75 | 90 | 2.8 | 2.2 | 1.8 | 1.2 | 0.9 | 0.7 | 0.4 |
| 110 | 110 | 3.5 | 2.7 | 2.2 | 1.5 | 1.1 | 0.9 | 0.6 |
| 150 | 140 | 4.4 | 3.5 | 2.8 | 2.0 | 1.5 | 1.1 | 0.7 |
| 200 | 180 | 5.6 | 4.4 | 3.6 | 2.5 | 1.8 | 1.4 | 0.9 |
| 250 | 210 | 6.7 | 5.3 | 4.3 | 3.0 | 2.2 | 1.7 | 1.1 |
| 320 | 260 | 8.1 | 6.4 | 5.2 | 3.6 | 2.6 | 2.0 | 1.3 |
| 360 | 290 | 9.0 | 7.1 | 5.8 | 4.0 | 2.9 | 2.3 | 1.4 |
| 400 | 320 | 10.0 | 7.9 | 6.4 | 4.4 | 3.3 | 2.5 | 1.6 |
| 450 | 350 | 10.8 | 8.6 | 6.9 | 4.8 | 3.5 | 2.7 | 1.7 |
| 500 | 390 | 12.2 | 9.7 | 7.8 | 5.4 | 4.0 | 3.1 | 2.0 |
| 600 | 460 | 14.4 | 11.4 | 9.2 | 6.4 | 4.7 | 3.6 | 2.3 |

## Step 3: Establish the tilt of the elements.

Once you have the diagonal visually centered in the focuser tube and offset the proper distance, you are ready for the tilt adjustment. If you were to carefully set the tilt of the primary mirror first, the setting would go amiss when the diagonal is finally adjusted. Thus, the tilt of the diagonal must be fixed before the main mirror is touched.

At this point, visualize the main mirror as painted white. All you can see at the primary are mirror clips jutting onto its surface. Ignore any reflections. A useful trick is to become painfully aware of dust on the mirror. Concentrate on the dust and the mirror clips. Look *at* the mirror, not *through* it. Figure 6-7a shows the diagonal with incorrect tilt.

Rotate the diagonal holder in the spider until it looks like Fig. 6-7b. Then adjust the screw in the holder base that tilts the diagonal either toward or away from your eye to center the main mirror clips as in Fig. 6-7c. Most diagonal holder bases don't contain springs. If you loosen one screw, you must tighten the other two.

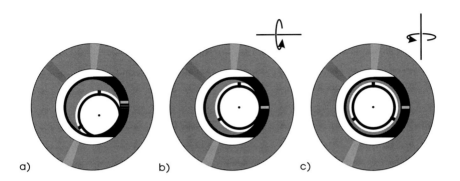

**Fig. 6-7.** *Setting the angle of the diagonal: a) A misaligned diagonal. b) After spinning the diagonal in the spider. c) After tilting the diagonal using screws at the base.*

Oddly, the two most common adjustments are rotating the whole diagonal about its axis and adjusting only one screw at the base. You may well ask why diagonal bases have three pesky and hard-to-reach screws. A spring-loaded hinge and one adjustment screw make more sense. One explanation is that telescope makers are extremely conservative, and diagonals have been mounted with three screws for a long time.

The above description had all of the wrong turns and frustrations removed. At first, it seems impossible to make these adjustments to simultaneously achieve diagonal alignment and keep the connectors tight. As the wrench is turned on the spindle, diagonal rotation is especially hard to prevent. Fifteen minutes of careful work can be lost while you try to torque the diagonal securely into place. What you eventually learn is how to predict the effect of the wrench. Ultimately, you will know how far to offset the finger-tight alignment to achieve wrench-tight alignment.

The last job of coarse collimation is setting the tilt of the main mirror. Finally, you may consider the reflection in the primary. The little hole through which you are looking is reflected somewhere near the mirror dot. By adjusting the screws on the back of the main mirror, move the hole reflection until it is behind the dot. Do not spend a great deal of effort on refinements of this adjustment. You will set it empirically with the star test.

Figure 6-8a is an example of a misaligned main mirror. Figure 6-8b shows correct coarse alignment. The stubby arrow shows the direction to the reflection of the focuser's base.

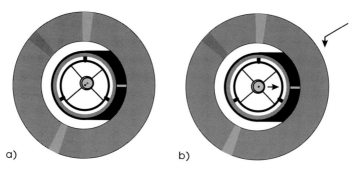

a)                                          b)

**Fig. 6-8.** *With the diagonal aligned, the screws on the back of the main mirror are adjusted until the dot is superimposed on the sighting hole: a) the starting appearance, b) correct coarse alignment after moving the reflection of the hole in the indicated manner.*

### Step 4: Repeat steps 1, 2, and 3 as an iterative procedure.

You are certainly allowed to start this process over again to correct any difficulties. Remember to order the steps properly. Don't adjust randomly, even though you are sorely tempted. A good example of one such temptation is the decentered appearance of the second reflection in the diagonals of Figs. 6-5 and 6-8b. Remember, these systems are correctly aligned, but the reflection of the bottom of the focuser is still decentered, an especially large effect in fast mirrors with big diagonals.

When they first notice this decentering, many first-time telescope collimators start tugging at the diagonal, and end up destroying their hard-won coarse alignment. People are unusually disturbed by this decentering, and they often skew the alignment until these circles are approximately concentric as well.

Unfortunately, this mistake has the same effect as tilting the focuser over, and by implication, tilting the focal plane. The eyepiece is no longer transported along the optical axis. Barlow lens performance may suffer, and the edge of photographic film frames become indistinct and blurry. Because of the natural curvature of field in Newtonian reflectors, one side of the frame is severely out-of-focus while the other is not. (Indeed, such photographic behavior can be used to diagnose a tilted focal plane.)

Supposedly, Fig. 6-5 is perfectly aligned. Why then, should a telescope in perfect collimation ever show any form of decentering? The problem is the three reflections that occur when you look though the telescope in this manner. The usual path of light is one reflection off the primary and one reflection off the diagonal. When we stare backwards through the telescope, the path is one reflection off the diagonal, a second reflection off the main mirror (okay so far), and *a third reflection off the diagonal.* We should expect centering only as far as the main mirror in Fig. 6-8b. Neither the diagonal as reflected in the main mirror nor the bottom of the focuser tube as reflected twice in the diagonal needs to be centered.

One modification should be made when you are satisfied with the coarse alignment of the instrument. Untwist the vanes of the spider so that they are once again perpendicular to the main mirror. This step is best done gently with a narrow-jawed crescent wrench. Cradle the vane near its middle or somewhat nearer the tube. Look through the sighting hole and twist the spider until it appears narrowest. This ensures that the spider obstruction causes as little blockage as possible.

**Step 5: Adjust only one element in fine alignment.**

Fine-align on a star. Use your accustomed configuration for high magnification. If you normally use a Barlow lens, include it in the optical train. You should be more concerned with hitting the axis of that Barlow than with attaining a pretty alignment of the dots. Pick out a moderately bright star of high elevation, and center it in the field. Rack the focuser out or in until defocusing aberration is about 10 wavelengths. If the telescope is severely misaligned, you see something like Fig. 6-9d. This pattern is unlikely if coarse alignment was done carefully. A misalignment of 12 arcminutes in our example means that the reflection of the sighting hole is decentered by 4 mm, or just outside the dot. (Consider how bad the alignment must have been before you started.)

The model used to generate these patterns is somewhat inadequate. The obstruction is still centered in the calculations, but it isn't centered in a real misaligned reflector. The sideways shifting of the secondary shadow is slightly enhanced outside focus and diminished inside focus.

More likely, you see less distorted patterns as in Fig. 6-9c or Fig. 6-9b, which are examples of milder misalignment. For these cases, the pattern Fig. 6-9b is difficult to distinguish from a perfect pattern when it is defocused as far as 10 wavelengths. Choose a dimmer star and defocus a smaller amount. Something like the images in Fig. 6-10 should appear. If seeing is excellent, you can perform the last critical adjustment on a focused star. Unfortunately, the seeing is seldom good enough to do so. Take comfort in knowing that if turbulence is bad enough to make star-test alignment difficult, seeing is probably the limiting factor in your wobbly stack of filters.

The optical axis in all of the figures is far to the right of the pattern. You need to move that axis back to the center of the field, so you want to move the image to the *left*. The real situation will not be so cooperative. The coma flare can be pointed at any angle. You must be able, somehow,

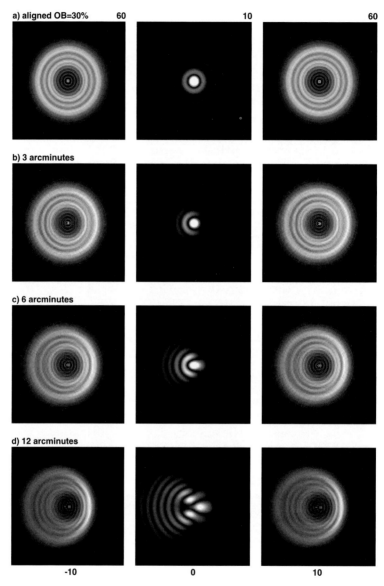

**Fig. 6-9.** *Star test patterns showing increasingly bad misalignment of a 10-inch, (250-mm) f/4.5 Newtonian reflector: a) the expected pattern if the telescope is perfectly aligned, b) misaligned by 3 minutes of arc (the worst misalignment that delivers a passable image), c) misaligned by 6 arcminutes, and d) misaligned by 12 arcminutes. The focused patterns are magnified 6 times compared to the unfocused patterns. See Appendix D for labeling information.*

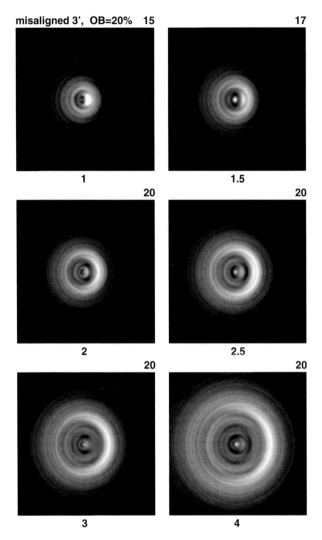

**Fig. 6-10.** *The 3 arcminute misalignment of Fig. 6-9 as defocusing is adjusted from 1 wavelength to 4 wavelengths. The misalignment is clearly shown.*

to correlate the pattern you are seeing with a cell adjustment screw.

A Newtonian has two mirror reflections, including one at a right angle. Perhaps some people can visualize the three-dimensional situation well enough to determine which screw to turn purely by logic, but they are few. The best technique to find this screw is to decide which clock angle you want to move the image—say, to 7 o'clock. Then rack the eyepiece a long

distance out of focus. Placing your hand in the optical path of the telescope and noting where the shadow intrudes on the defocused disk, you can
decide what part of the mirror corresponds to a certain clock angle. You
can bring the hand shadow either to 7 o'clock or 1 o'clock. Then follow
this orientation back along the tube to the mirror cell.

When you trace this line back to the mirror, you will emerge either close
to a screw or across the tube from one. Give that screw a small adjustment
in either direction. It is not important which way you turn it, just that
you remember the modification. Recenter the star and see if the situation
is worse or better.

If it's worse, undo the damage and turn it the other way. Look at the
image again. It should now improve. Pick a new adjustment direction, and
repeat the whole process. Always recenter the star before deciding on the
next step. If the cell adjustment bottoms out and you cannot tighten a
screw, remember that loosening the other two is equivalent.

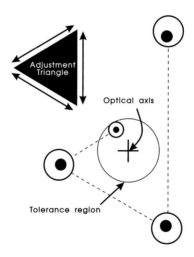

**Fig. 6-11.** *The adjustment triangle of a three-sided cell, and the first few steps
in fine alignment on a star-test image.*

As you home in on a fine-aligned mirror, you should be following a path
like that in the example of Fig. 6-11. You can only tilt the mirror along
the edges of the adjustment triangle. Please remember, what you are really
changing is the position of the optical axis, not the image, so you want to
move the image in a reverse direction to all of these adjustments.

I personally find image movement very confusing, so I don't even watch
the image shift in the field of view. I just decide the clock angle and use

the trial-and-error method described above. Again, it is more important to move slowly and methodically than to understand every twist and turn. The path of Fig. 6-11 is not the only solution to this initial condition or even the most efficient, but it succeeds.

### 6.5.2 The Refractor

Most smaller, less-expensive refractors cannot be collimated because the makers prefer locking down the factory adjustment. Reasoning that incompetent users cannot botch the alignment, they don't fit the telescopes with adjustments. Fortunately, small refractors use a long-focus design that can tolerate large misalignments, so the absence of adjustments doesn't often affect the image.

In recent years, partly because of the resurgence of interest in big refractors and the advent of new apochromatic and advanced glass designs used at low focal ratio, refractors are being supplied with adjustable cells once again. If your refractor isn't adjustable, you can still check it using the method described here. Unfortunately, telescopes lacking adjustments might have to be returned to the maker for collimation. So-called "telephoto" designs may also need to be returned. These instruments are permanently fitted with a hard-to-reach telenegative amplifier as the last lens group, far down the tube.

Refractors are not difficult to align. Geometric alignment is usually sufficient because their advanced optical designs yield wide, well-corrected fields. The problem is one of technique and equipment. A refractor is aligned sitting on a table with the lens cap on.

The usual device used to inject light into the darkened tube is called a Cheshire eyepiece (Sidgwick 1955, p. 185), a modified version of the sighting hole used to align the Newtonian. In that case, ordinary room light on the translucent film-can cap was sufficient to provide enough backlight to see the dot. For refractors, a great deal more light is needed. Ordinary glass only reflects about 5% of the energy that strikes it, transmitting the rest. Coated lenses reflect even less. The Cheshire eyepiece is designed to provide a target bright enough to see, even after inefficient reflections. You can obtain one commercially or make it yourself.

Figure 6-12 shows one such alignment tool. It has a long tube with a porthole drilled in the side to allow light to enter. A dowel cut at 45° is inserted in the end of the eyepiece and drilled so that you can see through it. The oblique side of the dowel is at least painted glossy white, and if its surface is polished metal, so much the better. The inside of the sighting hole is carefully blackened. The purpose of the defining stop is to put a crisp edge on the target. Such a refinement is not really necessary if the

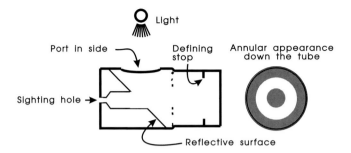

**Fig. 6-12.** *The Cheshire "eyepiece." The Cheshire is just an illuminated sighting hole; it contains no curved or high-quality optical surfaces. The reflective target pattern is shown at right.*

porthole is carefully placed.[2]

Taylor advocates the use of a white card tilted at 45° into which a sighting hole is placed, a "Cheshire" without the "eyepiece" (Taylor 1983). This suggestion, however, presumes that a great deal of care is taken with mounting the card and centering the sighting hole. Blacken a small elliptical area around the hole so you will see a circle at 45°.

Most adjustable lens cells use some variant of the push-pull system depicted in Fig. 6-13. This lens cell, when precisely adjusted and locked down, is extremely stable. A telescope flange is fixed on the tube, and the lens cell floats on three adjustable "push" screws threaded into that flange. Because the push screws are not sufficient to prevent the cell from dropping off, a matching pull screw associated with each push screw is added, making 6 screws in three groups around the tube. Since no springs are used, as one screw of each pair is loosened, its partner must always be tightened. Figure 6-13 shows a wide separation of the lens cell and the telescope flange to demonstrate the function of a push-pull pair. In fact, the starting configuration should always have the lens cell fitted nearly against the telescope flange. The adjustment will be longer-lived if the gap is small. Also, most real mirror cells carefully tuck the adjustment screws out of the way so they will not disturb the clean lines of the telescope. Some designers are so clever at hiding these screws that the instrument may not at first even appear adjustable.

If you can make this adjustment with a helper, you are strongly advised to do so. A couple minutes of alignment with two people quickly expands to an hour when you do it yourself. Put the Cheshire in the focuser

---

[2]If you use a Cheshire to align Newtonians, make sure you have sufficient in-focus travel to allow the eye to be placed close to the focal plane, and with fast mirrors make certain that the long sighting hole does not obscure the outside of the optics.

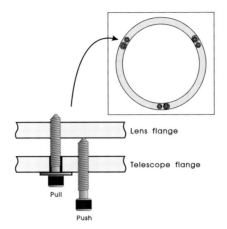

**Fig. 6-13.** *A "push-pull" adjustment screw pair. Inset shows three pairs making an adjustable cell.*

and shine light from the side, carefully shielding your eyes from the light source. If possible, use a low-magnification, close-focusing telescope looking directly through the rear hole. This ploy removes your eye from the bright sidelighting and expands the reflections so you can easily see them.

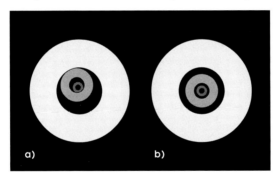

**Fig. 6-14.** *The Cheshire reticle reflection patterns from a 152-mm f/12 air-spaced apochromatic refractor: a) before collimation, b) after collimation. Neither alignment gave noticeably different images at the eyepiece.*

In one apochromatic refractor, the pattern of Fig. 6-14a was visible through a close-focusing finder telescope behind the sighthole of the Cheshire. The big annulus was a bright steely gray and was just about the size of the Cheshire. It must have been reflected from an air-to-glass surface of low curvature. The next annulus inward was pastel blue and somewhat dimmer. It was smaller, so it must have originated at a more sharply curved surface. The smallest ring was a very dull red or magenta and was not even observable with unmagnified vision. It perhaps relied on two or more of the inefficient reflections at coated interfaces.

This apochromat had six air-to-glass surfaces, and only three reticle reflections were seen. Fewer reflections are anticipated in a doublet. In fact, the Cheshire tool may not be very useful with some cemented doublets or refractors which use optical couplants (oils or gels) between the lenses. Only one reflection might be bright enough to see, and you wouldn't be able to compare it to others.

By adjusting the push-pull pairs, you can quickly make the reflection look like Fig. 6-14b. Turn the telescope over and check the pattern again. You will probably discover that the lens rattle designed into the cell compromises the centering. This condition is nothing to worry about; simply adjust it until it is about equally misaligned at each orientation. Even with the situation in Fig. 6-14a, misalignment was not noticed in the image.

After you achieve this grade of alignment, you are usually done. You can check the out-of-focus image but you probably won't be able to detect any astigmatism caused by misalignment (although other causes are still possibilities). The well-corrected field of a typical refractor is enormous.

If you do notice some astigmatism, you can certainly try to adjust it out using the star test. The direction of adjustment is less clear than it was with more coma present, since the direction of the optical axis can either be along the short dimension of the out-of-focus stellar disk or along the long dimension. For example, the optical axis may be found at 4 o'clock, 10 o'clock, 1 o'clock, or 7 o'clock, depending on whether you're inside or outside focus. With coma present, the angle was unique.

If the eyepiece is set inside focus, the optical axis can be found on either side of the *short* axis of the astigmatic oval. If the eyepiece is outside focus, the optical axis can be found along the *long* axis. For obvious reasons, you should decide on a certain side of focus and stick with it.

When the cell is adjusted at 90° to the proper direction, the stretch direction of astigmatism rotates rapidly. Also, undoing the adjustment and going an equal distance on the other side doesn't improve anything; it just reverses the rotation.

In star-test alignment, only a tweak of the push-pull screws will be enough. After all, the telescope should be very nearly collimated. Tiny changes at the screws mean enormous changes at the focal plane. If you are unable to remove the astigmatism by collimating it out, your telescope may be suffering from pinched optics or a true cylindrical deformation ground into the glass.

Let's review the general steps involved in alignment and see how they applied to refractors:

1. *Establish the axis line.* It was defined as the center of the tube.

2. *Center the optical components on this axis line.* Since most refractors have only one closely-spaced group of lens elements held in an accurately machined cell, this step was automatic. The focuser is assumed to transport the eyepiece along the axis. (In small, inexpensive refractors, this condition is not always met.)

3. *Establish the tilts of the elements.* This step was accomplished by centering the reflection of the annular reticle pattern of the Cheshire eyepiece.

4. *Repeat steps 1, 2, and 3 as an iterative procedure.* Check the alignment with the refractor turned over, and adjust until the Cheshire reflection looks about equally misaligned at all orientations.

5. *Adjust only one element in fine alignment.* This step was probably not needed, but if it were, it would have taken place on the objective.

### 6.5.3   The Schmidt-Cassegrain

Schmidt-Cassegrains of effective focal ratio f/10 have a primary mirror of about f/2 multiplied by a five-power convex secondary mirror. The center of curvature of the primary mirror must be behind the center of the secondary. Since the main mirror is not adjustable by the user on most Schmidt-Cassegrains, that adjustment must be set properly at the factory, or the telescope cannot be collimated.

An unacceptable main mirror adjustment is difficult to diagnose, but some clues exist. First, go through the rest of this collimation procedure to the best of your ability. Then, using a sighting hole (described above under Newtonian alignment), look back through the optical system. If you don't see absolutely concentric circles, rings within rings, your best alignment may be a kind of compromise. You will be offsetting the secondary to partially compensate for the aberrations induced by a misaligned primary. Still, the main mirror misalignment must be fairly serious before you are really able to detect non-circularity in these tiny reflections.

The front side of the instrument is an easier location to detect misalignment of the primary mirror. For 200-mm Schmidt-Cassegrains, place your eye a couple of feet from the front (about $1/2$ meter) and center the biggest reflection of the secondary outside the back of the secondary. By carefully adjusting the placement of the eye, you are able to see the reflection of the secondary as a thin annulus outside the true secondary. You are now nearer the alignment axis of the main mirror. If the mirror is seriously misaligned, it should be obvious that this axis does not coincide with the axis of the tube because the inside of the telescope will look tilted.

Another clue is derived from the way these primaries are mounted. The focusing action actually transports the mirror forward. The mirror's center is glued to a plate on the front of this axial focuser. Often, these mirrors get out of adjustment because of some sort of mechanical fault in the focuser. (Perhaps it has taken an enormous jolt during shipping.) As you focus the instrument, the image is not seen to defocus in a fixed location but reels or loops across the field. In any case, such anomalous focusing behavior, if severe enough, demands factory service.

For now, let's assume you have a well-aligned primary mirror. The only free adjustment is the tilt of the secondary mirror. If you have a severely misaligned Schmidt-Cassegrain, you may need to coarsely align by looking through it with a sighting hole. Center the reflection of the primary mirror in the secondary. Usually, this step will be unnecessary.

The final step is fine alignment with the star test. You can align the telescope in the daytime on an artificial star or at night on a real star. The Schmidt-Cassegrain is the most convenient of the example telescopes to align because of its compactness. If your arms are long, you can actually reach the adjustment screws while your head is behind the eyepiece. Of course, collimation is still easiest with two people, one calling out instructions and the other trying to obey them.

The secondary cell of a Schmidt-Cassegrain mount is a variation of the diagonal mount of the Newtonian. In both cases, loosening one screw is counterbalanced by tightening the other two. In changing the tilt of the secondary mirror, you must achieve alignment while keeping the mirror cell screwed tight.

It may seem expedient to overly tighten one screw as collimation is approached. Avoid such a shortcut. The secondary mirror is mounted in glass, and you might break the corrector. Also, the secondary mirror is held on a stiff plate, but this plate can be bent and the mirror strained. Finally, you might jerk the wrench out of the socket when forcing it and end up scratching the corrector. Tighten it snugly, but don't force it. If you have to move it a bit more, loosen the other two screws instead.

A misaligned Schmidt-Cassegrain will generate the same sort of star test behavior as depicted earlier for a Newtonian. Perform the star test without a 45° elbow. You will have one less potential source of aberration, and you will be able to observe the angle of the optical axis. The correct screw to turn is straightforwardly determined. Soon, you can center the shadow of the secondary in the image. (Use the same method as was used in the Newtonian.) Refine the alignment by turning to a dimmer star and defocusing it less or, if seeing is excellent, leave the telescope in focus and adjust the image for symmetry.

To review, the steps involved in aligning a Schmidt-Cassegrain were as follows:

1. *Establish the axis line.* That line, by definition, is coaxial with the tube.

2. *Center the optical components on the axis line.* Centerings are factory-set and hence are not adjustable.

3. *Establish the tilts of the elements.* The tilt of the corrector is, to first order, unimportant. The tilt of the primary is a factory setting and depends strongly on the condition of the focusing mechanism. Only the tilt of the secondary may be adjusted.

4. *Repeat steps 1, 2, and 3 as an iterative procedure.* Because so many of the coarse alignment adjustments are out of the owner's hands, iteration is impossible.

5. *Adjust only one element in fine alignment.* This step is combined with step 3. It is done on a star or artificial pinhole source placed at around 50 meters or farther; only the secondary is adjusted.

If your telescope still displays asymmetric images at the end of these steps, then it will have to be returned to the manufacturer. The primary mirror is probably tilted. The lack of adjustments on the main mirror is perhaps the weakest feature of commercial Schmidt-Cassegrain designs.

# Chapter 7

# Air Turbulence and Tube Currents

Some sources of aberration have nothing to do with the telescope itself. They come from the necessary immersion of the instrument in a changing optical medium. The light of astronomical objects must traverse a turbulent column of air that extends many kilometers from the top of the atmosphere to the focal plane of the instrument.

Little can be done by the amateur observer about turbulence high in the atmosphere, but it is easy to recognize in the star test. Many of the problems described in this chapter cure themselves after a time, particularly those having to do with the cooling of the telescope or of its immediate environment. The aim here is to teach you how to detect aberrations that originate in the motion of air, prevent them as much as possible, and recognize when they subside. Learning the star-test behavior of the atmosphere at your location will also allow you to identify those rare bouts of unusually steady seeing favorable to high magnifications.

## 7.1 Air As a Refractive Medium

The index of refraction of air is very near that of a vacuum, but it is noticeably different. At 0° Celsius, dry air at sea-level pressure has an index of refraction of 1.00029, while vacuum has an index defined exactly as unity (CRC 1973). Such a small difference doesn't seem worth worrying about, but the wave going through the air inside a 1.5-meter focal length telescope is slowed, relative to passage through vacuum, by about 791 wavelengths.

Assuming that air is approximately an ideal gas and that the fractional part of the index of refraction changes linearly with temperature, one can easily figure out the lag for a small temperature difference. Recall that 0° Celsius is 273° Kelvin in units of absolute temperature. Therefore, a 1° K difference in temperature over a distance of 1.5 meters results in a delay of $^{791}/_{273}$ wavelengths per degree Kelvin, or about 2.9 wavelengths/°K (1.6 wavelengths/°F). Now stretch the tube of air up through the atmosphere, many kilometers overhead, with each layer at a different temperature. Propagation delays can be profound.

However, it doesn't matter if the pencil of light is delayed uniformly. After all, the light has been on a long journey. Who cares if it arrives a little late? We are only interested in the variations in direction or time of arrival as the light enters different portions of the long, skinny cylinder of air in front of our instruments. We detect those differences when we see the image degraded by bad seeing. When we look through Earth's atmosphere, we hope for a pressure and temperature uniformity that does not often exist. Some parts of the wavefront are a small distance behind other portions of the wavefront. Such aberrations can form differences in intensity and apparent location (i.e., "twinkling"), but their most common effect on large apertures is to blur the image.

In defense of the sky, perhaps we are expecting too much when we peer upward through all of that material and demand perfect images. After all, the total pressure of the atmosphere is the same as the pressure of over 30 feet of water. Sub-arcsecond resolution would not be expected from the bottom of a diving pool. Yet such resolutions actually are witnessed for images seen through the atmosphere. On exceptional nights, the atmosphere surprises us by becoming beautifully tranquil.

Still, a mechanism producing small-scale differences in refractive index must exist before atmospheric effects become troublesome. Air, by its gaseous nature, doesn't tend to maintain differences in pressure or temperature—except for wide layering caused by the force of gravity. Air mixes together, averaging differences until layered uniformity prevails. Statistical inhomogeneity won't persist without mixing. The two mechanisms of most interest to telescope testers are atmospheric turbulence and tube currents.

## 7.2   Turbulence

If the atmosphere changed slowly, turbulence would never start. However, the atmosphere often is forced to move quickly. As sunlight deposits energy on the ground, it heats the air immediately above it. That air expands, becoming lighter than the mass of air immediately above it. The situation becomes unstable or "active," and the denser air falls to replace the warmer air below it. It moves quickly enough to generate turbulence.

This type of fluid motion is called a "Rayleigh-Taylor" instability. Completely fill an empty soda bottle with water and invert it with a playing card over the opening. Carefully remove your hand. The water does not fall out of the container (Walker 1977). If you were to suddenly remove the card, you would have a bottle full of water poised over a space of air.

All the water can't fall immediately. Air pressure holds the water up in the same way that a column of mercury is held up in a barometer. All of the water molecules are holding on to each other so they won't fall away individually.

Faster than humans can perceive, the random jiggles of the surface will cause one portion to deform slightly upward and another part slightly downward. That's all it takes. Once this process starts, it drives itself. A bubble rises and finally breaks off. The bottle empties, but it doesn't do so uniformly. The instability must form again and again. The bottle drains noisily, gently kicking in your hand.

Incidentally, the instability doesn't take place if a sufficient external force holds the surface level. With the card, the surface was constrained by the structural strength of the paper. By the time the opening is reduced to the size of a soda straw, surface tension alone provides enough force to overcome the instability. You can lift narrow columns of water by merely plugging the top of a straw.

For the atmosphere, no bottle circumscribes the unstable region, but essentially the same process occurs. As the cold air falls, inefficiencies ensure that the edges of the falling region aren't smooth. The fall is quick enough that tiny vortices form, but smaller swirls don't move with the speed of the main convective cell. Even tinier vortices form at the edges of these eddies. Finally the swirls become lost in complexity. At some small scale, the model of collective motion breaks down and the energy is expressed in heat. All realistic cases of fluid flow, such as streams and large convective cells, move macroscopically only on the average. When considered microscopically, they are turbulent.

### 7.2.1 The Aberration Function

Statistical variations of the wavefront are usually handled with semi-analytic procedures. These procedures, which commonly assume a Gaussian form for the random variations, are quite useful for calculating the long-exposure MTFs and other features associated with rough surfaces (Schroeder 1987, p. 315). However, they do not allow us to calculate the appearance of a single example image. They are the behavior averaged over many such roughened apertures.

The method used here to simulate the wavefront is called the midpoint displacement fractal algorithm. It is used to generate wonderfully realistic fractal landscapes (Peitgen and Saupe 1988, p. 96; Mandelbrot 1983; Harrington 1987). It can also render an artificial, pseudo-random wavefront just after it has passed through the aperture. Fractals were first applied to diffraction problems by M.V. Berry in the seminal article "Diffractals," in which a fractally-derived *phase screen* first appeared (Berry 1979, 1981). The method used here is an adaptation of an earlier article, where a one-dimensional variation of the midpoint deviation algorithm was used to calculate slit-type diffraction patterns (Suiter 1986a).

Because of the way the fractal must fill in the area of a two-dimensional grid, we may conveniently proceed by a two-step iterative procedure. The algorithm starts with the four corners of $129 \times 129$ point grid assigned arbitrarily to be of height zero (Fig. 7-1a). Only the location of the points are shown in Fig. 7-1; the deviation is perpendicular to the paper.

For the first half of the first iteration (Fig. 7-1b), the offset of the next finer division is calculated as the average of the previous four set points at the ends of the dotted curves (for the first iteration, this average is zero) plus or minus some random deviation $(\pm\Delta z)$. The center point is assigned this value. The points set only during each half-iteration are black; all previously assigned points are white. Points of the $129 \times 129$ grid that have yet to be assigned values aren't shown.

During the second half of the first iteration, the edges are filled in. The four nearest points are averaged again, assuming that the points off the edge of the area are zero, and to this number is added another plus or minus deviation. This time the maximum allowable deviation is divided by $\sqrt{2}$ before it is assigned. Notice that each complete iteration cycle averages the positions of the points first oriented at the diagonals to the point to be set, and then in the second half, averages at rectilinear angles. For obvious reasons, this algorithm can also be called the "$\times+$" method.

At the start of the second iteration, the maximum allowable offset is divided once again by $\sqrt{2}$ to make it $\pm\Delta z/2$. At the beginning of the third iteration, it is $\pm\Delta z/4$, and so forth. Thus, the cell sizes are decreasing at precisely the same rate as the maximum deviation, setting up conditions so that the apparent random slopes average out to be the same at all scales. This is called *statistical self-similarity*, or an independence of scale for averaged behavior.

Finally, when the seventh iteration is completed (it would be the 15th frame of Fig. 7-1, if the figure were allowed to go that far), the entire $129 \times 129$ grid is assigned. At this point, with the fractal algorithm finished, the area is conditioned to resemble a circular aperture. The aberrations and transmissions of points farther than 64 locations away from the center point are set to zero, and if a secondary is simulated, the same is done for all points within a certain radius. The outer parts of the $129 \times 129$ grid is cut off like the extra dough of a pie crust. The statistics of the clear aperture are then calculated, and the RMS deviation is scaled to the value

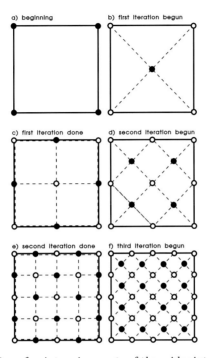

**Fig. 7-1.** *The ordering of point assignments of the midpoint deviation algorithm. Here the roughness is out of the paper.*

demanded by the individual computation.

An easy misunderstanding of Fig. 7-1 could occur here. Because of its superficial resemblance to the later image frames, readers could incorrectly assume that this non-physical mathematical procedure is used to calculate an image. This method merely simulates the random aberration function on the *pupil,* not an image. The image is calculated with the same Huygens-Fresnel theory used in other chapters (see Appendix B).

Physical reasons may determine that random variations do not persist equally over all scales. In fact, such is the case for turbulence. The characteristic width scale of turbulence, or about the distance between the "bumps," is on the order of 2–20 cm, with a good one-number estimate of 10 cm (Roddier 1981, p. 302; Schroeder 1987, p. 314). Abrupt deformations of the wavefront for slight lateral motions are not anticipated. The roughening of the wavefront is slightly rounded. This feature results in the well-known "small telescope" effect, where tiny instruments seem to give better images than large ones. Apertures smaller that 100 mm are looking through portions of the wavefront that are closer to a plane. Turbulence causes the image to jump around, but it appears to be well delineated from moment to moment.

For this reason, the algorithm is slightly modified. A *quenching factor* is applied to the $\sqrt{2}$ diminishing of each half iteration. The divisor in this case becomes $\sqrt{2q}$, where $q$ is the quenching factor. For $q$ greater than 1, the surface softens to make the gross variations more noticeable, with fine-scale roughness relatively suppressed. The surface resembles crumpled smooth paper instead of sandpaper. The quenching factor used here was between 1.1 and 1.6. No attempt was made to physically justify this model, but the lessening of finer scale eddies demands some sort of smoothing. The images generated with such quenching factors look the most authentic, and that realism justified their use in the images that appear here.[1] For quenching factors different from 1, the surface is no longer self-similar.

The other modification is a way of controlling the largest scale of the roughness. We would expect turbulence to show itself differently in a 24-inch behemoth than in a tiny refractor. In large telescopes, the image does less jumping around and momentary clearing of the blur happens less often. For the purposes of this chapter, the largest scale of the roughness was set at a significant fraction of the aperture. Thus, the calculations below are good for small telescopes with aperture of about 200 mm for most cases of turbulent air.

Some important characteristics of this fractal aberration will affect the quality of our simulation. First, the surface distribution is not Gaussian (bell-curve shaped). The surface distribution (shown in Fig. 7-2) is roughly Gaussian in that it is more-or-less peaked, but under no circumstance is it Gaussian nor would it ever be Gaussian, even if the iteration were allowed to continue forever. More commonly, multiple peaks are found in the surface distribution. Such unusual action allows us to simulate detail that would be washed out of Gaussian models.

Second, the surface is locally correlated. A surface with memory will allow our images to contain realistic streaks and bumps. The MTFs appearing below are calculated with the modeled "snapshot" surfaces and will show statistical variations. This procedure gives us an important view that could not be attained if we figured the MTFs from long-exposure averages.

One feature compromises the algorithm described above. The fictional exterior points are assumed to be zero, so one might expect some unusual distortions to occur near the edges. Because the surface was pie-trimmed, the worst effects are toward the four compass directions of the pattern nearest those edges. Distortions were indeed seen, but the problem areas were small and the effects did not readily appear in diffraction patterns.

---

[1] Readers interested in the more physical time-averaged models can find a survey and a good bibliography in the review article by Hufnagel (1993).

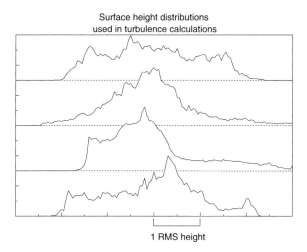

Surface height distributions
used in turbulence calculations

1 RMS height

**Fig. 7-2.** *Example wavefront-height distributions of the turbulent wavefronts, with the x-axis measured in units of the roughness RMS value.*

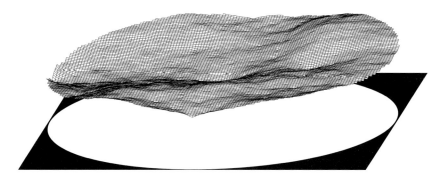

**Fig. 7-3.** *An example modeled aberration function of air turbulence.*

An example turbulent wavefront is shown in Fig. 7-3, with the wavefront conveniently elevated a small distance through the aperture. The most pleasing aspects of this pattern are the pseudo-random creases running through it. Creases should model the shadow-band behavior of real turbulent air currents that cause speckles and temporary spikes in the image. The quenching factor has acted to smooth the fine-scale variation, which will become more apparent when compared to the aberration function for primary ripple in the roughness chapter. Because earlier iterations were capable of much more movement, occasional dimples appear in the aberration function.

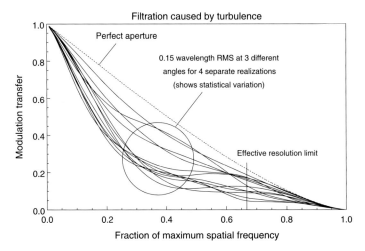

**Fig. 7-4.** *Twelve MTF curves associated with 0.15 wavelength RMS air turbu-lence. Aberration functions are calculated with the fractal model described in the text.*

## 7.2.2 Filtering Caused by Turbulence

These apertures are not circularly symmetric. Their ability to preserve contrast depends on the orientation of the bar pattern of an MTF target. Therefore, the MTF for each of the four generated surfaces was calculated along 3 axes. All 12 such MTF curves are shown in Fig. 7-4. The amount of RMS aberration used was about twice the $1/14$-wavelength Maréchal tol-erance. If one looks at Fig. 7-2 and replaces the RMS height with 0.15 wavelength, it is apparent that the total wavefront aberration is about 4 times that value, or 0.6 wavelength. This aberration is about twice as bad as can be tolerated for high-resolution observing, but such aberration is by no means uncommon for air turbulence. Often, seeing is much worse.

Also notice the extreme fluctuation at the high-frequency end of the chart. Because the curve flutters around rapidly there, resolution is limited to about $1/2$ to $2/3$ of the theoretical maximum for the aperture. With a 200-mm aperture, the central blur circle has a radius of about 1 to 1.5 arcseconds.

## 7.2.3 Observing Turbulence

In the focused image plots of Fig. 7-5, the modeled turbulence corre-sponds to a 5 on Pickering's 1–10 seeing scale, since the focused disk is always visible but arcs aren't often seen. This number corresponds to a

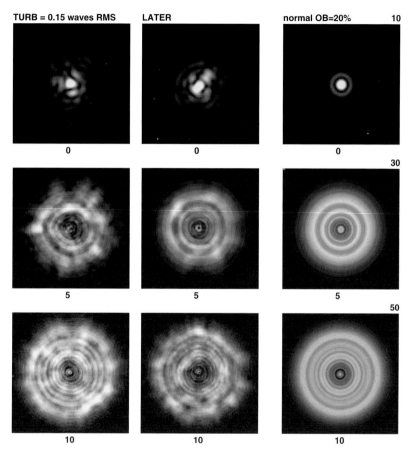

**Fig. 7-5.** *Image patterns calculated for 0.15 wavelength turbulence. Perfect patterns are to the right. Central obstruction is arbitrarily set at 20% of the aperture. (For a description of the labeling of image figures, see App. D.)*

"poor" seeing rating (Muirden 1974). Sometimes turbulence is much more severe. Good lunar-planetary viewing requires better.

Fig. 7-6 tracks the focused image as turbulence aberration becomes less objectionable. Fig. 7-6a shows long arcs and probably fluctuates between Pickering ratings of 6 and low 7. Fig. 7-6b has a rating of high 8, since the rings are complete but are always moving. Fig. 7-6c is about a high 9 or low 10, since the rings are stationary and the disk is crisply defined, but the weak ring still breaks up. With as much as $1/20$ wavelength of turbulence wavefront deformation, seeing still has a 10 out of 10 rating.

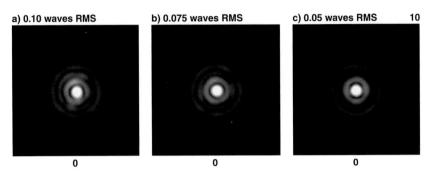

**Fig. 7-6.** *Focused images as turbulence is lessened. The ring structure reappears.*

The turbulence aberration is easily distinguishable from other aberrations:

1. It moves quickly. In less than a second you see an entirely different pattern.

2. It is balanced on either side of focus (unbalanced aberrations can modify the patterns, but the behavior is not caused by air turbulence).

3. If you pull the eyepiece outside of infinity focus, you can often focus on the disturbances themselves high in the atmosphere. They appear as bands or cells moving across the out-of-focus image.

### 7.2.4   Corrective Action

You can do little about high altitude turbulence, since it is beyond reach. High turbulence is more a function of the climate rather than a local phenomenon. However, you can start a log of weather and seeing conditions and see if you can come up with correlations. In general, the presence of clouds and high wind indicates that surplus energy is being transported around in the atmosphere and that seeing is bad. Good seeing is not always associated with transparent nights and may in fact be negatively correlated. Tranquil nights tend to be a little hazy.

Local seeing, or turbulence that occurs within a few hundred feet of the ground, is another matter. Local air turbulence may be caused by thermal currents from buildings or structures that have yet to cool from daytime heating. House shingles are notorious for their long cool-down times. Paving asphalt also retains heat and gives it up slowly. For this reason, observing over grass or trees is much preferable to observing over houses or roads.

Some authors have remarked on the interference caused by ground seeing (Muirden 1974), which is an effect located very near the telescope.

Personally, I have never had any trouble with turbulence very near the telescope that was not caused by setting the telescope directly on asphalt or concrete. One exception to this general situation, however, is that the nearby observer is a very good furnace. Body heat can waft across an open tube quite easily. This problem is not too great in the summer, when temperature differences are lower, but in the winter it can do serious harm to an image. A cloth drapery for an open tube framework often helps here.

One thing to watch when several people are observing together is that those who are waiting to look don't congregate near the optical path of a telescope, or upwind of it. Heated air from their bodies or breath can intercept the incoming light beam. If possible, when hosting a public observing session, arrange the line on the down-breeze side of the optical path. Finally, if you have to transport the telescope to the site, be sure to park the automobile or truck so that air rising from the hot engine cannot interfere with anticipated high-resolution observation.

## 7.3 Tube Currents

Air at different temperatures is affected by gravity because cooler air weighs more. When unconstrained by exterior structures, it forms the convection cells discussed above. Air inside a tilted tube tends to follow the wall—hot air on the high side, cool air on the low side. The tube resembles a tilted stovepipe. As air is heated at the bottom and becomes less dense, cool air falls down the tube and forces the hot air upward. It rises to hug the tube on its upper side and eventually exhausts to the outside.

With a telescope at or near ambient temperature, temperature differentials aren't bad enough to cause tube currents. However, when a telescope is first taken outside, thermal inertia causes problems until the instrument reaches the environment's temperature. The thick glass of the objective is particularly prone to slow cooling.

### 7.3.1 The Aberration Function

Clearly, every telescope cools off differently. Some have other problems that may obscure or modify the tube currents, like a hot mounting or an observing pad that retains heat from the day. Some have peculiarly shaped tubes or partial tubes that would change the patterns modeled here. All cooling telescopes have an unavoidable amount of locally induced turbulence. Some telescopes have only stubby mirror boxes and no real tubes, and these generate different patterns than shown below.

Schmidt-Cassegrains and refractors must cool off only through their rear exit portals or directly through the tube by radiative and conductive

cooling. One Schmidt-Cassegrain I examined displayed an extension of the
secondary shadow on one side of focus and streaks parallel to the edge of the
secondary on the other. At first, I thought it had a cracked corrector plate
near the secondary mounting hole, but when the tube orientation changed,
the pattern always followed an up-down direction. Presumably, a great deal
of the cooling was taking place in or around the mirror or corrector plate
perforations. An uneven thermal effect of the Cassegrain baffle tube may
also have caused the problem.

Even though it is not matched by every telescope, the behavior modeled
below is common enough in small to medium-sized Newtonians with round
tubes. The model assumes that the warm air is confined to the upper side
of the tube and that its effect is to advance the wavefront only along that
upper side, leaving the rest of the optical path comparatively untouched.
This behavior was described in Chapter 2 as resembling the turning of a
page.

The model used here is

$$W_{\text{tube}}(x) = \frac{A_{\text{tube}}(x - 0.3)^3}{(0.7)^3} \qquad (x > 0.3)$$
$$W_{\text{tube}}(x) = 0 \qquad\qquad\qquad (x \le 0.3),$$

$$(7.1)$$

where $x$ is the linear coordinate in one direction across the surface with the
origin at the center of the aperture. The value of $x$ reaches 1 at the edge
of the aperture.

The model does not allow variation in any other direction than the up-
down coordinate. No roughness is superimposed on the effect of the tube
current, even though it would surely be present.

The aberration plotted over the pupil is shown in Fig. 7-7, with the up
direction toward the right.

## 7.3.2   Filtering of Tube Currents

Again, the value of the modulation transfer function depends on the orientation of the bar pattern. The function was calculated for three angles:
up-down, left-right, and a 45° tilt. Fig. 7-8 shows two cases. The $1/2$ wavelength example is as bad as an observer should tolerate. The 1 wavelength
case is severe, but not unusual for telescopes that have just been moved
from warm surroundings.

This transfer function plot possesses a number of interesting features.
The first is the sudden drop of both the 45° and the horizontal MTFs.
The sharp fall is caused by the localized nature of the aberration. The
steep slope of the aberration kicks a lot of light out of the diffraction
spot, affecting spatial frequencies even $1/10$ of the maximum. For example,

**Fig. 7-7.** *The tube-current aberration function modeled over the aperture pupil.*

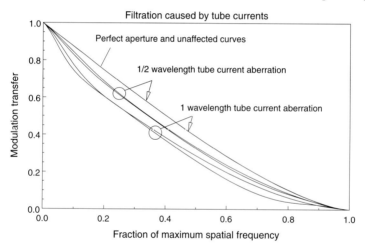

**Fig. 7-8.** *The MTF for the modeled tube current aberration. Two different aberrations are shown. Each aberration has three curves, but the up-down bar orientation results in no degradation. The up-down MTFs of both aberration values are plotted identically on top of the perfect pattern.*

if you had a 200-mm aperture, resolution of 5-arcsecond details would be noticeably degraded.

Second, for one curve in each aberration amount, the contrast is unaffected. The smearing of the image in the vertical direction doesn't affect resolution of MTF targets with the bars oriented up-down. Of course, the unmodeled roughness would tend to break up this symmetry a little.

### 7.3.3 Observing Tube Currents

Tube currents are easy to see. The problem lies in determining whether or not the aberration is in fact caused by a tube current or is present in the glass. These currents can be remarkably stable. You would think that they would dance and sway like high-altitude turbulence. The patterns do change, but they do so slowly, like candle flames. Even though you may know intellectually that a candle is a dynamic process, when you look at the fire, you easily slide into the comfortable viewpoint that it is motionless. A candle flame seems perched atop the wick.

Truly hot telescopes boil with turbulence, but they don't show this effect very long. As the telescope cools, the tiny temperature differences do not support the formation of massively turbulent air masses. The air moves slowly and smoothly upward. It drifts side-to-side languidly, but at any given time it is relatively quiet. Tube currents are always influenced by gravity and hence are oriented in an up-down direction.

You may easily determine the orientation of a suspected tube current wavefront deformation for refractors and Cassegrain-style instruments, just don't use a right-angled bend in the optical path. For a Newtonian reflector, however, determining the angle of the image is not straightforward. The cause is, of course, the built-in diagonal reflection.

Two remedies are suggested. The first is to use a star on the north-south meridian. Direction can be determined from the western drift by turning off the clock drive (if one is used). This trick cannot be used for an artificial source test. For such a telescope, a simple expedient is to rack the eyepiece far out of focus and then insert a fist or other obstruction from a known angle in front of the aperture. Up or down can then be easily located.

The diffraction pattern calculated for a total aberration of 1 wavelength appears in Fig. 7-9. The pattern is squeezed-in on one side of focus and stretched-out on the other.

Once you see a tube current, make certain that some other difficulty isn't the problem. First, change the tube orientation. Locate a feature of the tube along which the stretching is pointed. If no tube landmark exists, make a slight mark on the tube or attach a little curl of tape. Then, rotate the tube by some reasonable angle. Unfortunately, fork-mounted Schmidt-Cassegrains are impossible to rotate. Use a test source at a different location.

Tube currents will still point up and down with the new orientation, but they stretch toward a different tube feature. Other difficulties, such as warped or damaged optics, now show a non-vertical tilt in the eyepiece.

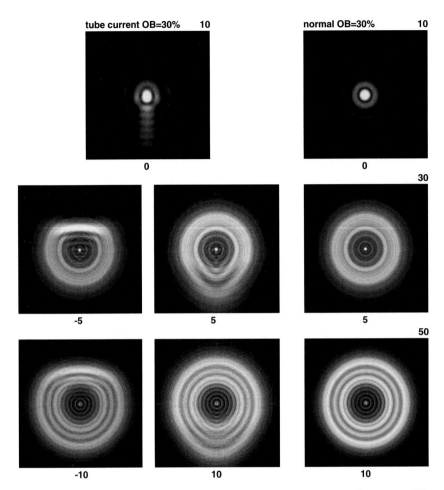

**Fig. 7-9.** *The star test patterns of 1 wavelength of tube current aberration. The perfect aperture is in the column on the right.)*

### 7.3.4 Corrective Actions for Tube Currents

Tube currents are not really that serious for very small telescopes. Just wait until the telescope cools down to the ambient temperature. If environmental temperature varies so much that the telescope never really catches up to the local temperature, atmospheric conditions are so unstable that seeing will be poor anyway.

Sealed telescopes, particularly refractors, do not display the same tube current effects that are common in open-tube reflectors. Refractors are typically made with metal tubes that leak heat readily, so they quickly cool down. Setting up small telescopes in the late evening, with enough time to reach the ambient temperature, is often sufficient to eliminate this optical problem.

The only observers who may find tube currents to be both objectionable and persistent are those using large or especially thick telescope objectives. I once worked on a 16-inch Newtonian mirror of 3-inch thickness (1:5 ratio). This mirror required half the night to cool down even under relatively benign conditions. Many nights it never cooled, but when it did, the mirror performed magnificently.

Such mirrors really should be prepared before they are required for observing. Transport in a warm automobile is one of the worst things that can be done to a thick mirror. Almost equally bad is storage in a sunlit shed or observatory. The optimum procedure is to open up the telescope or observatory in the early evening, long before the instrument is required. If the telescope is transported, try not to carry it in the heated passenger area of an automobile. Instead, haul it in a trailer or in the back of a truck.

Sometimes, the telescope must be set up on concrete or asphalt. Even with a properly stabilized instrument, the tube can catch external currents and act as a duct for them. In such situations, try closing the bottom end of a Newtonian's tube with a plastic bag and see if the aberration decreases.

# Chapter 8

# Pinched and Deformed Optics

At the start of each observing session, you should star test for problems that may change with transport of the telescope or a remounting of the optics after maintenance. This chapter will discuss the star-test pattern characteristic of one such warping and will present ways to relieve unusual stresses on the optics. Beyond the image improvements derived by giving careful attention to the deformations, you may be able to avoid catastrophic damage. Edge fractures are common among mirrors with too-tight edge clips. I have seen one mirror that was so severely strained that it broke in half.

## 8.1 Causes

Imagine a mirror or lens as a thick circular chunk of gelatin. Because we don't ordinarily notice tiny deformations, we think of some materials as rigid, but all objects warp with pressure and temperature changes. An object that looks solid to unmeasured eyesight and touch becomes soft and pliable when we look at changes as small as a wavelength of light. Optics are rigid only in a macroscopic sense.

If we place the gelatin on three support points, the shape of the surface distortion becomes a complicated function of the thickness of the slab and the placement of those supports. The problem is even more complicated if we tilt the gelatin; different supports carry unequal portions of the weight. Clearly, the edges sag between the support points.

The supports underneath can be placed near the edges, causing the center to sag, or near the center, causing the edge to bend down. They can be placed at 70% the radius, which causes the least deformation, but a more complex one. We can split each prop into 3 or 6, but what tradeoffs do we have to make?

That accounts only for the platform. What about the edges? If we screw on the edge supports too tightly, the surface pinches down around the three support positions. The clips could be properly adjusted, but when the telescope heels over, one clip may be forced to apply unusual pressure by the weight of the slab. Edge mounting has been solved a number of ways, ranging from the elegantly simple hanging-strap method used in Dobsonian mountings to a mercury edge-bag used in a few large equatorial reflectors.

Telescope mechanical design is far beyond the scope of this work, however. Only one example of surface deformation will be presented. Surface deformations cause an infinite variety of star-test patterns, none resembling the others. They may share some of the following characteristics:

1. They can be distinguished from turbulence because they are fixed patterns.

2. They often show 2, 3, or 6-fold symmetry.

3. They are usually weaker at high telescope elevations than low ones.

4. The pattern distortions may invert on passage through focus.

Although more common in reflectors, optics pinching is not unknown in refractors. One refractor I examined suffered a problem with a coupling agent used between the lens element. The material hardened or bunched up in three locations, yielding a star-test pattern similar to the classic three-point pinched mirror cell. See Fig. 8-1.

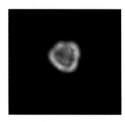

**Fig. 8-1.** *Star-test pattern taken through a large refractor. Its three-sided symmetry betrays a pinching effect. When repairing this problem, the maker reported that the optical coupling agent was causing undue pressure on the lens.*

Also, lens cells have to be made a bit larger than lens elements to account for the more severe shrinkage of metal with cooler temperatures. Glass constricts, but it does not shrink as much as metal. If the cell is made too small, the optics can actually be squeezed at low temperatures, resulting in an astigmatic or otherwise deformed image. If temperatures drop too low, a tight cell can crack the lens like an egg.

## 8.2 The Aberration Function

There are as many forms of surface warping as there are optical surfaces, but only one will be modeled here. The arbitrary choice will be clip pinching or perhaps a thin mirror that has too few bottom supports. What characteristics must the model have to simulate the effects of tight mirror clips? First of all, it must be strongest near the edge. If the optics deform, they can do so most easily at the edge. Second, the aberration function should have a tripartite symmetry. Optics, of course, can deform in other ways than the three-lobed pattern. However, since mounting cells usually have a three-sided aspect, such deformation is common.

Without physical justification, one can choose a softened[1] cycloidal dependence in angle and a third-order radial dependence to yield the aberration function shown in Fig. 8-2. The attractive feature of this pupil function is the asymmetry of the deformation; it ranges from creases in the valley to flat-topped humps. The aberration function could have been made symmetrical in the valleys and peaks, sort of like "three-lobed" astigmatism, but we will see astigmatic behavior later, so it would be redundant to dwell on it here.

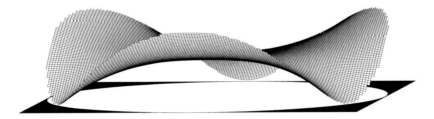

**Fig. 8-2.** *An aberration function of pinched or deformed optics.*

## 8.3 Filtering of Pinched Optics

Figure 8-3 depicts the modulation transfer functions of two unobstructed pinched systems. Because the pupil function is not neatly symmetrical, the transfer varies with the angle at which we place the lines of the MTF target. The figure shows three transfer functions, corresponding to bar patterns at the vertical, horizontal, and 45° angles. The MTF for this particular surface deformation is very similar to that for defocusing.

---

[1]The form used was a "curtate" cycloid. See the Glossary.

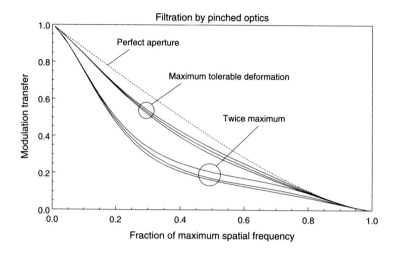

**Fig. 8-3.** *MTF degradation for three-lobed deformed optics.*

The least pinched curves of Fig. 8-3 yield a Strehl ratio of 0.8 (the same as $1/4$-wavelength spherical aberration error). Because of the details of this aberration function, however, the total pinching aberration is 0.4 wavelengths.

Doubling the total aberration to 0.8 wavelengths, the curve is stretched even further downward. At low spatial frequencies, such a telescope preserves contrast about as well as a perfect aperture of 60% the diameter.

## 8.4   Diffraction Patterns of Pinched Optics

In Fig. 8-4, we see the star-test patterns expected from a warped reflecting telescope that has a 25% central obstruction. At focus, the diffraction rings are squeezed together into knobby radial spikes.

Such perfectly balanced patterns will probably not be visible in real telescopes. One pressure point seldom induces precisely the same aberration as any other. Also, each deformed surface will display its own unique properties. One tricky pattern not handled by this model is a 6-sided spiking on one side of focus and a muted polygonal shape on the other. I witnessed this problem years ago when a mirror was screwed too tightly into a 9-point cell.

Nevertheless, this problem is easy to diagnose using the characteristics mentioned above:

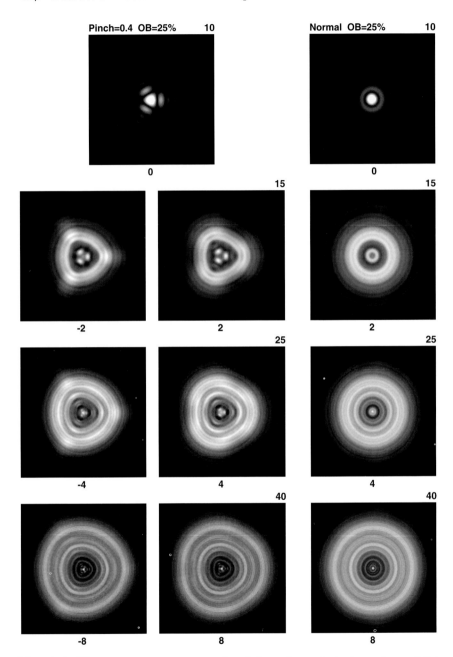

**Fig. 8-4.** *The star-test appearance of a deformed or pinched aperture of 0.4 wavelengths total aberration. Normal behavior is in the column to the right. Obstruction is 25%.*

1. *See if the warping changes with time.* If it is a fixed, unchanging image distortion, it cannot be caused by local heating, tube currents, or atmospheric effects. Look again in 15 minutes. Air optics change dramatically; pinching does not (unless the squeezing changes markedly with temperature).

2. *Count the points around the perimeter.* If you count 3 or 6, the mechanical supports are probably to blame. Three or 6-fold symmetry just isn't ground into the glass that often. Two-fold symmetry indicates pressure from one direction, or it could be an actual astigmatic error in the glass. If two-fold asymmetry is found, try to identify the axis of the astigmatism by putting your hand into the beam the same as you did during alignment. If the axis of the warping is precisely vertical, you can usually assume that either you are incredibly unlucky or the astigmatism results from gravitational forces applying non-uniform pressure.[2]

3. *Shift the telescope to look at a star near zenith.* The easiest confirmation that your difficulty is caused by mechanical supports is simply to change the direction of force on the optics. If the deformation lessens or changes, it could mean that the supports are warping the disk. In any case, it is rare not to change at least the magnitude, if not the flavor, of warping merely by changing the angle of the telescope. An exception is a pinched Schmidt-Cassegrain corrector plate. Because the plate is held so firmly, it gives the same distorted image at any angle.

4. *Rack through focus.* Some warped star-test patterns are similar to astigmatism on opposite sides of focus. If "points" in the image on one side become flat regions on the other, something could be straining the optics. Other deformations do not exhibit this behavior, however. It did not appear in Fig. 8-4, so it is not always a reliable indicator of pinching.

## 8.5   Fixing the Problem

The rest of the discussion will assume you have a reflecting telescope suffering from poorly held optics. Such a problem is rare in refractors, and you can do little about it anyway, except return the lens to the manufacturer for servicing.

If you see a two-lobed image warping in a Newtonian reflector, you could have the astigmatism in either the primary mirror or the diagonal. You need

---

[2]See Chapter 14.

an easy way to isolate the problem to the offending mirror. Rotate the tube by $20° - 30°$. If the deformation seems to be fixed at the same angle in the eyepiece, the problem is probably contained within the diagonal, because it rotated too. On the other hand, gravity has changed its direction with respect to the tube. If the pattern seems to have rotated by the same angle, or has otherwise changed, it is probably in the main mirror supports.

Nowadays, the telescopes that are often in the most danger of suffering from warped optics are large, thin-mirror Newtonian reflectors. Tube angle cannot be changed in many such instruments, so you can't isolate the origin of the aberration by the simple expedient of rotating the tube. Fortunately, patterns seen in thin-mirror reflectors should change drastically with elevation. Try comparing the appearance of a defocused star just above the horizon with one nearly overhead. If the appearance changes markedly, the most suspicious support is the one carrying the most weight—the main mirror's.

If the telescope is troubled by warping, you are better off to try mirror cell repairs blindly than to do nothing. First, you should verify that the mirror clips are not pressing down on the surface. Optimally, mirrors are not even held by such restraints. The purpose of mirror clips is to prevent catastrophic damage during transport and storage, acting as stops so the mirror does not fall face down in the tube. When the telescope is in operating form, these clips should hover above the surface.

You should make sure that the side supports are slightly loose. In many mirror cells, the clips and the side supports are the same units. Since most mirror cells are made to fit a nominal-sized mirror, the side supports are somewhat adjustable, either using a plastic set screw or by adding thin shims to the clip mount.

What you want to avoid is a situation where the mirror is held by excessive force, other than its own weight. One mirror cell I inspected a few years ago had too many shim washers removed from the combined clip and edge supports. This clip was attached with a screw, and the mirror was halting the screw before the metal of the cell did. In effect, the owner was tightening the side of the mirror down with a wrench.

If the mirror rattles a little when you shake the cell, it is mounted properly. Try for less than 1 mm of motion in any direction and even less vertical travel.

Thin, large mirrors in altazimuth Dobsonian mountings should not be held at the edge by point-like restraints. Their own weights induce unacceptable stresses. Thin mirrors should hang in a strap. But even if your mirror is held by a belt, it may still be maladjusted. In one telescope I saw, the strap had slipped and the mirror was sitting on the side of the box. Also, the belt should never support more than 50% of a mirror's cir-

cumference or hold the mirror too tightly.  Some mirrors are held with a
strap that is tightened by a screw, similar to an automobile radiator hose
clamp.  Such mounting methods should be replaced or modified, because
they squeeze the mirror excessively.

Of course, few acceptable cell designs exist for large thin mirrors supported in equatorial mountings.  As the instrument tracks across the sky it
also executes a rolling motion.  Thus, the direction of gravity changes orientation with respect to the cell.  Besides the mercury bag solution mentioned
earlier,[3] makers have tried many other tricks to avoid undue pressure at
points on the edge.  The most common of these is gluing the mirror to the
underneath supports, dispensing with edge holders and clips entirely.  Even
flexible aquarium cement occasionally suffers problems.  Gluing the mirror
down this way opens the possibility of other pressures being applied by
deformed mounting plates.  Perhaps you may be able to tune such a mirror
to work properly in some areas of the sky, but most likely you will have to
live with at least a little warping.  Compromises are sometimes unavoidable
when choosing to mount such a large, floppy mirror equatorially.

---

[3]This method involves large amounts of toxic mercury, a procedure that can be used
safely only by professionals.

# Chapter 9

# Obstruction and Shading

Modifying the transmission of the aperture pupil causes changes to the diffraction pattern. Obstruction and shaded transmission are not deformations of the wavefront in the same sense as aberrations. They can occur in officially "perfect" apertures. Nevertheless, they can affect the perceived image quality in a very similar manner.

Five main points are made in this chapter:

1. Central obstructions below 20% of the aperture are indistinguishable in practice from an unobstructed aperture, and for obstruction under 25%, performance can be very good.

2. Reckless efforts to reduce central obstruction can lead to even worse images than those resulting from obstruction.

3. A spider in front of an aperture hurts the image only for dim objects next to bright sources of interference or for low contrast objects imbedded in an extended field. For most dark-field observing, the spider's effect is only cosmetic.

4. Darkening the outside portion of the aperture results in contrast improvements at low spatial frequencies, but only at the expense of high spatial frequencies.

5. Dust and scratches are cosmetic errors, similar to spider diffraction except for certain types of observing.

## 9.1   Central Obstruction

The most obvious and potentially the most damaging kind of transmission change is caused by the centrally placed diagonal or secondary mirror.

Some observers are almost fanatical about central obstruction. In various astronomical publications, they have made blanket statements such as "obstruction reduces contrast" without giving the spatial frequencies at which that reduction occurs. They imply that obstruction so severely damages the image that no amount can be tolerated.

However, the negative consequences of central obstruction can be readily and precisely calculated. We will see that they worsen considerably beyond a fractional obstruction of 20 to 25% of the aperture. As long as the obstruction is kept inside that fraction, the image closely approximates that of an unobstructed telescope.

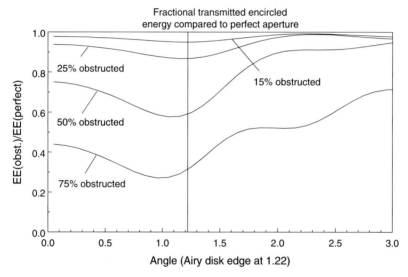

**Fig. 9-1.** *The fractional encircled energies of centrally obstructed apertures divided by the encircled energy of an unobstructed aperture. The performance drops off sharply at 20–25% obstruction.*

Figure 9-1 does not illustrate contrast but the closely related topic of encircled energy. In Fig. 9-1, the normalized encircled energies of the obstructed apertures are divided by the normalized encircled energy of a perfect circular aperture. Thus, the obstructed aperture ratios deviate from an ideal value of unity.

As the circle approaches the radius of the unobstructed Airy disk at 1.22, these ratios fall. The spot size is smaller in obstructed instruments, and the energy robbed from the core diffraction spot is mostly deposited in the first one or two diffraction rings. While the obstructed pattern is crossing the minimum between the central disk and the first ring, it encloses little additional energy and the unobstructed pattern gets ahead of it. Not

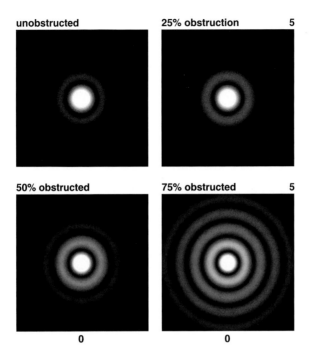

**Fig. 9-2.** *The in-focus diffraction patterns resulting from central obstruction.*

until the circle encloses the first rings of both patterns does the ratio begin
to recover.

In the focused diffraction patterns of Fig. 9-2, the intensities of the rings
swell as obstruction is increased. By the time a 75% obstruction is reached,
all pretense of optical quality is lost. Paradoxically, the diffraction disk is
smaller. All of these images are calculated at the same scale and printed
with the same central intensity, so this shrinkage cannot be explained as an
artifact of the reproduction. This phenomenon is real. In fact, the narrowest central disk is found in an aperture that is almost entirely obstructed,
but the powerful rings caused by such an aperture render it useless for fine
imaging.

Filtering appears in Fig. 9-3. Again, the bottom does not drop out
at middle frequencies until the obstruction is beyond 25%. An obstruction
diameter under 20% of the aperture can be viewed as acceptably small. The
narrower spot size shows itself as an increase in the MTF at high spatial
frequencies; contrast here exceeds even the value for a perfect aperture.

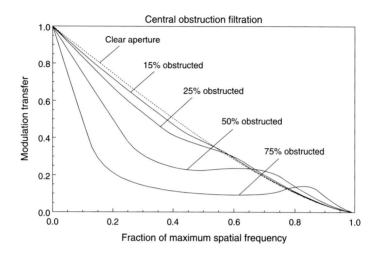

**Fig. 9-3.** *MTF curves of simple central obstructions.*

These curves demonstrate that a little breathing room is available between 20% and 25% of the aperture. The negative effects of central obstruction have begun to show themselves, but they are saving their full fury for obstructions beyond 30%. Any aperture that is 25% obstructed can be very good, and telescopes that block 20% of the diameter can be excellent. Instruments that have been modified to achieve less obstruction than 20% are obtaining very little contrast gain and are risking other optical problems. (See the end of Chapter 10 for more information on the degradation caused by obstruction in the presence of spherical aberration.)

In the absence of hard knowledge about the tolerable obstruction, telescope makers often cure this difficulty by immoderate measures. Commonly, they build Newtonian telescopes with overly squat focusers and minimum-size diagonals.

Unfortunately, reducing diagonal size often forces a compromise with the operation of other useful features of the telescope. Perhaps it even cuts into an unforeseen safety margin. For example, a long focuser tube baffles external light. Some telescopes are designed with eyepieces set so low that light can enter them directly, a problem especially common in open-tube telescopes. Another difficulty arises when a Barlow lens must be used. The focus should be far enough away from the optical path that the Barlow won't jut out in front of the mirror.

The diagonal is also prone to curvature near its edge, so telescopes that require every bit of the diagonal for on-axis imaging often have reduced quality. Certainly, small diagonals cause vignetting, and observers must be careful to make sure that the outer parts of the field of view are adequately illuminated for their favorite objects.

Thus, a well-meaning effort to improve contrast by reducing the diagonal size might have the opposite effect. The instrument may be so malformed by such efforts that contrast is much worse than it would have been with a slightly larger obstruction.[1]

## 9.2 Spider Diffraction

The support hardware that holds a secondary mirror causes some light diffraction. For linear spider vanes, the pattern takes the form of two or more radial spikes away from a point image. Spider diffraction takes a bright, extended image and smears it to either side.

Contrast is reduced, but by how much? Clearly, if the area of the vanes is not large when projected against the mirror, the spider cannot be scattering much light. That light *looks* brighter because it is blurred in only a few directions.

The MTF of a spider with vanes of thickness $1/128$ the diameter of the mirror appears in Fig. 9-4 (this MTF is compounded with the degradation of a 20% obstruction). The thickness is $1/16$ inch (nearly 2 mm) for an 8-inch (200 mm) mirror. Usually, small telescopes have vanes less than half that thick. Even so, the contrast is degraded only about 1.6% at first. The area of the vanes is also 1.6% of the aperture's area. Thus, a simple relationship exists between the area of small-scale obscuration and the amount of abrupt degradation in the MTF.

Spider diffraction causes the quick drop of the MTF, and thereafter the degradation is about a constant fraction of the normal behavior.[2] One can see from the very slight decrease that spider diffraction is a cosmetic defect for most dark-field observation. Only in exceptional situations does it significantly affect image contrast. If, for example, a dim star resides in the spider diffraction spike of a bright companion star, this light could become a problem. The spider diffraction does not cause difficulty if the dim star is alone or at a different angle to the spike, but because the nearby star is so bright, the spike may illuminate the whole area around the dim star. Fortunately, many telescopes allow rotation of the spider or tube.

---

[1]These examples are not meant to imply that a small secondary mirror is not a laudable goal. If telescope designers are aware of the risks, they can avoid them. The key is not to reduce the secondary size to the exclusion of every other optical consideration.

[2]For modulation patterns at 45°, the MTF will recover at 71% the maximum spatial frequency and even slightly exceed the value expected in its absence. MTFs for horizontal or vertical bar targets display less violently-changing structure. See Zmek 1993.

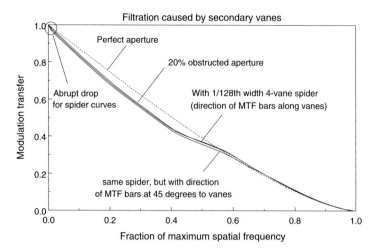

**Fig. 9-4.** *Modulation transfer function for spider diffraction. The degradation is slight compared to a spiderless 20% obstructed aperture. The lowest curve is for an MTF pattern at 45° to the vanes.*

On extended bright objects such as planets, spider diffraction causes a much subtler degradation. Each point on the object has its own spikes. Low contrast details can be washed out by weak light diffracted from the spider. A realistic thin-vaned spider has a surface area of about 0.5% the area of the aperture. Thus, the signal-to-noise ratio could be as low as 23 dB. Luckily, much of the stray light is beyond the edge of planets. If the vanes are as narrow as 0.5 mm, the width of the diffraction spikes is about 100 arcseconds. Spider-vane diffraction would greatly exceed the size of even a large planetary image, such as the 50 arcsecond angle subtended by Jupiter during oppositions. SNR exceeds 30–40 dB for planetary observation. Light diffracted from spider vanes becomes troublesome chiefly for lunar and solar observations, where the extent of the image is larger than the angle of diffraction.

Despite the conclusions from Fig. 9-4, spider diffraction can be an important design consideration. If the diagonal support vanes are much too thick, the diffraction spikes become brighter. More area of the mirror is intercepted, and more light is diverted. Thicker vanes also have shorter diffraction spikes. Since the light diffracts into a smaller area, it is relatively brighter.

You can see the effect of a wide spider vane by stretching a strip of black electrical tape across the front of your instrument (this experiment even works for refractors and Schmidt-Cassegrains—just keep the tape away from the lens). Direct the telescope towards a bright star and use a medium-

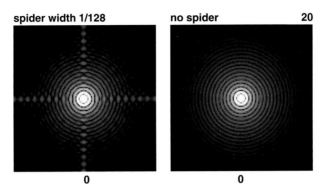

**Fig. 9-5.** *An "overexposed" monochromatic spider diffraction pattern compared with the same pattern calculated with no spider.*

to-high magnification eyepiece. You should see a bright spike of light at right angles to the tape. This spike glistens with sparkles of color. If the star is bright enough, the spike fades out with increasing distance from the star and then brightens again, perhaps doing so many times. You're observing the side peaks of spider diffraction, similar to the rings of circular aperture diffraction.

Another design mistake is the use of extremely thick, curved-vane spiders or a diffraction-spike suppression mask. Two such masks were suggested by A. Couder using curved-edge vane covers (Ingalls, Book Two 1978, p. 620). The images don't suffer the diffraction spikes caused by conventional spiders, but an increased level of scattered light is still there—just spread around in angle. In imaging of extended objects (such as planets), it doesn't matter whether the light is confined to a diffraction spike or has been averaged over various angles. Contrast is lowered the same amount. The most important factor is the *fraction* of the mirror such vanes cover. The only acceptable change to spider vanes is the use of *thin* curved-vane spiders, or eliminating them entirely by supporting the secondary on an optical window.

A focused spider image is shown in Fig. 9-5. This rendering is not a very realistic picture because it is calculated for monochromatic light, such as a laser would produce. The dips in the spikes will be filled in with other colors in white-light images, giving only a hint of structure.

While spider diffraction is only a minor annoyance for small telescopes, it can become a major object of concern in the design of large instruments. Because mechanical structure does not scale linearly, the support requirements of large reflector secondaries can be very great indeed. Heavy Cassegrain secondaries must be supported rigidly enough that alignment does not suffer. Thick vanes are necessary, and diffraction from the vanes becomes considerable (Beyer and Clune 1988).

One should make certain at the end of coarse alignment that the secondary support vanes present the minimum interception area to the beam of incoming light. This maintenance costs nothing, and can improve the image substantially.

## 9.3   Shading or Apodization

Diffraction rings are among the most objectionable features of the perfect circular diffraction image. This problem is perhaps most observable at the boundary between a bright area and a dark sky background. If seeing is sufficiently good, this boundary does not appear sharp, but shows "echo" images, one or more thin lines at the edge. Observers must be aware of this phenomenon, or else they will report spurious detail in the image. It is particularly prominent in images that are strongly colored or viewed through color filters. Planetary disks display limb-darkening, so this effect is difficult to notice at the edge of a planet. However, the problem is observable elsewhere and is always a source of interference with any clustering of spotty detail. Several diffraction rings may add to create another spot where one didn't exist before.

Changing the transmission characteristics of an aperture is called *apodization*. "Apod-" literally means "without feet" and refers to a shading of the entrance pupil that results in lowered diffraction rings. Apodization existed informally before it was named. Jacquinot and Couder made a one-dimensional apodizer in the 1930s to suppress the dim side lines that appeared next to bright lines on spectrographic plates (Jacquinot 1958).

R.K. Luneburg widened the definition of apodization by suggesting a set of generalized problems that don't necessarily lead to smaller rings but induce modifications of the diffraction pattern to optimize any given characteristic.[3] Based on Luneburg's investigations, it can be stated with some confidence that the best pupil shape *in most cases* is an unobstructed one (Luneburg 1964, pp. 344–359). One can set any sort of condition on the diffraction image, however, as long as some other parameter is allowed to swing freely.

For example, the diameter of the central spot can be minimized if the height of the diffraction rings does not matter. In fact, G. Toraldo di Francia designed a complex pupil shading that results in arbitrarily fine resolution and suppression of diffraction rings out to a specified radius (di Francia 1952). Unfortunately, such a shaded pupil is fantastically inefficient for all

---

[3]For this reason, I personally prefer the term *shading,* which comes from antenna and acoustic array theory.

realistic apertures, diverting most of the energy of the beam to a bright ring beyond the specified radius. The field stop must be inside of this radius to prevent the bright ring from dazzling the super-resolved star.

Similarly, C.L. Dolph (1946) derived a shading technique for linear-array radar antennae that balances resolution and diffraction. It also works for slit apertures. Dolph's technique features arbitrary suppression of side lobes to a specified level surrounding the central peak. This method is also inefficient but helps most for strong sources where interference from multiple directions is troublesome.

An early systematic investigation into partially transparent coatings of lenses to achieve enhanced resolution was made by Osterberg and Wilkins in 1949. They were able to theoretically achieve a central spot diameter only 77% that of the usual Airy disk. The Strehl ratio of such an aperture is 0.21, so this resolution comes at considerable optical costs. The first diffraction ring is about $1/10$ as high as the central peak. This behavior is similar to that of the obstructed apertures mentioned earlier, but it is carefully optimized to do the least damage and at the same time achieve the highest resolution.

All of these advanced solutions have the same general features: high-resolution pupils look like soft-edged obstructed apertures, while low diffraction-ring pupils become darker toward the outside in a slow taper (Barakat 1962; Jacquinot and Roizen-Dossier 1964).

Also, these advanced techniques generally don't feature simple shading, such as would be provided by a variable strength neutral-density filter (particularly for resolution enhancement). They shift the transmission back and forth between positive and negative. Admittedly, the notion of negative transmission sounds odd. One imagines light springing from the eye and going back through the telescope in a reversed direction. The truth makes more sense—negative transmission refers to places on the aperture where the phase is reversed, or areas that have a uniform aberration of $1/2$ wavelength. Of course, jerking the aperture to both sides of the phase severely reduces central spot intensity. Such filters are also difficult to make.

The only pupil shading considered here is a truncated Gaussian function. The Gaussian is the familiar bell-shaped curve representing statistical deviations in measurements. It is similar to the curve teachers sometimes consult when they assign students' grades. A Gaussian aperture starts with full transmission at the center and gradually tapers off until the edge is reached. The transmission coefficient of an aperture pupil is modeled by

$$T(\rho) = e^{-\rho^2/w^2}, \tag{9.1}$$

where $\rho$ is the radial coordinate and $w$ is related to the width of the Gaussian. Figure 9-6 shows this transmission pattern. The word "truncated"

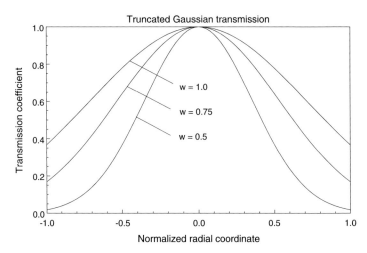

**Fig. 9-6.** *The transmission coefficient of the Gaussian pupil as it varies with radius. The outside of the aperture is at a radius of 1.0.*

refers to the sharp drop at the outside edge of the aperture. As the width is decreased, this drop is less important, but the clear area in the center of the aperture decreases with smaller widths. If the transmission at the edge of the aperture is small, the usable window is also smaller.

The Gaussian function has a unique mathematical property. When one calculates the diffraction pattern of a perfect circular aperture, the result is a complicated expression that goes through many oscillations—the cause of diffraction rings. When the same calculation is made for an untruncated Gaussian-shaded pupil, the result is another Gaussian. Once a Gaussian function dies away, it does not rise again. Therefore, the diffraction pattern has no rings around it.

If the Gaussian function has a small drop-off at the edge (as it does for the truncated examples in Fig. 9-6), the rings reappear, but they are strongly suppressed. Figure 9-7 shows the focused appearance of a truncated Gaussian with $w = 0.75\rho$. First, note that the pattern is definitely a bit larger. Second, muted rings remain around the central spot. If we turn the pattern sideways, the longitudinal slice of the diffraction pattern from this truncated Gaussian pupil is seen in Fig. 9-8. We still see nodes, but this behavior is severely diminished. Another interesting characteristic of this diagram is the boxy appearance of the central lozenge. Compared to the regular aperture, the image seems to display a cohesiveness more tolerant of defocusing.

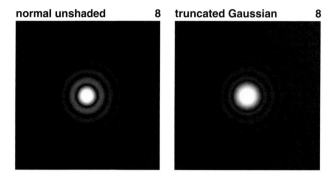

**Fig. 9-7.** *In-focus pattern of perfect unshaded and truncated Gaussian pupils.*

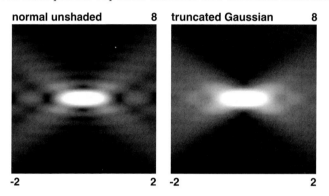

**Fig. 9-8.** *Longitudinally sliced image pattern of a normal and Gaussian pupil.*

What sort of changes to the image take place? The encircled energy of a $w = 0.75\rho$ truncated Gaussian appears in Fig. 9-9. Remember, this diagram is corrected for the simple darkening of the aperture. Thus, the ratio of the encircled energies goes to 1 as the circle becomes very large. Amazingly, the ratio for the Gaussian-apodized aperture sweeps upward to enclose more of the transmitted energy than the normal aperture over most of the range.

This strange behavior is related to the suppression of diffraction rings. For a Gaussian pupil, all of the stray energy that normally is in distant portions of the image has already been gathered. A normal pupil encloses only 83.8% of the energy in the Airy disk, 91% inside the edge of the first ring, 93.8% inside the edge of the second ring, 95.2%, 96.1%, and so forth. Gaussian pupil transmission is the same as taking a broom and traveling around the image, sweeping all of the remaining intensity toward the center. This sweeping is not as tidy as one would like, so the energy raked inward is piled up at the edge of an enlarged diffraction disk.

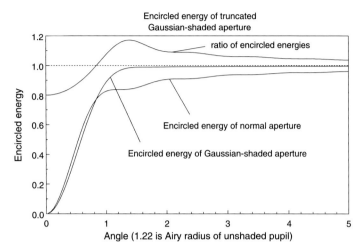

**Fig. 9-9.** *Encircled energy transmitted by a truncated Gaussian pupil compared to a normal unobscured pupil.*

Figure 9-10 shows the effect on filtering. Gaussian transmission enhances low spatial frequencies at the expense of high ones. The lowered response at high spatial frequency is understandable if one remembers that the central spot is bulkier. The enhancement at low frequencies is related to the gathering of energy from distant portions of the image. Low frequency modulation targets have wide bars. If the energy is piled close to the center of the diffraction disk rather than spread out, less light leaks from the light areas into the dark ones.

Thus, Gaussian apodizers will not show detail very near the resolution limit of the telescope with higher contrast, even though the diffraction rings are suppressed. On the other hand, much of an image's content is at low spatial frequency. The Gaussian filter will help the contrast of features that don't require every scrap of the resolving power. Another useful benefit of lowered diffraction rings is resolution of unequal double stars just outside the resolution limit, where the bright ring is inconveniently coincident with the dim star. For general extended images, however, making the rings less apparent does not help high resolution.

Apodization came to amateur astronomy with a series of letters and articles in the "Amateur Astronomer" column of *Scientific American* in the early 1950s. These articles culminated with a suggestion for pupil shading using layers of periodic screening (Leonard 1954). This suggestion was a clever and practical way of achieving a peaked pupil shape.

In spite of their mixed performance on the MTF chart, apodizers have been used in planetary viewing for many years. They have been vigorously

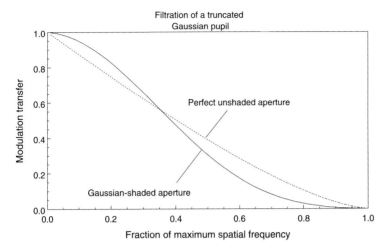

**Fig. 9-10.** *The MTF of a $w = 0.75\rho$ truncated Gaussian pupil. The normal MTF is plotted also for comparison. The Gaussian shifts the frequency response from high spatial frequencies to low ones.*

promoted by several amateurs, who claim that they are useful as "seeing" filters, although their explanations of the cause differ (Van Nuland 1983; Gordon 1984). This popularity, even though it has been confined to a small number of observers, is difficult to dismiss.

Is there a mechanism by which these filters can act to steady an image? Edberg (1984) suggested some indirect benefits, including stopping down the aperture, lessening the dazzling brightness of the planets, and covering poor optical fabrication. Gordon (1984) suggested that the moving rings associated with turbulence blur over into the Airy disk. If no rings are present, this blurring is reduced.

Another article suggested that a Gaussian filter could shift contrast rendition from high spatial frequencies—where turbulence was destroying the image anyway—to low spatial frequencies. Thus, coarser details that were still visible through the turbulent atmosphere were being rendered with higher contrast (Suiter 1986b). The MTF of a circular aperture troubled by turbulence provides evidence for that claim. Figure 9-11 illustrates the Gaussian pupil transmission MTF for a single moment of turbulence.

This figure shows how contrast is being shifted. Below a spatial frequency of about 0.4 maximum, the Gaussian-filtered system performs better than the open telescope. Below 0.1, the Gaussian-filtered instrument transfers contrast better than a perfect unaberrated system.

For example, a perfect 10-inch (250-mm) telescope can resolve MTF targets with bars separated by about 1/2 arcsecond. However, when troubled

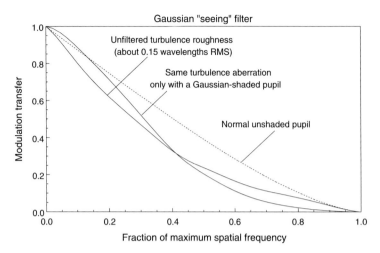

**Fig. 9-11.** *Improvement of the contrast transfer of low spatial frequencies for a $w = 0.75\rho$ Gaussian-filter pupil suffering from 0.15 wavelengths RMS of turbulence aberration. The same aperture when unshaded is also shown. A single MTF orientation angle during one snapshot is depicted. At higher spatial frequencies, the curve is unstable.*

by 0.15 wavelengths RMS turbulence, the MTF curve fluctuates wildly for bars separated by about 0.8 arcseconds and below. We may then choose to throw away contrast at high resolutions—where the behavior is unreliable anyway—and shift it down to spatial frequencies where it can be profitably used. With Gaussian filtration, bar separations of about 1.5 arcseconds and higher are imaged with higher contrast than the unapodized aperture. Above 4 arcseconds, the apodized aperture is behaving better than a perfect circular aperture on a steady night.

Thus, a Gaussian apodizing filter does seem to help during bouts of poor seeing, but it does so only in a backhanded manner. The seeing filter is perhaps useful in order to transform bad seeing to passable, but for critical resolution nothing less than steady skies and full aperture are necessary.

## 9.4   Dust and Scratches on the Optics

We can formally use the admittedly esoteric topic of superposition of apertures to explain the effect of central obstruction. The central obstruction can be mathematically replaced by a negative oscillating aperture that just cancels the positively oscillating area of the full aperture on top of it—Babinet's principle. This procedure works the same for lesser obstructions such as dust particles, only in this case, the dust grains or scratches act like a myriad of pinhole or short slit apertures.

Tiny pinholes and slits do not have good resolution. They emit a diffuse glow that is spread throughout the field of view. This behavior is observable in certain benchtop experiments. If a bright image is barely hidden from view by a straightedge (as in a Foucault test), dust flaws can actually be seen shining on the darkened aperture.

We can predict the curve of the modulation transfer function without calculating it. It is very similar to the MTF calculated for spider vanes. If an outrageous fraction of the mirror or lens were covered with dust or scratches (say, 1%) the contrast would lurch down suddenly by 1%. After that, the degradation of the MTF would remain fairly constant. The reason for the sudden drop is simple. The MTF must always start at 1, but the diffuse glow affects narrow bars and wide ones equally. Not until the bars are very wide does the leakage from a bright bar not extend over the dark region.

Apertures with 1% of their area covered with dust are very grimy optics indeed. Nearly everyone keeps lenses and mirrors cleaner. Imagine how spotted the optics would look if, for each square centimeter, 1 square millimeter (about the area of the head of a pin) was blocked. A 200-mm aperture has an area of over 314 cm$^2$. Sprinkling salt on the mirror or lens could scarcely produce 1% obstruction.

Dust and scratches, like spider diffraction, are mostly cosmetic errors except for unusual situations that feature bright, non-interesting objects close to the object to be observed. If a dim deep-sky object were observed quite near a dazzling star (NGC 404 behind Beta Andromedae or NGC 2024 near Zeta Orionis, for example), then the diffuse glow surrounding the bright star would invade the image of the dim object. Observing tricks, such as obscuring the star behind a field stop, can diminish scattering in the eyepiece and the eye, but if the main lens or mirror is dusty, the damage is already done. The stray light will peek out beyond the edge of the stop anyway. Excessive dust on the optics can also damage the detection of low contrast details on bright extended objects, such as planets, because the scattered light exists in a general haze.

The maximum amount of dirt the observer should tolerate on the optics is about $1/_{1,000}$ of the surface area. We have already seen in Chapter 3 how this can lead to signal-to-noise ratios as low as 30 dB.[4] Luckily, most of the

---

[4]Conventionally, noise varies with time and is random in location. Thus, my calling scattered light "noise" is incorrect in the sense that light scattering appears motionless and is completely determined by details at the aperture. Nevertheless, I use the concept of the signal-to-noise ratio because scattered light similarly degrades the quality of the image. SNR is used throughout this book to compare a scattered or diffracted haze of light with the underlying "true signal," giving relative weights to widely different phenomena. Please remember, however, that such a usage should be viewed only as an analogy or beneficial fiction, and it should not be pushed too far.

halo extends beyond the edge of a planet. Hence, much of the scattering is ugly but not harmful. Like spider diffraction, the worst SNRs are reserved for very large bright-field objects, such as the Sun and Moon. It is difficult to estimate the fraction of the optics covered by dirt, but $1/_{1,000}$ of the area is the size of a single obstruction about $1/_{30}$ of the diameter. On a 200 mm mirror, the accumulated grime would cover a spot 7 mm across—slightly smaller than the size of your little fingernail. Even a telescope that is that dirty will not contribute much additional scattering to a reflector with spider vanes, and the tolerance for dirt could perhaps be relaxed somewhat for such instruments.

The observer should heed one additional warning. Some telescope owners, after reading the above comments, might be tempted to clean their mirrors or lenses too frequently. Optics possess delicate coatings for which the safest prescription is to *leave them alone.* Overuse of even the most gentle of cleaning materials leaves a myriad of tiny scratches in coatings. Don't decide to clean mirrors on the basis of shining a light down the tube at night. All mirrors fail such a harsh inspection.

The best procedure for clean optics is not washing but prevention. Keep them covered and dry. Clean them only when you believe they have been chemically attacked or when the dust begins to visibly affect the images. Of course, specialized observers might need cleaner surfaces at all times, but no doubt these people have already learned of the considerable risks and expenses involved (more frequent aluminization, etc.). By following good maintenance procedures, you should not have to clean optics very often.[5]

---

[5]Frequently, enthusiastic mirror-makers will aluminize a mirror before it is truly polished. They are either covered with a haze of pits or have a fuzzy ring out toward the edge. Unfortunately, such mirrors cannot be "cleaned" at all and are usually unsalvageable. They need to be returned to polishing.

# Chapter 10

# Spherical Aberration

The most common error on the glass is called spherical aberration. It resides to some degree on all surfaces and need not become debilitating, though that depends on its severity.

The star test for spherical aberration is surprisingly sensitive and easy to interpret. This chapter will make five points:

1. Wavefronts deformed by simple spherical aberration (fourth-order curves) are recognizable by noticing that light approximately follows the behavior of the ray-optics caustic. On one side of focus, light is taken from the outer parts of the out-of-focus disk and deposited at its center. On the other side of focus, light taken from the center brightens the outermost rings.

2. The strength of lower-order spherical aberration can be roughly estimated by utilizing a central obstruction and comparing the breakout points of the central shadow on both sides. Correction error must be the only contributing aberration for this estimation technique to be valid.

3. Higher-order spherical aberrations, although noticeable in star tests of certain designs, are practically never seen in pure form.

4. By calculating the energy deposited within an angular radius of $\lambda/D$ (near the edge of the diffraction disk), the telescope user can usefully add together the combined effects of spherical aberration and central obstruction. This encircled energy ratio yields a number similar to the Strehl ratio, but it includes the degradation of obstruction in a single standard.

5. A quarter wavelength of correction error delivers images of extended objects that are noticeably soft, but barely acceptable.

## 10.1    What Is Spherical Aberration?

Because they seem to have the form of shallow bowls or protrusions, it is natural to assume that perfect mirrors and lenses are sections of spheres. However, spheres are not the best geometrical form to produce an image. The following thought experiment makes this point obvious. Imagine the inner surface of a hemisphere as a mirror and light as incident from infinitely far away on the right, as in Fig. 10-1. Light striking the edges is hardly deflected; it kisses the interior and bounces around the half dome. Light incident more toward the center is deflected towards a sort of focus, but the light striking near the axis is directed the farthest away. The focus region is expanded in Fig. 10-2 to demonstrate that the focus is bent from a geometric point to a horn-shaped caustic envelope.

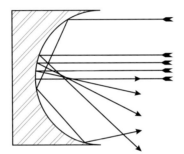

**Fig. 10-1.** *Half-dome spherical mirror. The focus is more poorly defined as the incoming ray approaches the edge.*

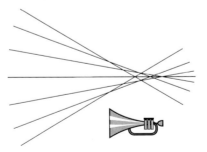

**Fig. 10-2.** *The caustic "horn."*

The original meaning of *caustic* was "burning," so an optical caustic is at or near focus. In ray tracing, the term acquired a slightly different meaning. A caustic is a curve or surface along which rays seem to pile up.

It refers to locations where the geometric spreading or convergence of a ray bundle does not give the correct value of the intensity. Caustics are places where one must resort to diffraction theory.

The type of spherical aberration shown in Fig. 10-1 is called spherical undercorrection. With overcorrection, the order is reversed. Centrally incident light crosses the axis too near the objective, and light incident at the edge crosses the axis at the most distant point. In overcorrection, the horn points the other way.

The best surface configuration to image light varies from telescope to telescope. Some objectives, such as compound refractor lenses, correct for spherical aberration by bending or separating spherical surfaces. Here the designer uses a trick to retain the easily made spherical shape. A similar bending occurs in the Maksutov design. The meniscus shell doesn't really possess much focusing power because the rear surface has about the same curvature as the front. The real purpose is aberration modification. Other telescopes share the burden of correcting the main focusing element's spherical aberration with an oddly deformed corrector plate, as in the common Schmidt-Cassegrain telescope.

For telescopes with only one focusing mirror (i.e., Newtonian reflectors), the proper geometric form is a paraboloid. The flat secondary diverts the beam so the observer's head doesn't get in the way, but it doesn't actively participate in forming the image. The paraboloid is one special case of a family of surfaces called *conic sections of revolution.*

Classical Cassegrains combine a paraboloidal primary with a hyperboloidal secondary to achieve the requisite spherical correction. One can take out the secondary mirror of a classical Cassegrain and install a diagonal to use it as a Newtonian. The secondary mirror must correct its inherent spherical aberration independently. One might reasonably guess that the secondary would have to be a convex paraboloid, but the secondary doesn't do the same job as the primary, so it must be curved differently.[1]

Other Cassegrain-style instruments, such as the Dall-Kirkham type, only correct part of the spherical aberration of the whole system in each mirror. The convex secondary remains spherical. This small mirror adds a component of spherical aberration of opposite sign to a concave spherical primary mirror, but the amount is not sufficient to correct the system completely. As a consequence, the properly made primary mirror of a Dall-Kirkham is deformed to a prolate spheroid (between a sphere and a paraboloid). Dall-Kirkhams are popular with telescope makers because the spherical secondary is easy to make. However, they suffer severe off-axis coma.

---

[1] One peculiar Cassegrain-style design, the afocal Mersenne, has a paraboloidal secondary mirror. This curious telescope doesn't need an eyepiece (King 1955, pp. 49–50.)

The Ritchey-Chrétien design goes the other way. By putting stronger hyperboloidal curves on both the primary and secondary mirrors, the designer can achieve a degree of coma correction superior to the classical Cassegrain. However, these telescopes are hard to make, and are usually of interest only to professional observatories. The Hubble Space Telescope was designed as a Ritchey-Chrétien.

## 10.2   The Hubble Space Telescope

The summer of 1990 featured an event making the previously esoteric topic of spherical aberration front-page news. The Hubble Space Telescope (HST) was revealed to be improperly manufactured. Newspaper reports said that it suffered from approximately $1/2$ wavelength of spherical aberration and that the edge of the mirror was nearly 2 microns (or 2 $\mu$m) off.

At first, these statements were confusing. A 2 $\mu$m surface error would result in a wavefront improperly curved by about 4 $\mu$m, or about 7.25 wavelengths of yellow-green light. If focus is adjusted to the minimum disk size rather than the focus of the center, that value is reduced by a factor of 4 to 1.8 wavelengths.

This number was clarified when an article in *Sky & Telescope* mentioned that the $1/2$-wavelength aberration had been measured as a root-mean-square (RMS) deviation (Sinnott 1990a). To derive the peak-to-valley value from the RMS value, we have to multiply by a factor of approximately 13.4/4, because for correction errors

$$\frac{1}{4} \text{ wavelength (peak-to-valley)} = \frac{1}{13.4} \text{ wavelength (RMS)}$$

$$\text{so } \frac{1}{2} \text{ wavelength RMS} \times \left(\frac{13.4}{4}\right) = 1.68 \text{ wavelength.}$$

(10.1)

The comparison that is best known to amateurs—with Rayleigh's $1/4$-wavelength tolerance—in this calculation comes to 1.7 wavelengths for the Hubble Space Telescope, assuming the $1/2$-wavelength RMS error was exact.

The root cause of the error was an improperly assembled device called a null tester used in the manufacture of the primary mirror. This null tester was supposed to generate a wavefront with precisely the reverse correction as the main mirror. Thus, a mirror that undid that correction would be exactly right. Unfortunately, the null tester was spaced incorrectly and presented the wrong reverse correction (S&T 1990; Capers *et al.* 1991).

## 10.3 Generalized Spherical Aberration

From the point of view of the star test, you don't have to think about the form of the optical surfaces, or even remember their long names. Consider only the shape of the final wavefront as subtracted from a perfect sphere. This difference can be expanded in the form of a simple polynomial function:

$$W(\rho) = A_0 + A_2\rho^2 + A_4\rho^4 + A_6\rho^6 \cdots, \qquad (10.2)$$

where $\rho$ is the radial coordinate with range 0 to 1. The symbol $W(\rho)$ stands for the total distortion of that wavefront away from a sphere with a center at the focus. If $W(\rho)$ is zero, then the curves are the same. Let's look at each of these terms and the coefficients in front of them (the "A's") and discuss what they mean.

The first is a constant, $A_0$, that only advances or delays the wavefront. We can think of this number as the "time" or "phase" constant, and it should be chosen so that the comparison sphere is not too far removed from the wavefront. This constant represents propagation, with different values of $A_0$ representing snapshots taken at different times. Usually, the constant is set to zero just as the wave passes through the aperture or else adjusted for convenience.

The term $A_2\rho^2$ is a smooth bending, either pushing the wavefront in a small amount or pulling it out somewhat. If our reference sphere has its center placed at the wrong focal point, this term bears the brunt of the increase. Thus, $A_2\rho^2$ is called the "defocusing aberration" here and is the same one appearing in Fig. 4-15.

The $A_2$ defocusing term can be conceptually included in the spherical aberration expansion, and from the point of view of star-testing, defocusing should be considered as just another aberration. However, defocusing is not a feature of the glass, so it isn't customary to refer to it as a spherical aberration term. Defocusing is so important that it is set aside and considered separately.

The fourth-order term, $A_4\rho^4$, is what is usually thought of as *spherical aberration*. Another name for this term is *primary spherical aberration*. Errors here are said to be "correction" errors, such as undercorrection or overcorrection.

The terms $A_6\rho^6 \ldots$ are usually small but can become important with unusual optical systems. You can see by the ellipsis that this expansion goes on forever, but each factor $A_n$ is usually much smaller than the previous coefficient. We can regard the $A_6$ coefficient as the last important term in this chapter.

Spherical aberration can be expressed by a number of equally valid conventions. Another way of referring to the fourth- and sixth-order wavefront terms is to call them third- and fifth-order spherical aberration. These names are derived from the slope of the wavefront, not the wavefront itself, and how far the light is shifted sideways from the center of the diffraction spot. Some authors find it more convenient to consider the residual changes in focal distance with $\rho$, or "longitudinal aberration" (Kingslake 1978, p. 114). In this way of looking at errors, primary aberration is the coefficient of the $\rho^2$ term. Thus, we can find the same primary spherical aberration expressed as fourth-, third-, or second-order coefficients, depending on whether the polynomial expansion refers to the wavefront, to the residual slope, or to the longitudinal aberration respectively. In this book, we will always refer to the wavefront.

## 10.4   The Aberration Functions

The aberrations are usually measured at the position of best focus[2] because the spurious disk is smallest there. It's what we think when we say "the telescope is focused." When $A_2$ is zero, Eq. 10.2 has the position of focus arbitrarily set at what is called "paraxial" focus, or the focus of the center of the mirror or lens (the narrow end of the caustic horn above). Although a convenient place for the mathematics of wavefront shape, it has nothing to do with the location where we visually perceive the tightest disk.

If we make the constant $A_4$ non-zero, for example, we find that some defocus must be added to chase best focus as it scoots away. If we change $A_4$ a second time, we must move the focus again. The term $A_6$ creates even more complications. If we wish to consider pure higher-order spherical aberrations at the best focus position, we must subtract out just the right amounts of lower orders. Removing these terms can be tiresome although the process is computationally straightforward.

It is much more convenient to encapsulate just enough of the lower-order aberrations to automatically cancel them out of each term as it is increased. This step was taken, in a considerably more complicated form, by Fritz Zernike, and the resultant terms are called orthogonal Zernike polynomials (Born and Wolf 1980). The interesting terms are limited here to 4th- and 6th-order, but they exist for higher orders as well:

$$W_4(\rho) = 4A_4' \left( \rho^2 - \rho^4 - \frac{1}{6} \right)$$
$$W_6(\rho) = -\frac{A_6'}{2}(20\rho^6 - 30\rho^4 + 12\rho^2 - 1).$$

$$(10.3)$$

The primes are placed on the coefficients to indicate that they are not

---

[2]also called "diffraction focus"

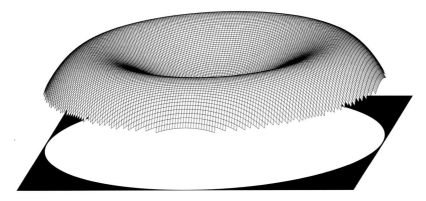

**Fig. 10-3.** *Aberration of Zernike function $W_4(\rho)$, illustrating overcorrection at best focus.*

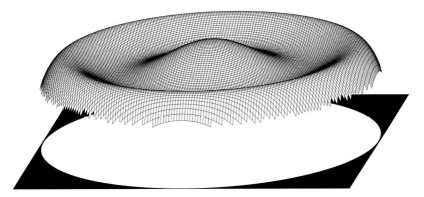

**Fig. 10-4.** *Aberration of Zernike function $W_6(\rho)$, describing higher-order spherical aberration.*

the same size as in Eq. 10.2. These complicated-looking equations simplify somewhat when displayed as aberration functions (see Figs. 10-3 and 10-4). All focused patterns appearing below are referenced near the focus positions implied in these functions.

The functional form of the fourth-order Zernike polynomial has just one doughnut-shaped ring, whereas the higher order has an elevated center. The 8th-, 10th-, and higher-order polynomials add one extra curl each. In fact, as we go higher, the pattern appears increasingly corrugated. But remember, the sum of these polynomials represents smooth surfaces. The signs and amplitudes are chosen so that the washboard appearance goes away. Only for the zonal defects of Chapter 11 do anomalous contributions of high-order polynomials add up to give a non-zero result.

Although it is not plotted, the 6th-order function has a more involuted caustic shape. Imagine if a very powerful individual reached into the bell of the musical horn of Fig. 10-2 and pulled the mouthpiece halfway back through it. The resulting damage would look much like that caustic (Cagnet *et al.* 1962).

Another minor point is that the position of diffraction focus moves slightly if the telescope is obstructed. Most of the patterns appearing in this chapter take into account this change. The longitudinal slice patterns are an exception.

## 10.5   Correction Error (Lower-Order Spherical Aberration)

### 10.5.1   Filtering of Spherical Aberration

The modulation transfer function (MTF) is depicted in Fig. 10-5. The drooping lines show the way contrast is reduced as spherical aberration is steadily worsened. One interesting feature is the mild increase that occurs for small aberrations near a spatial frequency 0.5 to 0.6 of maximum. This recovery corresponds to a frequency where the separation of the target bars is about the distance to the first diffraction ring. It sags on either side.

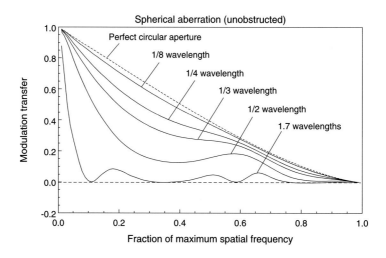

**Fig. 10-5.** *MTF characteristic of correction error.*

The MTF worsens significantly when the aperture pupil goes from $1/8$ to $1/4$ wavelength of total aberration, emphasizing that optical quality begins to fail at around $1/4$ wavelength of correction error.

Spherical aberration shifts light from the central disk to the outer parts of the diffraction pattern. A peculiar feature of spherical aberration is that it leaves the central core of the image alone (until the aberration is quite strong) other than to sap it of its intensity. Spherical aberration drains energy from the central Airy disk and feeds it to the rings. In Fig. 10-6, the encircled energy ratio of increasing low-order spherical aberration is shown plotted against reduced angle. Note the flat or near-flat appearance of the encircled energy ratio out to the radius of the Airy disk. This signature identifies spherical aberration of any order (even mild defocusing displays this peculiar behavior). Energy has been removed from the central disk of the aberrated pupil, but it holds the unaberrated shape fairly well until out beyond the first ring. Also in Fig. 10-6, the encircled energy ratio for 1/4 wavelength of spherical aberration intercepts zero radius at 0.8, just where the Strehl ratio says it should.

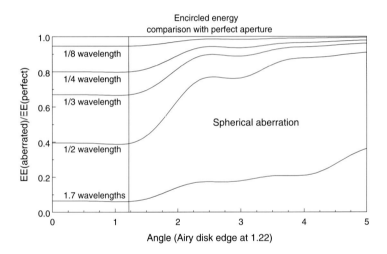

**Fig. 10-6.** *Encircled energy of unobstructed apertures suffering from spherical aberration divided by the encircled energy of a perfect circular aperture.*

The effect of draining the energy in the core image is to maintain a more or less equivalent (but dimmer) Airy disk surrounded by a blurring that lessens with distance. Planetary detail suffers considerably, because low contrast dark markings are often very close to bright areas that bleed or wash over. The MTF chart indicates that the worst effects of correction error begin to occur for surface markings having separations of about 1/3 to 1/2 the resolution limit of the instrument. Thus, an aberrated telescope capable of resolving stars separated by 1 arcsecond shows planetary detail (such as banding separated by less than about 2 or 3 arcseconds) with markedly reduced contrast.

## 10.5.2  Star-Test Patterns of Correction Error

When star testing, you may wish to view the image through a color filter to avoid color mixing effects. Because the maximum sensitivity of the human eye is around yellow or green, you probably can derive the most information from a filter centered on these colors. If you use an artificial source (such as a flashlight) some serendipitous filtering is caused by the lower color temperature of the filament. You may discover for yourself the helpful effects of filtration when star testing a telescope on Arcturus during a hazy night. The star is naturally yellow and so heavily colored by passage through the haze that it becomes orange. Few color filters cut out all of the lights of other bands, however. You shouldn't expect the monochromatic diffraction patterns calculated here to be precisely reproduced.

Of course, you are welcome to try other filters, but be aware that as you go from blue to red the wavelength error lessens. Red filters may help subtract small amplitude trash from a diffraction-pattern image when you are trying to see broad deformations of the wavefront.

The behavior of the in-focus image is depicted in Fig. 10-7, where spherical aberration runs from 0 to 1.7 wavelengths. All correction errors are different from the perfect aperture, but the first ring brightens badly for aberrations greater than $1/4$ wave. Since the use of a secondary is so common, a similar comparison is made for a 33% obstructed aperture in Fig. 10-8.

Out-of-focus behavior appears in Figs. 10-9 and 10-10 with each successive pair having slightly worse undercorrection. Each of these patterns is calculated for 10 wavelengths defocusing aberration. The severe 1.7 wavelength case is calculated for overcorrection (note the reversed appearance of the patterns). Here the strong outer ring appears *outside* of focus. We are viewing slices of the horn-shaped caustic in these figures. On one side of focus, the horn is sliced near the flaring bell. As a consequence, most of the energy is confined to a thin outer ring. On the other side of focus, the horn is sliced near the mouthpiece, so much of the energy is concentrated near the center. Still, a lot of energy spills out into the surrounding area to make the disk appear blurred.

Again, the out-of-focus behavior is depicted for a 33% obstruction in Figs. 10-11 and 10-12. The 1.7-wavelength error doesn't precisely reproduce the pattern expected of the Hubble Space Telescope before the repair mission, but this behavior is a good approximation.

With lesser amounts of spherical aberration, you need to defocus less to show the patterns well. Figure 10-13 shows the appearance when defocusing aberration is only 5 wavelengths.

### 10.5.3    Estimation of the Severity of the Problem

Correction error creates a marked contrast between the inside-focus and outside-focus star-test patterns. An experienced observer under excellent conditions can certainly detect errors smaller than $1/10$ wavelength and possibly $1/20$ wavelength (Welford 1960). Ironically, the star test for spherical aberration is almost too sensitive. It is so revealing that nearly any telescope fails casual inspection.

A high-resolution light detection system would allow measurements over the expanded stellar disk and determination of exactly how the aberration affects the telescope. Because the eye is a terrible radiometer, it cannot be trusted to measure brightness. People who use the eye to determine the magnitude of variable stars are only successful if they follow a careful procedure using similar comparison stars. Estimating brightness of extended objects (like defocused star disks) is hopeless. Meticulously calibrated light sensors have been used to perform this job, but such a solution requires precise knowledge of the defocus distance. It is not practical for those wishing to do a fast test. (For an example of these difficult measurements, see Burch 1985.)

A method must be developed that uses the strengths of vision instead of its weaknesses, some sort of tool that does not rely on the eye's absolute ability to determine brightness. A hint of the method appears in *The Amateur's Telescope*, by Rev. William F.A. Ellison, which was reprinted in *Amateur Telescope Making Book One:* (Ingalls 1976)

> It is easy enough to see, by the out-of-focus images of a star, what is the state of correction of the mirror. A truly corrected mirror, out-of-focus, will give an expanded disk, uniformly illuminated except for faint traces of diffraction rings, having a clean, sharply defined edge, and a round black spot in the center. This black spot is the shadow of the flat, and it should be *the same size at equal distances inside and outside focus.*
>
> If it is larger inside focus, the mirror is under-corrected. If it is larger *outside,* it is over-corrected. And many a time on a night when temperature was variable, the writer has watched a mirror *change through all these phases* within not very many minutes, the changes of the black spot answering faithfully to those of the thermometer... [italics in original].

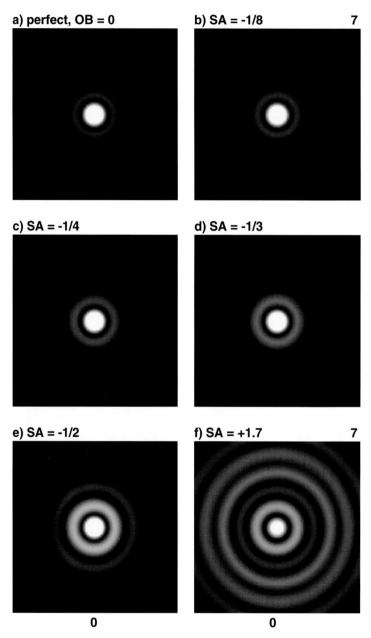

**Fig. 10-7.** *Focused patterns for 0, ⅛, ¼, ⅓, ½, and 1.7 wavelengths of lower-order spherical aberration. The aperture is unobstructed.*

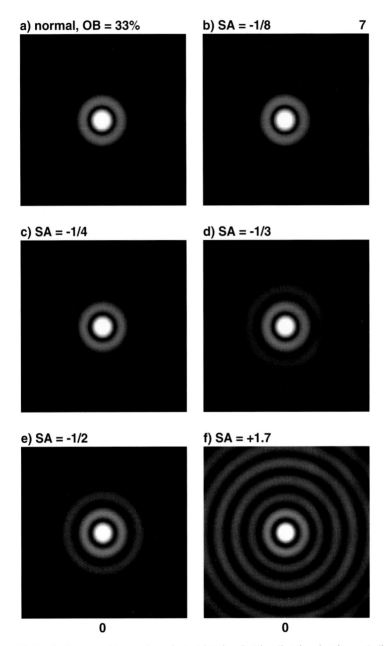

**Fig. 10-8.** *In-focus patterns for a) 0, b) ⅛, c) ¼, d) ⅓, e) ½, and f) 1.7 wavelengths of lower-order spherical aberration. Aperture has a 33% centered circular obstruction.*

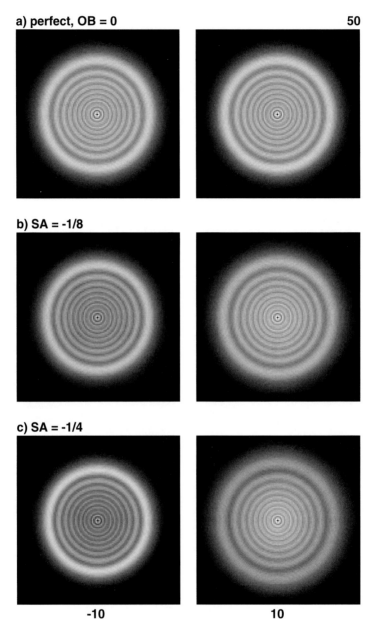

**Fig. 10-9.** *Undercorrected apertures inside focus (left) and outside focus (right). Defocusing aberration ±10 wavelengths. a) 0, b) ¹⁄₈, c) ¹⁄₄ wavelength lower-order spherical aberration. Aperture is unobstructed.*

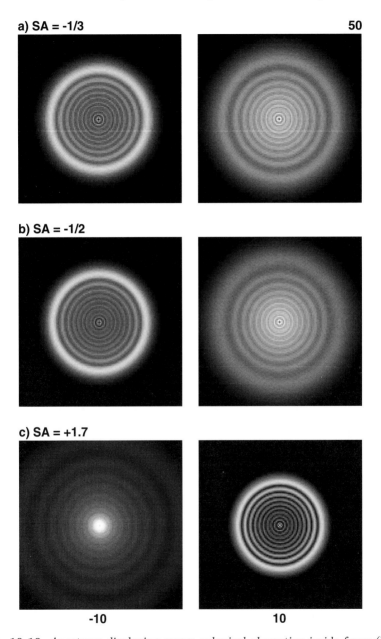

**Fig. 10-10.** *Apertures displaying severe spherical aberration inside focus (left)
and outside focus (right). Defocusing aberration ±10 wavelengths. a) ⅓ wavelength undercorrected, b) ½ wavelength undercorrected, c) 1.7 wavelengths overcorrected. Aperture is unobstructed.*

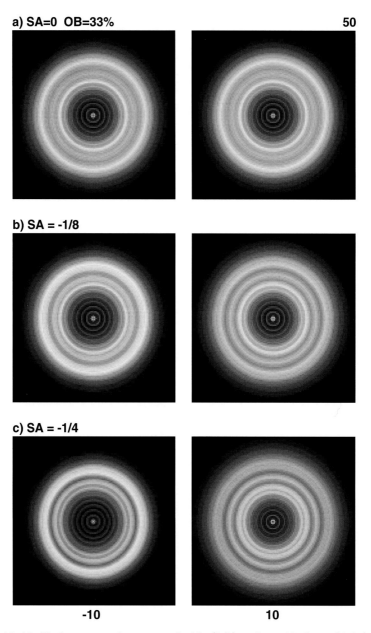

**a) SA=0  OB=33%**                                          **50**

**b) SA = -1/8**

**c) SA = -1/4**

**-10**                                        **10**

**Fig. 10-11.** *Undercorrected apertures inside (left) and outside focus (right). Defocusing aberration ±10 wavelengths. a) 0, b) ⅛, c) ¼ wavelength lower-order spherical aberration. Aperture is 33% obstructed.*

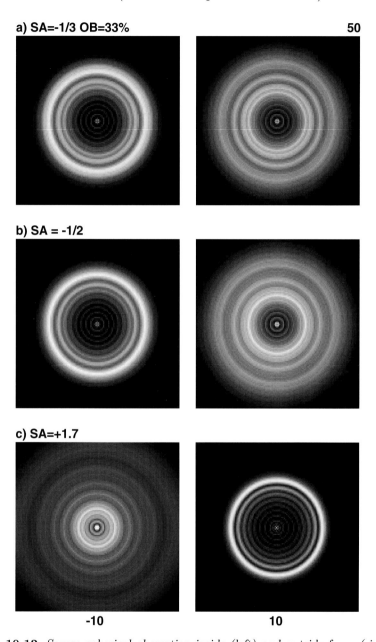

**Fig. 10-12.** *Severe spherical aberration inside (left) and outside focus (right). Defocusing aberration is ±10 wavelengths. a) 1/3 wavelength undercorrected, b) 1/2 wavelength undercorrected, c) 1.7 wavelengths overcorrected. Aperture is 33% obstructed.*

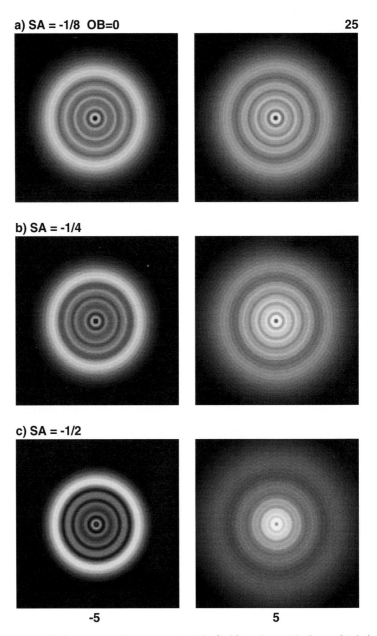

**Fig. 10-13:** *Undercorrected apertures inside (left) and outside focus (right). Defocusing aberrations ±5 wavelengths. a) ⅛, b) ¼, and c) ½ wavelength undercorrected. The aperture is unobstructed.*

As it turned out, these comments were imbedded in an argument that seemed critical of star testing. Perhaps many of Ellison's readers were confused by this discussion into thinking that the star test was inadequate. Ellison's point, however, was valid. The plate glass mirrors common at that time were untestable in an environment that was rapidly varying in temperature. Any test would have failed in this situation.

Modern materials used in mirror substrates are much less prone to deform with temperature changes. As long as the telescope is close to ambient temperature, the optics are reasonably well-behaved. The test is reliable for slowly changing exterior temperatures.

In any case, the shadow spot gives testers a way to estimate the aberration. Figure 10-14a shows a longitudinal slice through a perfect aperture's focus point. The objective lens or mirror is to the left, the outside-focus direction is to the right (for an explanation of labeling, see Appendix D). Except for the spot activity along the axis, looking like beads on a string, the out-of-focus profile is almost smooth and uninteresting. In 10-14b, we are looking at the same situation with a 33% obstruction. The aperture is otherwise perfect, and this situation is symmetric.

In dark cones emerging from the center, the shadow of the diagonal seems to break out of the defocused image at a finite distance close to either side of focus. Since the image is quite small, the bright spot at the center delays the appearance of the central obstruction until the defocusing aberration is close to 2 wavelengths on either side. (See Chapter 5 for the conversion of defocusing aberration to focuser motion.) The eyepiece must be moved a little more until the spot is clearly defined. Nevertheless, notice that the breakout points for a perfect mirror are balanced; they are the same distance on either side of focus.

What happens when we add some undercorrection to the obstructed aperture? The answer is shown by Fig. 10-15.

The first point of interest is that the best focus point slides a little forward with progressively worse undercorrection. The aberration was entered as a Zernike polynomial, but those functions have a slight focus shift for obstructed apertures.

The next peculiarity is the small size of the disk inside focus compared with that of the outside. This condition is caused partly by the obstruction focus shift, but it is noticeable in Fig. 10-12 above, which has been corrected for this shift. No unique focal point exists for the aberrated wavefront. Approaching focus, the wavefront must buckle and change shape, manifesting itself in these different sizes.

Energy conservation also plays a role. In the longitudinal slice figures, a vertical line cannot be drawn that doesn't intercept an illuminated region. The intensity is never allowed to turn itself off everywhere in a sliced plane.

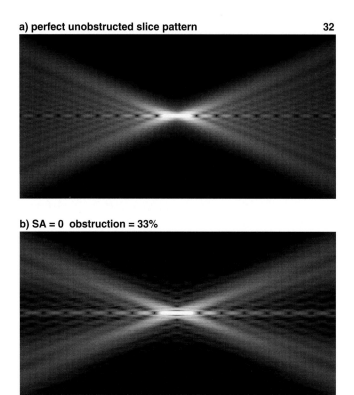

a) perfect unobstructed slice pattern                              32

b) SA = 0  obstruction = 33%

-8                                                                  8

**Fig. 10-14.** *A longitudinal slice through the focus of a) a circular unobstructed aperture, b) a 33% obstructed aperture. Neither pattern has any aberration associated with it. The slice is taken from defocusing aberration of −8 wavelengths to +8 wavelengths. The corner angle of 32λf/D corresponds to the ray-tracing edge of geometric shadow ±8 wavelengths defocusing. Thus, the picture has been squeezed until it resembles the cone of an f/1 system.*

In fact, if we very carefully keep track of the total energy at any value of defocus, we discover it to be the same as the total energy that passed through the aperture. The gnarls and knots are just an arrangement. An appearance of a bright ring is counterbalanced by a dark ring showing up elsewhere in the sliced plane.

The dark cones of the secondary shadow are no longer at equal offsets in the presence of correction error. This is made clearer in the stick-figured drawing of Fig. 10-16. In the 1/4-wavelength diagram, the central obstruction does not show itself until it is *about twice as far from best focus.*

Two effects are conspiring to offset the secondary-shadow breakout point. One is the clustering of energy around the rim of the horn-shaped

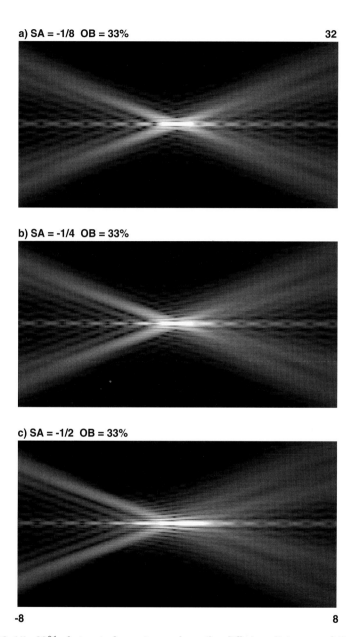

a) SA = -1/8  OB = 33%                              32

b) SA = -1/4  OB = 33%

c) SA = -1/2  OB = 33%

-8                                                      8

**Fig. 10-15:** *33% obstructed apertures show the differing distances of the emergence of the secondary shadow from the center of the diffraction disk. Correction error is a) $-1/8$ wavelength, b) $-1/4$ wavelength, and c) $-1/2$ wavelength (all undercorrected).*

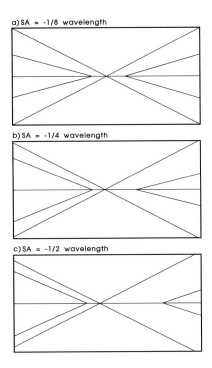

**Fig. 10-16.** *Diagrams sketching overall behavior of Fig. 10-15. The distance of reappearance for the secondary shadow is significantly different if correction error exceeds* 1/4 *wavelength.*

caustic on one side of focus. This fierce excavation of energy from the center allows the secondary shadow to burst forth more quickly. The other effect is the pile-up of energy toward the mouthpiece of the horn on the other side of focus. This intensity fills in the secondary shadow and retards its reappearance. Not until the eyepiece has been moved well past the caustic region is the secondary shadow allowed to poke free.

A criterion can be defined for low-order spherical aberration. We will demand that the ratio of the breakout distances be no more than 2:1. Of course, the evaluation must be performed on a 33% obstructed aperture. This test is different than the one described by Ellison. He defocused equal distances and compared the size of the shadows. Here, we will estimate the relative distances on either side of focus that the shadow firmly shows itself.

Such a criterion would be exceedingly weak if it were based only on a single theoretical plot. It comes from long experience with star-testing telescopes for which other tests had also been performed. This tolerance is not absolute by any means. The reappearance of the shadow can depend on the brightness of the star, the seeing, and the admixture of other aberrations. The tester must take into account the general performance behavior of the telescope before rejecting it for failure of the "2:1 test" alone. Nevertheless, I have seen no mirror having 1/4-wavelength correction error (as determined by the zonal Foucault test) give a lower ratio.

## 10.6  Testing for Correction

This 2:1 ratio test is useful for other telescopes besides reflectors. The telescope should be obstructed even it has no natural secondary. Refractors can be artificially obstructed by centering a piece of paper over the telescope opening.

Reading the offset, however, is by no means a well-controlled process. If the obstruction is 25%, the cutoff drifts up to about 3:1. Since most Newtonian reflectors have obstructions of less than 33%, this test can be standardized by making a larger mask to attach to the back of the spider. Of course, the native obstruction of most Schmidt-Cassegrains is very close to 33% already.

Also, finding the breakout points of obstruction shadow is a much more straightforward process on medium to high focal-ratio telescopes. It is much easier to read on telescopes with focal ratios above f/8. The difficulty of making this estimate on faster instruments is exacerbated by rack and pinion focusers and the tiny depth of focus.

This procedure seems to work well in white light, because having a multiplicity of colors tends to wash out the minima in surrounding diffraction rings, or at least make them less distinctive. The secondary appears in all colors, but details in the disk depend on the color. Unless you're testing a refractor, try removing the color filter to check for spot size.

The source should not be too bright. Since you're inspecting the image close to focus, examining a bright star could overpower the eye and make seeing details difficult at the center of the image. If you are doing the test with an artificial source, you may want to put the illuminator at a greater distance, use a smaller reflector, or use a neutral-density eyepiece filter. If the telescope seems to have an unusually high offset, try again with a dimmer star.

The behavior of one color is shown in Fig. 10-17. The diagrams go from slightly inside focus at top left to somewhat farther outside focus at lower right. Keep in mind that this diagram is reproduced here at too great a magnification. If you have difficulty seeing where the shadow permanently and strongly reappears in Fig. 10-17, place the page at some distance. You'll find that the shadow isn't really apparent until well beyond focus.

The shadow appears to have equivalent central depressions at about $-1.5$ and 3.75 defocusing aberration.

3.75 compared to 1.5 seems to be a bit more than the estimate of 2:1, but recall that this transition point is a rough one. Many compromises have been made in generating these image patterns on paper. The most important approximation is that the figures are not self-luminous. Absolute image brightness and contrast have also been allowed to slide so that they could be printed on a medium with limited dynamic range. The point at which you should become concerned about the correction of your telescope is when the ratio exceeds 3:1.

An additional effect of defocused spherical aberration is demonstrated in Fig. 10-17. As you defocus toward the bell of the caustic (inside focus for undercorrection), the shadow breaks out abruptly and cleanly. On the other side, the shadow first appears as a soft central depression or a navel. The secondary shadow uncurls or blooms as it appears. The point of undoubted appearance is less crisp but is still appreciably different than the other side. Because of this uncertainty, the method is not suggested as a precise measurement. It is only a way of detecting unusual amounts of correction error which could cripple your telescope. You cannot use this ratio method to measure spherical aberration precisely.

If an otherwise good telescope is failing this test, you could have an interfering aberration of a different type. If you suspect that the location of the shadow breakout is giving you the wrong answer, shift to a fixed-distance pattern comparison (as in Fig. 10-13) by looking up the value of the defocus in Table 5-1. Be careful of Ellison's warning. Let the optics cool down completely. Pyrex is a better material than plate glass, but its shape is not completely independent of temperature change.

## 10.7 Higher-Order Spherical Aberration

Sometimes the $A'_6$ coefficient is neglected or uncorrected. In most telescopes, this aberration makes little difference, but it can be a problem for some unusual instruments.

For example, the shape of a Schmidt corrector plate is similar to the fourth-order curve in Eq. 10.3 with a different amount of $\rho^2$ cleverly chosen to minimize potential chromatic aberration. The fast spherical primary produces an aberration function with many terms in the expansion in Eq. 10.2, but the corrector plate is capable of easily correcting these terms out only to fourth order. A small value of sixth-order aberration may remain uncorrected. Various lens designs can also add trifling amounts of "secondary" spherical aberration of sixth order on the wavefront (Kingslake

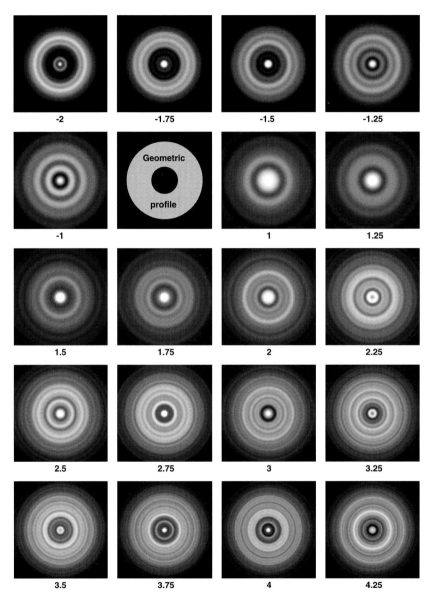

**Fig. 10-17.** Defocused stellar images of a 33% obstructed aperture having $1/4$ wavelength undercorrection. Each frame is magnified so that the perfect geometric profile is the same size as the labeled frame. Thus, the edge is at 10 units of angle for 2 wavelengths of defocusing, 20 units for 4 wavelengths, etc. The bottom of each box is marked with the defocusing aberration in wavelengths.

1978, p. 114).

Higher-order spherical aberration can be safely neglected in most instruments. Nevertheless, in certain ultra-fast catadioptrics or complicated refractor designs, you should not be surprised to see small amounts of the aberration described in the next section.

### 10.7.1   Star-Test Patterns of Higher-Order Spherical Aberration

An $A_6'$ coefficient in Eq. 10.3 yields the patterns of Fig. 10-18. Like a fourth-order correction error, an $A_6'$ with the opposite sign results in these patterns being reversed in focus direction.

The error looks worse in the star test than it behaves in the image. To reduce the Strehl ratio to the same 0.8 value that it possesses for $1/4$ wavelength of lower-order spherical aberration, $A_6'$ would have to be increased to about 0.4 wavelength.

The description of the higher-order caustic as a horn pulled back halfway through itself helps explain these complicated patterns.  The correction error star-test patterns that appeared earlier in the chapter went from a bright outer ring on one side of focus to a fuzzy bright core on the other side. Here the fuzzy bright core appears on the same side of focus as a hole in the center (Fig. 10-18, $-3$ wavelengths defocused).

For that reason, high-order spherical aberration might be called the "ring aberration." It bears more than a passing resemblance to the zonal defects appearing in Chapter 11. Indeed, this aberration can be viewed as the broadest of the zonal aberrations.

Of course, higher-order spherical aberration is rarely seen in clearly identifiable form. As a residual aberration in a normal telescope, its amplitude is very low. This aberration is usually swamped by other effects. I have seen a slight amount only in one Schmidt-Cassegrain, where a dark secondary shadow was coupled with diminishing brightness toward the edge of the out-of-focus diffraction disk. The other side of focus revealed the opposite behavior, with a light secondary shadow and a strong outer ring showing simultaneously.  The only reason I was capable of unambiguously seeing this small aberration was the almost complete absence of simple correction error in an exceptionally good instrument.

### 10.7.2   Filtering of Higher-Order Spherical Aberration

The filter graph for higher-order spherical aberration appears in Fig. 10-19. Clearly, $1/4$ wavelength of aberration does not seriously affect the optics. Not until the aberration has been increased to 0.4 wavelengths does the damage become considerable.  The worst part of the decrease occurs at

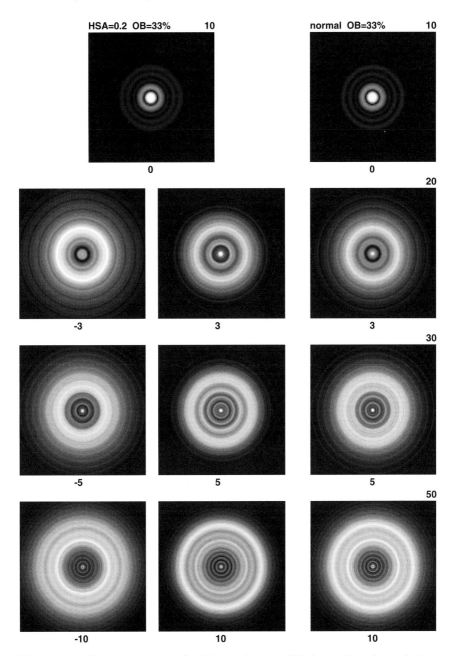

**Fig. 10-18.** *Star-test patterns for $1/5$ wavelength of higher-order spherical aberration at best focus. Obstruction is 33%.*

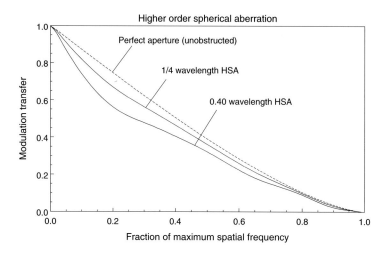

**Fig. 10-19.** *MTF curves caused by 0.25 and 0.4 wavelength of higher-order spherical aberration.*

a lower spatial frequency than it did in Fig. 10-5 for low-order spherical aberration. In this case the fall occurs at about 20% of the maximum spatial frequency instead of 35%. Recalling that the maximum resolution of a 200-mm aperture is about 0.6 cycles/arcsecond, this aberrated system transfers surface details separated by less than 3 arcseconds with reduced contrast.

When the "elbow" of the MTF curve appears farther to the left, it is a sign of a more corrugated appearance of the aberration function. The surface error becomes more localized. As the optical error becomes smaller and goes through more wiggles, the corresponding MTF exhibits a sharper decline at lower spatial frequencies. As the optical errors become more localized, the MTFs at higher spatial frequencies are also reduced but don't oscillate much. The damage is already done at lower spatial frequencies. However, it should be emphasized that pure higher-order spherical aberration of this magnitude is unlikely to trouble ordinary instruments. If the optics are fabricated poorly, the bulk of the aberration is usually expressed in simple fourth-order correction error.

## 10.8   A Compact, Uniform Standard for Optical Quality

Consumer telescope makers and observers alike tend to divide aberration and obstruction into separate compartments, treating the two as incomparable phenomena. However, a single standard can easily be defined to cover them both. It is based on the *encircled energy ratio* (or EER($\theta$)). The encircled energy ratio gives a way of comparing these two degradations on an equal footing.

Here's the way such ratios are calculated: First, we find what fraction of the energy from a point source is focused by the imperfect telescope on a tiny circle of specified angular radius at the focal plane. This number is then divided by the same fraction for a perfect, unblocked aperture of the same diameter. For example, a moderately obstructed telescope that also has a trifling amount of spherical aberration encircles 72% of its energy at a certain angle and a perfect aperture encloses 84% at the same angular radius. The encircled energy ratio would then be $^{72}/_{84} = 0.86$ at that angle.

The encircled energy ratios appearing in Figs. 9-1 and 10-6 are complete curves. For a single number that represents a quality criterion, one needs to take the EER($\theta$) value at a specific value of $\theta$. The question arises: what angle is best?

Unfortunately, no one angle is the last word on optical quality. We could choose an angle (or circle) very near the center of the image, or EER($\theta \rightarrow 0$). This number is close to the normalized brightness ratio at the center of the diffraction disk. In fact, it is identical with the Strehl ratio in unobstructed apertures. EER taken near the center of the image, however, seems excessively tolerant of obstruction, as Fig. 9-1 demonstrates. EER($\theta \rightarrow 0$) does not dip below 0.8—the cutoff point of good optical quality in the Strehl ratio—until obstruction is above 45%. One could also define the quality factor as EER within a circle of radius $\theta = 1.22\lambda/D$ (Eq. 1.1), or the edge of the Airy diffraction disk. Fig. 9-1 shows that the values of EER(1.22) sag considerably, and have even started to rise again.

Somewhat arbitrarily, this book will use an angular radius of $\theta = \lambda/D$, or the angular spacing where the MTF always goes to zero. This angle has the practical advantage of catching obstructed apertures at their low points in Fig. 9-1 and has the philosophical advantage of always being related to the maximum spatial frequency of the MTF chart. This ratio will be called EER(1). In Fig. D-2, you can see the edge of the frame is at an angle of $1.22\lambda/D$. Thus a circle drawn here would be sitting in the darkness between the rings. The integrated area of EER(1) is slightly inside the bright edge of the disk.

EER(1) of apertures mixing the two optical problems of obstruction and lower-order (Zernike) spherical aberration have been collected together in Table 10-1. We see a very similar behavior to the Strehl ratio in the unobstructed top row. A quarter wavelength of spherical aberration still results in a degradation of EER(1) to 0.8. It is the second axis that is most interesting, however. It is possible to compare the loss of encircled energy ratio of obstructed, but otherwise perfect apertures. EER(1) = 0.8

for obstructions slightly less than 33% of the full diameter.

Notice that obstruction does not always diminish quality. The case of $1/2$-wavelength correction error shows a curious inversion, with increasing obstruction serving to *cover up* the poor figuring.

Table 10-1
EER(1) for apertures with
lower-order spherical aberration.
Wavefront is refocused.
Obstruction is fraction of diameter covered.

| Obstruction | Peak-to-valley correction error on unobstructed aperture | | | | | | |
|---|---|---|---|---|---|---|---|
| | 0 | $1/8\lambda$ | $1/6\lambda$ | $1/5\lambda$ | $1/4\lambda$ | $1/3\lambda$ | $1/2\lambda$ |
| 0.00 | 1.00 | 0.95 | 0.91 | 0.87 | 0.80 | 0.67 | 0.39 |
| 0.15 | 0.95 | 0.91 | 0.87 | 0.84 | 0.78 | 0.66 | 0.41 |
| 0.20 | 0.92 | 0.88 | 0.84 | 0.81 | 0.76 | 0.65 | 0.42 |
| 0.25 | 0.88 | 0.84 | 0.81 | 0.78 | 0.74 | 0.64 | 0.43 |
| 0.30 | 0.83 | 0.79 | 0.77 | 0.75 | 0.71 | 0.63 | 0.44 |
| 0.33 | 0.79 | 0.76 | 0.74 | 0.72 | 0.69 | 0.61 | 0.44 |
| 0.40 | 0.71 | 0.69 | 0.68 | 0.66 | 0.63 | 0.58 | 0.45 |
| 0.50 | 0.58 | 0.57 | 0.56 | 0.56 | 0.54 | 0.51 | 0.44 |

My personal experience with a large number of telescopes having various amounts of correction error suggests the following empirical ratings. These cutoffs are necessarily hazy, and the "good" point is deliberately chosen to match the Strehl ratio (i.e., 0.8), where optics are conventionally called "diffraction-limited."

1. 0.88–1.00 excellent to perfect

2. 0.80–0.88 good to excellent

3. 0.70–0.80 poor to good

The only acceptable instruments with EER(1) below 0.70 are special-purpose telescopes, such as astrocameras or richest-field telescopes. No instrument having $1/3$ wavelength of correction error, even if unobstructed, reaches up to this minimum standard. No aperture with an obstruction slightly larger than 40%, even if figured perfectly, ever meets it.

## 10.9   Tolerable Errors

All telescopes are made with some spherical aberration. The perfect Newtonian paraboloid, for example, is an unattainable goal between an infinite number of prolate spheroids and hyperboloids. The question is whether the telescope suffers under the load. Once EER(1) is over 0.88 or so, spherical aberration is gratifyingly small and the optics could justifiably be called "perfect."

We saw in Chapter 3 how modulation transfer functions stacked individually. Most obstructed telescopes are teetering on the brink already. It takes very little to push them over. By such logic, we should be intolerant of any correction error, but that attitude is unrealistic.

Commercial telescope optics have always been corrected to a tolerance of about $1/4$ wavelength. The way that accuracy is stated has changed, but commercial telescope makers still fabricate the same $1/4$-wavelength optics they always did.

Let's recognize a simple fact. Making objectives to higher accuracy than $1/4$ wavelength is expensive. The scaling of price with quality is similar to the scaling of price with diameter. Incremental improvements in surface accuracy cost much more because we are paying not for glass but for an optician's valuable time. For better or worse (usually worse), buyers use price as a strong deciding factor.

Is more accuracy really needed? In informal tests, a telescope with a $1/4$-wavelength correction error has been found difficult to distinguish from a very good telescope unless seeing is excellent and the observer is skillful (Ceravolo *et al.* 1992; also see Chapter 15). For most people who observe under average skies, a $1/4$-wavelength correction error represents an acceptable compromise between quality and the price of optics.

In the previous section, we defined those apertures with encircled energy ratios greater than 0.88 as excellent. We see this designation only applies to the upper left corner of Table 10-1, i.e., to obstructions less than about 25% or correction errors less than $1/5$ wavelength. Notice that a 25% obstructed aperture with only $1/6$ wavelength of correction error is still "good" at 0.81, but that a 15% obstructed aperture with a $1/4$-wavelength error is below the cutoff at 0.78. The lesson is clear. Accurate figuring allows the telescope to get away with other difficulties.

Personally, I find the images of optics that are nudged against the Rayleigh limit a bit too soft. However, of the telescopes I've tested, most of them that obviously didn't perform well on the sky have been much worse than Rayleigh's limit. A quarter wavelength of correction error is barely acceptable if it is the only significant problem. With a reasonable 25% obstruction, such an aperture has EER(1) = 0.74, and has a transfer function better than a perfect, unobstructed aperture $1/2$ to $2/3$ of its size. Even with optical problems of this magnitude, a 6-inch f/8 reflector is at least as good as a perfect 3 to 4-inch apochromatic refractor. At some spatial frequencies, it is better.

# Chapter 11

# Circular Zones and Turned Edges

This chapter discusses zonal defects and a common type of zonal error, a turned edge. It will make four chief points:

1. On mirrors of amateur size, interior zones are seldom large enough to be troublesome.

2. Zonal defects can be detected by defocusing a larger amount than is usual.

3. Turned edge is a persistent problem that yields contrasts worse than the smaller aperture inside the turned annulus.

4. Narrow turned edges can be treated by masking or painting the edge.

## 11.1  Causes of Zonal Defects

Zones are slight circular corrugations in the polished surface of the glass. The improper use of fast polishing materials may lead to zones in optical elements. For example, the lap is typically pressed against the optical piece to achieve uniformity of polishing action. If too little pressing is done, or if part of the lap overhangs during pressing, sections of the polisher can ride the optical piece with more pressure than the rest. Because the lap and the stroke direction rotate with respect to the mirror, this uneven pressure digs a trench around a certain radius of the mirror. Many other mechanisms can also result in zonal defects. When too short a stroke is used, good statistical averaging of the two surfaces doesn't take place. Channeling a lap with a centered pattern will often result in a profusion of thin rings. If a piece of the brittle pitch breaks off and is trapped beneath the rest of the lap, it will plow a furrow in the mirror during the next few minutes until the piece is forced back into the lap.

201

However, these causes are minor compared to the chief reason for zones. Fast aspherical mirrors demand the use of smaller polishers. The old style of optical work (common in the days of long-focus mirrors) involved the use of two identical disks. Telescope makers modified their stroke slightly for a few minutes, but still used an equal-diameter lap to achieve the aspherical figure. Unfortunately, that method won't work on mirrors of low focal ratio. The sphere is so different from the correct shape that the maker struggles for proper conformance. A lap of equal size won't ever reach the correct form. The natural tendency toward statistical averaging will keep dragging its curve back toward a sphere. Also, full-diameter laps are cumbersome when the optical piece is large, regardless of its focal ratio.

The optician chooses a sub-diameter lap, usually one about half the size of the disk being worked (unless the optical piece is really huge—then it's even smaller). The aspherical shape can be approached merely by rubbing the center of the disk more than the outside. Using a smaller lap is dangerous though. The optician must enforce an artificial randomness on the polishing machine to prevent the unnatural precision of the mechanism from digging trenches at fixed radii and, by implication, leaving ridges at other radii. A partially worked surface must be blended or smoothed.

Happily, interior zones on most commercial mirrors are detectable in sensitive bench tests, but they are usually so slight that they are unseen in the eyepiece. Most common is a small depression or nipple at the center, an error that is largely obscured by the secondary mirror. In leaving this error untreated, the optician is saving time and money by ignoring an error that will not be illuminated. (A central zone is shown in Fig. A-3.)

Another common type of interior zone consists of one or more ghostly thin rings appearing about halfway out. They can usually be seen in the Foucault test when the surface figure is very near a sphere, but such an error is only cosmetic. The slight ringing is evidence that the blending is going well.

On the other hand, if the maker is hurried and testing is inadequate, a severe zone may be left in the mirror. One form of interior zonal defect has two competing radii of curvature—one inside the zone, the other outside the zone. This condition may be more damaging to the image than light scattered from the vicinity of the zone itself. Light deflected from the immediate area of the zone will appear as diffuse glow if the zone is sharp enough, but these large areas of the mirror on either side of the zone are directing a great deal of light on interfering focal points. They cover sufficient area that light is attempting to come to two tight disks at different focal distances.

The most debilitating form of a zone is turned edge. It can result from even a full-diameter lap. It is caused by excessive wear at the edge of the disk during polishing. If too much pressure is applied while the tool is teetering on the edge of the optical surface, or if the lap is not maintained in good conformance to the shape of the disk being worked, a turned edge can result (Texereau 1984). Turned edge also seems to be a problem associated with a rocking motion of the mirror disk during polishing.

Turned-down edge, because it happens at the very periphery of the optical surface, is not limited in amplitude. Interior zones are temporary intruders. If good contact between the mirror and tool is maintained and the stroke is not too short, the averaging effects of many strokes at many different angles will eventually average the zone out. It will be automatically blended away.

Turned edge, on the other hand, is derived from bad figuring habits or improper use of materials. Once it starts, the cause generally doesn't go away. It just keeps on occurring or even becomes worse. Turned edges are usually deep, and since the edge is on the perimeter of the optics, it covers a surprisingly large fraction of the aperture's surface area. A 5% turned-edge zone is struck by about 10% of the light incident on the aperture.

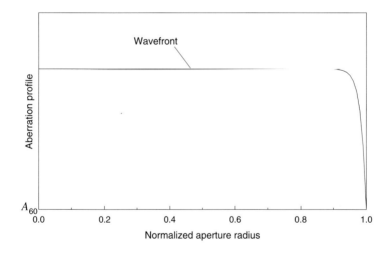

**Fig. 11-1.** *Turned edge is modeled by a 60th-order term of Eq. 11.1.*

Zonal aberration is connected to the expression for general spherical aberration. Remember, the equation for the wavefront involved terms like

$$W(\rho) = \text{constant} + \text{focus term} + A_4\rho^4 + A_6\rho^6 + A_8\rho^8 + A_{10}\rho^{10} + \cdots. \quad (11.1)$$

Normally, for global figuring errors, the coefficient of $\rho^4$ is largest, with a smaller coefficient of $\rho^6$. All of the remaining terms are much smaller. But a zone is a special case where one or more of the higher order terms contributes. A zone is like a switch that turns on very high-order spherical aberration, suddenly waking up errors that were best left asleep.

A simple example is graphed in Fig. 11-1. Turned edge is modeled as a term $-A_{60}\rho^{60}$. There is nothing special about the 60th order. Similar results would have been derived from 58th order or 62nd order.

Interior zones are more complicated. They are combinations of many high-order terms. Broad zones are described by lower orders than sharp zones.

## 11.2   Interior Zones

Something should be emphasized at the beginning to avoid frightening the reader. Interior zonal defects on amateur-sized optics are rarely more than cosmetic defects. Although they are common during brief periods of fabrication, reasonably careful work is enough to lessen them. Few opticians would release a small mirror with a significant interior zone on it. Large mirrors, however, are typically figured face-up with polishers much smaller than their diameters. Such optics often show persistent zones. These mirrors require more careful evaluation to determine if their zonal defects are negligible.

Two types of interior zones are considered here. The first is a narrow trench where the deformation is isolated or does not persist over the rest of the surface. Huge observatory optics often suffer from this type of zone, because the surface is worked by very small polishers. Usually, opticians working on large optics are no fools and will not let conditions that generate these zones endure for long. Still, the skeletal remains of zonal grooves will sometimes appear on test photographs from big mirrors.

The star-test pattern in Chapter 2 was calculated from such a $1/4$-wavelength trench zone. It was modeled as a narrow Gaussian-function dip in an otherwise flat mirror. The particular extrafocal patterns shown in Fig. 2-9 had defocusing aberrations of 20 wavelengths. A general feature of the star test for zones is that one must rack farther out of focus to see the effect of zones well.

A zone produced commonly in the fabrication of small mirrors has a profile that looks like an "S" or "Z," and is called an "S-zone" here. The zone remains after global figuring errors below sixth order are subtracted from the wavefront. This zone can have different radii on either side of its sharpest slope.

### 11.2.1 Aberration Function of S-Zones

Zones can be described by linear combinations of many spherical aberration terms, but that method is somewhat cumbersome. Instead, the zone is specified here with three parameters: amplitude, width, and radius. The optical surface is then divided into three regions, and the surface is constructed by fitting cubic polynomials through the points defined by those three parameters. At the border of each region, the slope of the wavefront is set to zero. Figure 11-2 shows a narrow zone at a 40% radius. A cupped plateau is inside the zone and a shallow dish surrounds it. Less evident is the slightly different curvature of those areas.

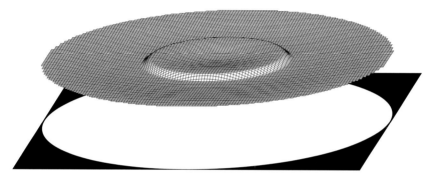

**Fig. 11-2.** *A sharp S-zone at a radius of 40% of the aperture. It divides up the surface into two broad areas with different radius of curvature, as well as providing a rapidly inclined scattering ridge.*

### 11.2.2 Filtering of S-Zones

Interior zones have two characteristic scales. Light diffracted from the vicinity of the zone itself is scattered into a broad fuzzy halo, so one anticipates that the modulation transfer function should dip rapidly at low spatial frequencies. When such zones have a large diameter, more or less like a big central obstruction, the MTF oscillates similarly at higher spatial frequencies.

The behavior of the MTF matches both predictions in Fig. 11-3 for two radii and two amplitudes. One radius is just the 40% zone described in the last section. The other is the same zonal defect moved out until it is centered on 70% of the radius. Both zones are plotted with total aberrations of $1/8$ and $1/4$ wavelength, and both zones have width equal to 0.1 aperture radii. The $1/4$-wavelength zones yield a slightly better Strehl intensity ratio than the 0.8 value that marks the Rayleigh $1/4$-wavelength limit

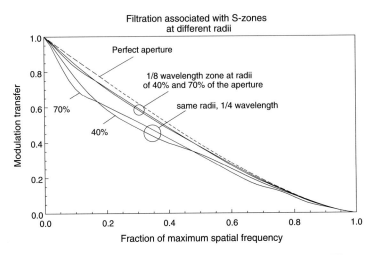

**Fig. 11-3.** *Modulation transfer functions for a single zone. The MTF curves are for two values of zonal aberration (¹/₄ wavelength and ¹/₈ wavelength) and two zonal radii (0.7 and 0.4 of the full aperture). The aperture is unobstructed.*

for spherical aberration. The ¹/₈-wavelength amplitude zones are well inside of the 0.8 Strehl ratio tolerance.

The slight wiggles of the zonal defect MTF at high spatial frequency don't concern the tester much. More troublesome is the brisk drop at low spatial frequency. It is this degradation that Danjon and Couder were talking about when they made the distinctions between the slope of the defect and its amplitude (mentioned in Chapter 1). A smooth surface is the difference between merely adequate optics and those rare instruments that take the observer's breath away.

Notice another characteristic of these plots. A zone appearing at 70% of the aperture is much worse than an equal-depth zone appearing closer to the center. At low spatial frequencies, the contrast drops more precipitously for the larger-radius zone. Lowered performance in this case is purely a function of how much area the defect covers.

Of course, interior zonal defects are not well described by peak-to-valley wavefront error. The RMS deviation is a much better way of characterizing zones. Zones are unacceptable when their RMS deviation is ¹/₁₄ wavelength, which corresponds roughly to the ¹/₄ wavelength curve of Fig. 11-3 at a radius of 0.7. This deviation is much worse than any self-respecting optician would tolerate. For deviations half that size, the MTF only shows a slight dip. This amount of aberration is acceptable.

### 11.2.3  Detecting Interior Zones in the Star Test

In his 1891 work on star testing, Taylor gave a brief description of how he detected a zone in a refractor:

> In order to detect such zonal aberration, which is caused by imperfect figuring of one or more of the surfaces, it is best to direct the telescope to a very bright star, using a moderately high power, and rack in and out of focus as before, only it is best to rack out until 8 to 20 interference rings can be counted, for the irregular zonal effect is most easily detected under such conditions.... Counting from the edge inwards, it may be noticed, for instance, that the outer ring is poor and weak, while the next one or two appear disproportionately strong, the next two or three weak, while those about the center are strong again... (Taylor 1983).

Even though Taylor was writing about refractors and referring to smoother deformations that those modeled here, he described the two essential techniques to detect zones. First, bright stars are used to test for zonal defects. Second, the telescope is defocused farther than is recommended to detect other types of aberration. Defocusing long distances is especially handy because it lessens the effect of other aberrations almost to the vanishing point. Also, because light near focus is hopelessly muddled together, the zone doesn't tend to isolate itself from the rest of the diffraction structure.

Star-test patterns for unobstructed optics with an S-zone at 40% the radius of the aperture and $1/8$-wavelength total aberration on the wavefront are shown in Fig. 11-4 (corresponding to one curve of the MTF chart in Fig. 11-3). The defocusing aberrations are 10 and 20 wavelengths, whereas most of other aberrations appearing in this book are all depicted inside of 8 or 10 wavelengths. The telescope is a long way out of focus, but still this zone is easily visible.

The zone is most distinct at $\pm 20$ wavelengths, where it appears near its proper radius, but it has some anomalous features even here. It dips before it crests. In fact, the zone seems to be located at the crossover point between the extra bright ring and the depressed ring, presumably because it is an S-zone. Trench or hill zones are located at the correct radius but are bracketed by opposite-brightness rings. A dark area is always associated with a bright one because energy must be conserved. Energy that makes one ring look brighter always must be scooped from a nearby ring.

The patterns at $\pm 10$ wavelengths defocusing aberration show another interesting zonal property noticed by Taylor—the pattern at 10 wavelengths

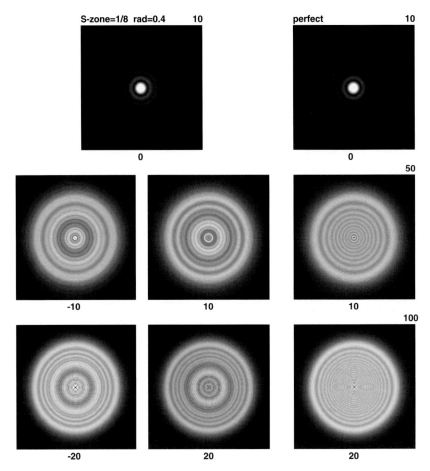

**Fig. 11-4.** *Star-test patterns for an S-zone at 40% radius with amplitude of* $^1\!/_8$ *wavelength. The perfect patterns are in the column on the right. The aperture is unobstructed.*

seems to be the complement of the $-10$ wavelengths pattern. The reversal is not perfect, only approximate. In portions of the disk far from the edge and close to the radius of the zone, the pattern seems to be a negative of the pattern on the other side of focus.

The in-focus pattern indicates that such a zone will frighten a tester more than it will disturb an image. The Strehl ratio is reduced only to about 0.95, well within the tolerance for excellent optics.

Another pattern appears in Fig. 11-5. This time the zone has been moved to a radius of 0.7 of the full aperture and the aperture is obstructed by 20%. Here we see really complicated behavior. The localized effects of the aberration have not yet unmixed from the image at 20 wavelengths defocus. This fact teaches something important about identifying zones. Zones are easy to detect, but their radius and number is hard to pin down. The most we can say, unless very clean separation is seen, is that the surface exhibits zones.

In casual conversations, one hears star-testers speaking confidently about locating zones, saying things like "I detected two zones, one at 50% and the other at 75% of the radius." These claims assume that the structure of the out-of-focus pattern is completely unmixed, which is probably false. Figure 11-5 is a calculated pattern from one zone at a known radius, yet this aperture seems afflicted with many zones. The multiple ringing will separate out at 30 or 40 wavelengths defocusing aberration (not shown) but in an obscure manner. Since this zone is so far out on the aperture, it interferes with the ever-present dark ring on the inside of the bright outer ring.

One final conclusion can be drawn from both Figs. 11-4 and 11-5. The star test is almost too sensitive to interior zonal aberrations. The filtration of $1/8$-wavelength total aberration of either situation is mild. The in-focus patterns are nearly the same as the unaberrated optics. Yet the zones look severe when defocused. If you can only barely detect the existence of zones with defocused optics, then you have nothing to fear. They will not damage the focused image in most dark-field observing situations. In fact, I have never seen a zone as bad as the one depicted in Fig. 11-5.

## 11.3 Turned Edges

Turned-down edge is common enough in both amateur and commercial mirrors although it usually takes different forms. In amateur-made mirrors, it is often wide and shallow, starting at a radius somewhere around 80% or 90% of full aperture and rolling gradually toward the edge. In commercial mirrors, turned-down edge is usually right at the perimeter, but it is steeper. The reasons for this dichotomy are obscure. Perhaps amateurs, who usually work by hand, are capable of putting less pressure on the mirror, or maybe they use a pitch with different working characteristics. Commercial mirrors are likely polished with stiff pitch and hence are not prone to turned edge, but the machines are capable of putting enormous force on the tools.

For the purpose of this chapter, which is less concerned with mirror making than mirror testing by observers, the type of turned edge described is the narrow one. Wide turned-down edges will be classified as zones that happen to be at the boundary of the mirror. Their behavior at best focus is similar to simple spherical overcorrection. Since lower orders of spherical aberration (4th and 6th) have already been discussed in Chapter 10, this

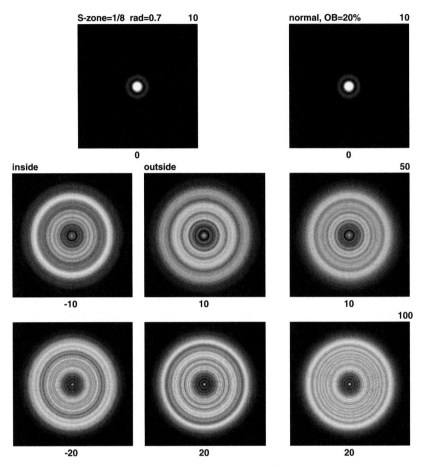

**Fig. 11-5.** *Star-test patterns of an S-zone at 70% of the disk radius. Total aberration is* ⅛ *wavelength. Normal patterns are in the column on the right.*

section will concentrate on the other limiting case.

Turned edge seems to be more prevalent in fast, large, or thin mirrors, but this rule is not rigid. It appears often enough in slow, small, or thick optics. One mirror-making author advises that during design of large thin-mirror telescopes, observers plan a larger surface than will be expected in the final instrument. Then they can cheerfully (and somewhat fatalistically) mask the far edge (Kestner 1981).

### 11.3.1   Aberration Function

Again, a turned edge can be handled by a very high-order term in the spherical aberration equation. Here we choose a much easier path. It is much more convenient simply to allow the mirror to be flat out to a certain radius and then start a quadratic fall toward the edge. The quadratic nature of the downward trend is not based on any physical evidence or theory of the way these edges are put on optical surfaces. It is chosen arbitrarily. Other ways to describe the descent were tried, and the results didn't change much.

Figure 11-6 shows such a turned edge as a skirted table. This figure is not quite accurate. Best focus for turned edges demands that the inner flat area become a very shallow bowl. The aberration function actually used to generate the patterns was modified so that it had a minimum variance.

### 11.3.2   MTF of Turned Edge

The filtering of a turned edge is shown in Fig. 11-7. This aberration is very compact and highly sloped, so it is no surprise that the light diffracted from the edge is diverted far from the center. The MTF drops quickly to reflect the damage to the widely spaced bar patterns of a low spatial frequency target. At the other end of the scale, the contrast preservation at high spatial frequency is much like that of a smaller aperture with a radius the size of the unturned area. Light is driven so far from the central core that it doesn't interfere with the focused spot, but the outer portion of the aperture is not contributing appreciably to the image. A telescope with a turned edge behaves no better than a smaller telescope. Worse, at low spatial frequencies, the spurious light from the edge region actually harms the image.

### 11.3.3   Image Pattern of Turned-Down Edge

Figure 11-8 shows a focus run of the previous section's turned edge. Since this aberration is much more common with reflectors than refractors, a moderate obstruction has been added for realism.

A diffuse glow spreads over the field of view inside focus. Contrast between the rings is appreciably lessened. The reverse is true as well—the contrast between the rings visible outside of focus is increased. Of course, this effect is easier to see with a filter that passes only one color (perhaps a deep green or a crimson red), but using such a filter requires a very bright source of light. Also, the edge of the diffraction disk softens inside focus. Turned edge, like other zones, is easier to detect at long defocus distances.

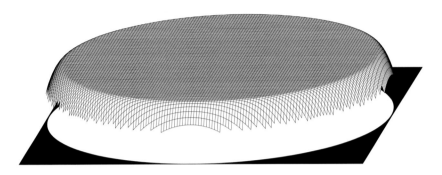

**Fig. 11-6.** *An example aberration function of a turned edge.*

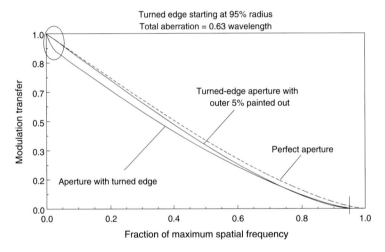

**Fig. 11-7.** *Filtration of an unobstructed aperture caused by an example turned edge that reaches 0.63 wavelength at the far edge. The flat area inside covers 95% of the diameter. The Strehl ratio is slightly higher than 0.8, so this error is about the maximum tolerable. A comparison is made to an aperture with the turned portion masked or painted out. The MTF goes to zero at about 0.95 of the maximum spatial frequency just as the smaller aperture would.*

At greater distances inside focus, the hazy glow of turned-down edge condenses into a smaller bundle, and the edge of the disk seems to bleed light into the outside. This behavior appears in Fig. 11-9, where the defocus is shown at 30 wavelengths inside and outside of focus.

Other aberrations also render the diffraction rings more distinct on one side of focus than the other—an example is lower-order spherical aberration—but none of them show a uniformity of disk illumination. One might well wonder if a turned edge is detectable in the presence of spherical aberration or if it is too difficult to tease out of the confused image.

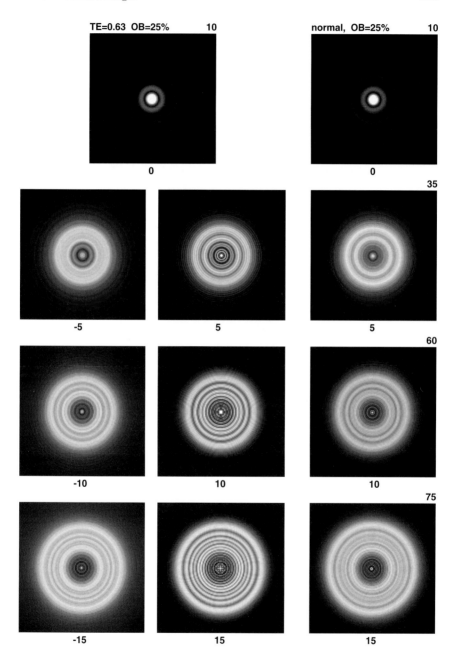

**Fig. 11-8.** *Image patterns of turned edge starting at 95% the radius and having the value of −0.63 wavelength right at the edge. Obstruction is 25%, and the normal unaberrated patterns appear in the column to the right.*

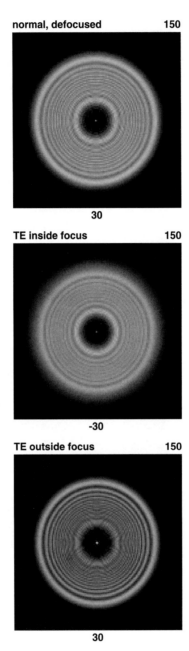

**Fig. 11-9.** *Turned edge ±30 wavelengths out of focus. Normal appearance is also shown. The Maltese crosses are a moiré effect caused by the sampling rate of the calculated image. They would not appear in a real view.*

If, say, a turned edge as severe as Fig. 11-8 is added to $1/4$ wavelength of spherical aberration, the turned edge would be visible beyond 20 wavelengths defocus (image not shown). The spherical aberration becomes hard to detect with 20 wavelengths defocusing aberration, but the turned edge is still there to see. Thus, turned edge can indeed be detected in the presence of mild correction error.

When the image is focused inward a long way, the low-brightness soft edge of the disk becomes hard to see. Low contrast in the rings is a surer indicator of turned edge, and the delicate appearance of the boundary is further evidence.

Ellison and other subsequent authors pointed out that the edge of the disk inside of focus looked "hairy" (Ingalls 1976). It would not be surprising if the uncontrolled way a turned edge is applied to a mirror would lead to some structuring in the scattered light, thus causing a "hairy" edge. However, I have never been sure such an effect is generated by the turned edge or is caused by the common turbulence-induced aberration acting on slight low-order spherical aberration.

With the wider and less deeply turned edges characteristic of amateur-made mirrors, some modifications of these patterns should be expected. The turned area diverts light to lower angles and looks more compact. Also, the optimum distance for detecting a soft edge is somewhat nearer the focus than the 20-wavelength number recommended above.

Refractors can have turned-down edges, too, but the appearance is reversed. Contrasty rings are found inside focus; the soft edge and low contrast rings are outside. However, refractors don't tend to exhibit turned edge unless it is wide. Normally, the lens cell hides the far edge of the objective behind retaining rings. In a way, this advantage compensates for not being able to hide a central zone behind a secondary. Few refractors are made so badly that they show noticeable turned edges.

The in-focus images of Fig. 11-8 display the almost negligible effect of turned edge on high-resolution applications. The diffuse glow is still there, but is unseen compared to the dazzling stellar image. Other than the slightly reduced effective aperture, turned edge disturbs low spatial frequencies (or wide details) preferentially.

### 11.3.4  Signal-to-Noise Ratio of a Turned Edge

The effect of turned edge is very similar to dirty optics in that it "scatters" light throughout the field of view. Therefore, it is instructive and revealing to make an equivalent signal-to-noise calculation. In most dark-field observing situations, turned edge is like dusty optics or spider diffraction in that small amounts matter little. A tiny fraction of an already dim object's light is negligible. However, in the case of lunar-planetary astronomy or attempted observation of a dim object next to a bright one, turned edge can become a serious source of trouble. How much can be tolerated?

For planetary astronomy, two things are important: 1) the diameter of the induced halo of the turned edge and 2) the amount of light removed from the image. The diameter is easy to estimate. Consulting the MTF chart in Fig. 11-7, we see that the halfway-down point in the initial sharp drop (marked with oval) occurs at about 2% the maximum spatial frequency. This number inverts to a radius of about $50\lambda/D$, or about 40 Airy disk radii for a 5% turned edge. In a 200 mm aperture using yellow-green light, the radius of the glow is about 30 arcseconds. For a turned-edge amplitude of only $1/8$ wavelength, the amount of energy removed from the image (and reappearing as noise) is slightly less than 1% of the total energy. Thus, the SNR can be as bad as 20 dB.

The really disturbing thing about turned edge is the relative compactness of the halo. It doesn't throw the light as far from the image as dust does. Thirty arcseconds means that much of the offending light is *still inside planetary disks.* Turned edges are pernicious errors that remove contrast far in excess of their nominal magnitudes. The amplitude of a 5% turned edge zone must be decreased to $1/25$ wavelength before it reaches the 30 dB SNR that was given as the tolerance for dust. That amount is scarcely measurable. Of course, a turned edge of such a small magnitude hardly behaves in the manner of a turned edge. It has begun to compete with interior zones and roughness errors.

The best way of reducing turned-edge diffraction is to make sure that it is extremely narrow. The turned-edge halo will then appear much larger and correspondingly dimmer. It will divert light outside planetary disks and diffract less light to begin with. For a 2.5% turned edge of the same $1/8$ wavelength amplitude as the case above, a 24 dB SNR is diffracted to a halo with twice the angle. Now, because much of the stray light misses the image and the area of the turned edge is smaller, the true SNR increases to 28–30 dB.

### 11.3.5   The Width of the Turned Edge

Usually, when turned edge is less detectable than in Figs. 11-8 and 11-9, you have very little to worry about. But if you have a serious problem with an edge zone, the radius at which the zone begins to roll is a useful bit of information. You can perhaps do further tests with edge masks to try to determine the turning radius and severity of the zone, but such checks are difficult to interpret.

Turning radius is easier to determine using a variation of the Foucault test. Try an occluding knife outside the focus of an artificial-source star test done at night. The source should be very bright, so move the flashlight close to the sphere or use a larger sphere. Mount the knife over one half of an empty tube of the same diameter as an eyepiece. (A fragment of a playing card or opaque slip of paper works almost as well as a true knife and offers less opportunity for accident.) You can do fine adjustments by rotating this "eyepiece." Defocus should be 5 mm or more. Arrange the telescope so the knife's shadow covers either $1/4$ or $3/4$ of the aperture, but not half. Do not replace this knife edge by a Ronchi ruling. The side-order images of the grating disturb interpretations of the edge.

If the shadow is perfectly straight on the aperture and seems rock-solid, try to put the knife nearer to the focus. If you see a blurred, quavery shadow that is disturbed by the slightest touch, you are probably too close to focus. Set the knife farther away. You are looking for a slight curl of the shadow very near the edge of the aperture. The curl becomes severe beyond the turning radius.

If you can detect the width of a turned edge in this manner, then the rolled region is probably too wide to paint as suggested below. What you want to see is little or no evidence of a turned edge from this crude test. You only want to paint a narrow turned edge. If you detect a wide turned edge, you will find it easier to mask the offending region. Use the turning radius determined here to calculate the size of the aperture through which you wish to allow light transmission.

## 11.3.6  Remedies for Turned Edge

As was shown in the MTF diagram above, the mirror with a turned edge performs no better than a smaller perfect aperture at high spatial frequencies and worse than the smaller aperture at low spatial frequencies. Clearly, the last bit of aperture on the periphery is doing less than nothing for the imaging performance. Turned edges gather worthless, imperfectly focused light and corrupt otherwise perfect images with it.

Masking is not an irreversible step, but it requires a little mechanical skill. Generally, it involves constructing a narrow annulus and finding a way of holding it over the mirror. A mask holder mounted above the mirror works best for open-tubed, Dobsonian mountings. Access to the region just above the mirror is easy with such a telescope, and installing and adjusting an edge mask is convenient.

Those mirror owners who have a definite diagnosis of turned edge and who are willing to accept the considerable risks involved, may significantly improve the performance of a telescope mirror by painting it. Painting should not be attempted with wide turned edges. The definition of "wide" depends on aperture diameter. Ten millimeters sounds wide for a 150-mm mirror and narrow for a 500-mm mirror.

Painting the mirror, however, works with any telescope and requires only a steady hand. Remove the mirror and place it on a lazy-susan or other rotating platform. Make sure the mirror is larger than the rotating table under it. Spend some time carefully centering and leveling the mirror on the pivot, so that it doesn't wobble or rotate eccentrically.

Slowly spinning the disk, brace your hand in one spot and introduce the brush point gingerly onto the mirror's surface, working in from the edge. You are in no hurry, so try to lay down a clean line over many revolutions. I don't advise using a permanent marker but if you do, be advised the solvent tends to wipe up existing marks, so you may have to make repeated passes before the ink stays on the mirror. Brushes are less controllable, but painting in this manner results in a more saturated obscuration. Do not use an airbrush or spray paint of any sort.

Perform the painting operation in two steps. The first time, paint out just 1 or 2 mm of the far edge. If you are fortunate, this narrow ribbon will largely cure the edge problems. Star test the mirror again. If the image doesn't improve, extend the painted zone inward. At the end of such a procedure, the ugly appearance of the mirror can be shocking. Keep in mind, however, that you have, in effect, trimmed off the poorest part of the aperture.

The effect of a corrected turned edge can be seen in the star test. How it will improve actual observing is not immediately apparent. Remember, the most objectionable feature of a turned edge is a hazy glow in the vicinity of the bright point image—20 to 40 Airy radii out. Inspection of the MTF chart reveals a quick dip at low spatial frequency. For this 5% wide zone, most of the damage has already occurred by the time 2 to 5% of the maximum spatial frequency of the MTF target has been reached. If the aperture is 200 mm (8 inches), then detail separations less than about 10 to 30 arcseconds are degraded. Masking the turned edge will have the most benefit with richly-detailed large objects, such as the cores of tight globular clusters or planetary disks.

# Chapter 12

# Chromatic Aberration

A simple refractor lens focuses light at different distances behind it, resulting in color errors. One can choose only one focus at a time, so the remaining colors appear as defocused disks. Also, because of the differing focal points, the magnification of each color is different and white-light edges are blurred into spectra.

To get an idea of the difficulty involved, hold up a simple one-element lens and look at the transmitted image with a low power eyepiece. Such a lens often appears in toy telescopes or binoculars. Obviously, chromatic aberration is profound. Every bright object appears to be surrounded by a rainbow-hued glory, and reasonable imaging only occurs for fields comprised, not surprisingly, of only one pure color.

Early astronomers reduced the importance of simple-lens color error by increasing the focal ratio to enormous values. This stratagem increased the depth of focus until it encompassed the spread of colors, and they found that performance improved. The battle was hard to win, however, because modest increases in aperture had to be accompanied by huge increases in the focal length, and operational difficulties worsened considerably (King 1955; Bell 1922).[1]

Even today, residual color error is visible in nominally color-corrected instruments. Focus binoculars on a bright edge against a darker background (a good target is a window from the inside of a large room), and then decenter the image. Because the color correction is only approximate for these instruments, you will see the smearing associated with color error. In some binoculars, the color fringes are violet and green, depending on whether the bright edge is to the inside or outside of the field.

---

[1] Many $5 \times 24$ finders on department-store telescopes are actually stopped-down simple lenses. If a roughly 8-mm stop is visible immediately behind the objective, it is not corrected for color. The finder is useless. Discard it.

219

Color errors are not really aberrations in the narrow sense that aberrations are departures from the ideal spherical shape of the wavefront. One could easily describe an aperture that focuses each color precisely on a different axial point. In any given color, the wavefront converges spherically. Such an aperture could justifiably be called perfect, yet it would not work as a telescope objective.

Another important distinction between wavefront (or "geometrical") aberrations and chromatic aberrations is the absence of interference effects in chromatic aberrations. Different colors do not mutually interfere. For most of the discussions appearing in this chapter, *wave optics and ray optics are identical.*

Whatever the origin of the optical degradation, color error is objectionable, and one goal of the star test is to make certain that it is as small as possible.

## 12.1   Dispersion

All of the image patterns presented in this book have been calculated for a single wavelength of light, so-called monochromatic radiation. An ideal lens would focus all colors at the same lens distance, and lenses would be indistinguishable from mirrors.

Unfortunately, all simple lenses are dispersive. The word *dispersion* represents the inability of all colors of light to move at the same speed in glass. Like the word *propagation,* its source is botany or agriculture. "Dispersion" originally referred to randomly spreading seed. Its optical meaning refers to the spreading of colors, but such dispersion is anything but random. In fact, if it had not been applied already to color error, *dispersion* might have been a better word for what is known today as "light scattering."

Red light typically has a higher speed in glass than blue light. Thus, red-light waves outrace blue-light waves while they are traversing the material. The net effect is that after passing through a prism blue light is diverted to a larger angle than red light.

Say we have two prism materials, as in Fig. 12-1a, that divert or *refract* light to the indicated angles. The average behavior of the two prisms is the same. Each kicks yellow light to 10°, but the behavior at either end of the spectrum is somewhat different. One glass (let's call it "crown" glass) diverts red light to 9° and blue light to 11°. The other glass (call it "flint") spreads the spectrum twice as far, to 8° and 12° respectively. This second sample of glass is said to have higher dispersion because of this spreading property.

We can combine these prisms to produce interesting effects. If we invert the flint prism and place it snugly against the crown, as in Fig. 12-1b, we have made an approximately plane-parallel window. The combination passes yellow light undeflected, but red is pushed up to 1° and blue is bent down to −1°. What we have envisioned here is a straight-through dispersive element, one that spreads light into its color components, but does not refract it on the average. Such a device was once made and marketed as an objective prism by the firm of Merz and Mahler, but its expense prevented wide adoption (King 1955, p. 294). The advantage of such a prism was that the telescope could be immediately directed at the region of interest.

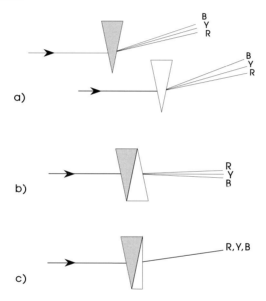

**Fig. 12-1.** *Simplified achromatism: a) "crown" glass (dark prism) showing dispersion of light and "flint" glass exhibiting the same average refractive power but twice the dispersion, b) the two glasses combined to generate a "straight-through" rainbow (dispersion without diversion), c) a combination that results in an achromatic prism (diversion but not dispersion).*

Figure 12-1c depicts another clever trick we can perform with these two materials. This time, we divide the flint prism in half, making another prism that only deflects yellow light to 5°. Blue light would exit this half-prism at an angle of 6° and red light at 4°. If we invert this prism as before and place it close to the crown prism, the exit angles of the combination become: yellow, 10° − 5° = 5°; red, 9° − 4° = 5°; and blue, 11° − 6° = 5°.

If one were designing a crystal chandelier, this prism combination would be a disaster. Instead of dividing the light into a profusion of sparkling rain-

bows, the compound prism keeps the light packed tightly in a white beam.
It diverts all colors equally. On the other hand, if one were designing telescopes, it is just what is required. This device has two important characteristics. It bends light and does so colorlessly. What has been demonstrated
here are all of the essential elements of an achromatic refracting telescope.

## 12.2   The Achromatic Lens

Figure 12-2 shows the progression that must take place to get from
the achromatic prism to the achromatic lens. If we envision the lens as
composed of little prism pieces, and allow the divisions to get finer and
finer, we eventually get to a cylindrical lens. It takes very little imagination
to rotate the other way and extend the situation to a spherical lens.

Almost as soon as the concept of dispersion was developed, this trick
of achromatism was envisioned. All that was left was to find suitable materials. Isaac Newton conducted limited experiments where he compared
the dispersive power of different media with their refractive power. His
hasty conclusion was that dispersion and refraction were inextricably linked.
Thus, dispersion could not be counterbalanced without also eliminating
bending of the light beam. He reached this erroneous result by perhaps
relying too much on a visceral feeling that dispersion was a property of
light itself. By this argument, materials didn't matter; dispersion was proportional to refraction and thus always existed until lenses were weakened
to be no different than windows. Therefore, achromatic refractors were
impossible.

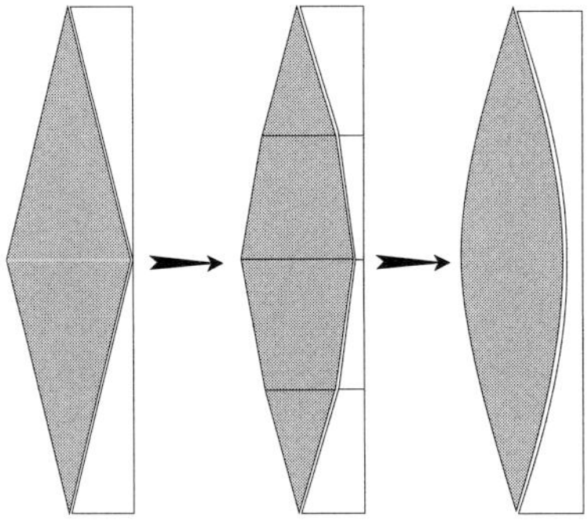

**Fig. 12-2.** *How a prism achromat leads directly to an achromatic lens.*

Various conflicting statements about Newton's mistake have been made.
Bell (1922) said that Newton had never published this result, and King
(1955) referenced a section of Newton's *Opticks* in which the great physicist

despaired of ever curing chromatic aberration but didn't give his reasons. The confusion can perhaps be reduced by referencing yet another portion of *Optics,* where Newton said (Book One, Part II, Prop. III, Prob. I, Exper. 8):

> I found moreover, that when Light goes out of Air through several contiguous refracting Mediums as through Water and Glass, and thence goes out again into Air, whether the refracting Superficies be parallel or inclin'd to one another, that Light as often as by contrary Refractions 'tis so corrected, that it emergeth in Lines parallel to those in which it was incident, continues ever after to be white. But if the emergent Rays be inclined to the incident, the Whiteness of the emerging light will by degrees in passing on from the Place of Emergence, become tinged in its Edges with Colours. This I try'd by refracting Light with Prisms of Glass placed within a Prismatick Vessel of Water.

In other words, conditions leading to the straight-through spectrum of Fig. 12-1b do not occur, implying Fig. 12-1c is also impossible. He followed this experiment with some speculative theorems elaborating his ideas. In Newton's defense, I don't believe that discrediting the idea of achromatism was the main thrust in this section of *Optics,* but the experiment was among those interpreted by later readers to be a stronger condemnation than it actually was.

Partly because of Newton's powerful reputation, opticians gave up on achromatic lenses for 50 years. Then, an English gentleman named Chester Moor Hall made the first reduced-color lens from two different materials. He kept the lens design hidden, although the trick was reverse-engineered by a nosy lensmaker who happened to be subcontracted to work on both lenses at the same time. The lensmaker didn't realize the importance of the invention, and news of it languished until it was redeveloped a generation later by John Dollond. When it appeared to be a profitable development, lawsuits were filed by London opticians saying that Dollond had stolen the idea.

Dollond likely had heard rumors about Hall's lens, but certainly he did enough experimentation himself to be justly credited with reinventing it. Perhaps it would be more accurate to say that Dollond was the first to reduce the achromatic lens to common practice. He was certainly the first to announce it publicly (King 1955, pp. 144–150).

## 12.3   Residual Chromatic Aberration

Unfortunately, the ideal materials of Fig. 12-1 do not exist. Most dispersion in the range of visible wavelengths originates with resonances in the ultraviolet. In the frequency bands of these resonances, the wonderfully transparent materials go opaque. The transparent nature of these materials (called *dielectrics*) in the visible spectrum does not persist for every wavelength. Over much of the spectrum, the materials are content to accept energy at the entrance side and emit it at the exit side with very little loss. The energy brushes over the molecules, disturbing them little. However, at certain frequencies these materials are unusually excited by the incident energy. For wavelengths near resonance (usually about 100 nm), the glass molecules suddenly absorb energy and convert it to heat rather than pass it along.

The material behaves like a child's swing. If the swing is pushed once every quarter hour, the pendulum motion does not build. If the swing is pushed three times per second, most pushes are poorly timed and once again, pendulum motion does not build. If the impulses are carefully timed, the energy lost to the swing (or glass) steadily increases. The swing is driven at the resonance frequency. The energy contained in the light wave doesn't float through glass anymore because it must drive the oscillation in the material. Transparency is destroyed (Hecht 1987, p. 63).

The presence of resonances in the ultraviolet causes the refractive index of optical materials over the visible spectrum to increase sharply toward the blue end of the spectrum. Most glasses also have a distant resonance in the infrared caused by molecular vibration, but this resonance affects the slopes less profoundly in the visible band.

One aim of the lens designer is to choose powers of the lenses in such a way as to cause the dispersion of the "crownlike" lens elements to cancel the opposite dispersion of the "flintlike" lens elements. Because the dispersion tilts sharply at the violet end of the spectrum and the number of acceptable materials is limited, the color correction cannot be perfect. Lens designers are unable to choose lens powers for every color so that the dispersions nest like spoons. If they are combining two lens materials, the differences of refraction toward the blue means that they can probably choose only two colors with the same focal points. The remainder of the spectrum must go where it will. Each color, naturally, will be paired with another color from the opposite side of the spectrum, but the designer can deliberately choose only two.

For most visual telescopes, the two colors that the designer attempts to bring to a common focus are red (the Fraunhofer C line at 656 nm) and blue-green (the Fraunhofer F line at 486 nm). The focal point of yellow is slightly closer to the objective, and the far ends of the spectrum (deep red and violet) are beyond the C-F focus. Violet is farthest away, but that doesn't matter. The human eye is not sensitive to violet except at high brightness, so the defocused halo of violet light is mostly invisible. The residual color spread of achromatic objectives between the two chosen colors is known as the *secondary spectrum*.

Color corrections do not scale with size. As the diameter of the objective increases, it must be made at higher focal ratios to squeeze the light between C and F inside the Airy disk. While small 80-mm lenses can still perform admirably at f/10, a conventional achromat six inches in diameter must be made at f/18.5 to focus the different colors as well (Sidgwick 1955, p. 67; Rutten and van Venrooij 1988, p. 55). A.E. Conrady is even more conservative, stating that the focal ratio for an 80 mm lens must be f/15 and a 6-inch should be f/29 (1957, I p. 201). Since secondary spectrum is $1/2000f$ for ordinary achromats, we can use Appendix E to show:

$$F = \frac{D[\text{mm}]}{8.8\Delta n} \qquad (12.1)$$

where $\Delta n$ is the number of wavelengths defocusing error we are willing to tolerate in the secondary spectrum, $D$ is the aperture diameter, and $F$ is the focal ratio. Following the depth-of-focus discussion in Chapter 5, we place $\Delta n$ at $1/2$ wavelength. The formula becomes $0.23D[\text{mm}] = F$, or f/18 for the 80-mm aperture and f/35 for the 6-inch. This result is as conservative as Conrady's. Nevertheless, I have observed through a 6-inch f/15 refractor and was only moderately bothered by the excess color. Perhaps the restriction can be eased to 1 wavelength without too much loss. In this case, it drops to $0.12D[\text{mm}] = F$, which is the same as Sidgwick.

This focal-ratio discussion sounds a disturbing note about the so-called perfection of conventional refractors. Perhaps it also says something about the human tolerance for chromatic errors.

Lens designers have found other useful telescopic color corrections besides pulling C-F into common focus. In the early years of astrophotography, special-purpose achromats were corrected for the orthochromatic emulsions then in common use. Orthochromatic plates were most sensitive to blue through near-ultraviolet light, and completely insensitive to red. Photographic telescopes could only be focused by the tedious process of taking actual exposures, but they gave sharper images on the plate than a visually-corrected lens.

Since the designer had to take the whole optical system into account, the personal preferences of the observer were figured into the design. Color correction curves published by Bell (p. 91) showed that the finest makers of the 19th century favored bringing the F (blue-green) line into common focus with the deep red at 680 nm (the B line). Much of this color correction shift is presumably caused by the chromatic aberration inherent in the eye and in the eyepieces used at the time (Taylor 1983).

## 12.4   The Apochromat

Achromatism can be compared to tying the spectrum in a knot. The brightest parts of the visual spectrum are deliberately folded into the tightest bundle, with the deep red and the violet ends hanging out like shoelaces. Some of the earliest optical workers (most notably Peter Dollond, son of the achromatic lens developer) tackled the cause of these spectral defects. Dollond could choose from only a handful of glasses. He reasoned that if a flint element were "designed" from a composite of two glasses, then the dispersion of that element could be tuned so that it would nest more closely with the opposite dispersion of the crown element.

He made and marketed such a triple objective, but apparently the lens was designed by trial-and-error. In any case, the glasses of the time were not yet good enough to consistently allow such refinement. It was not until 1892 that H. Dennis Taylor produced an apochromatic lens using comprehensive optical theory. He not only corrected secondary spectrum more fully, but folded the violet tail of the spectrum close enough to the visual to allow the blue-sensitive photographic plates of the time to use the same focus as the human eye (King 1955).

Using three different forms of glass (or two, if exotic glasses are used) allows the lens designer to put an extra kink in the dispersion curves, which in turn allows the simultaneous focus of three chosen colors. The color spread is knotted yet again. Often, the colors selected for common focus are further separated than the Fraunhofer C and F lines. One such correction brings the line C, e, and g into common focus, or red, yellow-green, and violet (Kingslake 1978, p. 86). The deep-violet and deep-red ends of the spectrum are tucked in closer to the visual focus. Typically, the residual tertiary spectrum has been reduced a factor of five to $1/10,000f$ (Rutten and van Venrooij 1988, p. 54).

However, the proper behavior of the bright portions of the spectrum is no guarantee that the spectral tails are close to focus. Much depends on what the designer has in mind. Some apochromatic refractors might be designed for purely visual use, minimizing the spread of focus between C and F. These apochromats might bring violet only a little closer than ordinary doublets. Others may be designed for pinpoint photographic images without using filters, focusing deep into the violet with only slightly improved visual correction.

## 12.5 Testing Refractors for Geometrical Aberrations

Since each color, in effect, goes through different apparent thicknesses of glass, one would anticipate that the correction for other aberrations might vary over the spectrum. In fact, some aberrations aren't corrected at all. Much depends on how many free parameters the lens designer is allowed to play with.

For example, the variables of a doublet are all four of the curves, the separation of the lenses, the position of the aperture stop, and the glass formulations (of which there are hundreds of important types). If allowed to vary these parameters at will, designers can focus two chosen colors simultaneously and adequately correct for coma and spherical aberration over much of the spectrum. However, if designers are deliberately hamstrung by cost limitations or other considerations, they may make a cemented achromat out of inappropriate glasses. Such conditions can be so confining that the designer cannot correct spherical aberration and coma at the same time, even though it is possible with careful choice of glasses (Kingslake 1978, p. 171). Most makers of quality astronomical refractors are not constrained in this manner, but the cheapest consumer refractors may well offer limited aberration correction.

An apochromat focuses three chosen colors to the same point (for a more precise definition, see Buchdahl 1970). Enough free parameters remain in three-element apochromats that the designers can make a superbly corrected lens, minimizing chromatic variation of spherical aberration (spherochromatism) at more than one wavelength and suppressing coma. Also, apochromats can be adequately corrected at faster focal ratios. Six-inch apochromats are routinely made at f/9. An apochromat should present as good an image as diffraction will allow, and should accordingly be tested thoroughly.

You should test for geometrical aberrations in refractors by using an eyepiece filter. In fact, using such a filter to suppress the polychromatic nature of white light is recommended even for inspection of reflector optics. A very deep yellow or green filter is recommended. After you have tested at a central color, you may wish to change filters to red or blue to verify that other aberrations are small at the edges of the visual spectrum. Except for limiting the color band, testing refractors for other aberrations is the same as testing reflectors.

## 12.6 The Star Test for Chromatic Aberration

Different colors do not mutually interfere. Hence, chromatic aberration does not manifest itself in modifications of the diffraction rings, either focused or defocused. Chromatic aberration appears as a different focus position for each color. The shift can be a lateral one, as for a mild prism, or it can be a longitudinal offset. For all real lenses, each color has a slightly different focal length.

To see color effects, *pull off all filters and focus on a white star or an artificial source.* Be sure to filter the flashlight for a nighttime artificial-source test of chromatic aberration (see Chapter 5).

### 12.6.1  Wedge, Assembly Errors, and Atmospheric Spectra

Look for smearing of the focused image into a short lateral spectrum, the effect of decentering or wedge in optical components. Either of these problems puts a red fringe on one side of the image and a blue fringe on the other side, although the yellowish light of the outer planets often mixes with this light to make it appear green. Decentering may also cause other aberrations, depending on the details.

Decentering is a sideways shift of the elements with respect to one another. Wedge is an extremely shallow prism that is added to the optical system. It results from having an element thicker on one side than the other. After years of trouble-free use, wedge can appear suddenly after the lens is disassembled for cleaning. Makers sometimes cleverly remove the last bit of wedge in their objectives by canceling it between lens elements. Thus, if the crown element has a wedge of 0.04 mm and the flint element has a wedge of 0.03 mm with a maximum tolerance of 0.02 mm, the total wedge can be reduced to 0.01 mm by putting the thick part of the crown next to the thin part of the flint. An unsuspecting owner can turn these elements to yield a total wedge of 0.07 mm, or more than 3 times the tolerance. Upon reassembling the lens elements, look for alignment marks, either arrows or scratches, on the edges of the disks.

Another accident can also occur when refractor lenses are taken apart for cleaning. Refractors are so long-lived that even well cared-for instruments will eventually acquire too much internal grime. Occasionally, owners improperly invert the crown element during cleaning. This error sometimes happens even to huge observatory instruments, as is documented in Leslie Peltier's *Starlight Nights* (1965). He had obtained a 12-inch Clark refractor that had a hideous purple glow around star images. Doubting that the Clarks would deliberately release such a poor instrument, since it would damage their reputation in professional circles, Peltier speculated that the crown element had been inadvertently flipped during washing in the past. He inverted the element once again, and recovered the fine performance of the original lens design. Any instrument that is air-spaced may suffer this indignity, regardless of size. I once saw it in a good 2-inch refractor, but in the case of this miniature doublet, the inversion also damaged the spherical correction.

Usually, the direction of spectral dispersion is vertical. In this case, the atmosphere and not the telescope is at fault. The same spectrum would appear in a similar-sized reflector, and certainly no mechanism exists in a reflector to cause the same dispersion. The presence of a vertical spectrum could either be caused by cool air puddling at the bottom of the telescope, or (more likely) a slight prismatic effect in the atmosphere itself.

Observers commonly witness a color spread in low-lying planets and bright stars. Any object below 45° elevation is likely to be smeared to a small extent. Such errors are unlikely for artificial sources, but in the sky they are all too prevalent. Rotation of the tube will serve to isolate this error to air effects. Choose a star closer to zenith.

### 12.6.2  Star Test for Conventional Astronomical Visual Doublets

The design of the crown-flint refractor lens froze into place in the 19th century. Individual makers chose slightly different residual dispersions curves, but all were more-or-less bound by the availability of materials. The quality and homogeneity of materials have improved, but the simplest astronomical refractors are still made using designs that would have been recognized by makers in the 1800s.

The following star test does not apply to modern advanced refractors made from uncommon materials. It is based on a star test done by the author on a 4-inch f/15 Alvan Clark refractor built in 1889. This test used Polaris as a target. It is essentially the same description found in Taylor (in 1891), who probably used similar instruments, and would apply to ordinary doublets even today.

Inside focus, a very pale yellow-green disk with a trace of a magenta fringe is visible. Just beyond focus to the outside, a somewhat surprising red spot appears in the center. This wonderfully tiny crimson point of light is astonishing to someone who has never noticed it before. Taylor says that its origin is in the deep red beyond the C line.

An additional factor contributes to the appearance of this red dot. It approximately coincides with the location for which yellow-green is 1 wavelength out of focus. The diffraction pattern of yellow-green light for this situation looks like Fig. 12-3a, which shows an annulus with a hole neatly punched in it. Eq. 5.1 gives the focus shift to +1 wavelength defocus as $8F^2\lambda$. The fraction of the focal length is just $8F^2\lambda/f$. For a 4-inch f/15 refractor in yellow-green light this ratio amounts to $8(225)(2.2 \times 10^{-5})/60 = 0.00066$.

**a) yellow-green**                    **b) red, same position**

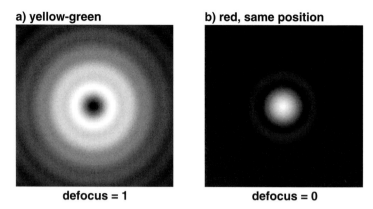

defocus = 1                              defocus = 0

**Fig. 12-3.** *The "red dot" effect just beyond focus in conventional doublet refractors.*

For conventional doublet refractors, the difference between yellow-green and C (red) focus is 0.0005 times the focal length. For the same location as the yellow-green focus of Fig. 12-3a, red light slightly beyond the C Fraunhofer line is being focused in the pattern of Fig. 12-3b. Thus, a convenient little hole is present in the bright yellow-green diffraction pattern through which the red focus peeks.

Beyond the red spot, the pale greenish disk expands once more. Taylor says that sometimes a green fringe appears on this disk, but it didn't appear or was very weak in the Clark. Farther out, an indefinite blue focus is supposed to form at the center. Focus is much too strong a word, however. The 4-inch showed a blue-violet fuzzy ball that never condensed well enough to form what could be termed a focus.

Taylor's observations were done with a Huygenian eyepiece while the modern views were supplied with a modified Orthoscopic eyepiece. This difference probably accounts for the few changes, together with variations in optical design. Also, the Clark was not coated, and it had the residual coloration of glasses at the time it was made, thus slightly affecting comparisons with modern doublets.

A dim in-focus image is mostly colorless. Its most objectionable feature is a watery purple or violet glow that forms around bright objects such as the planet Venus. Taylor said it best when he described a planetary image as a sketch in black and white, where the artist made a last pass dabbing on the far red and violet colors with a sponge. However, the bad effects of this halo should not be exaggerated. It attracts notice on only the most dazzling objects, and even then it seems to interfere only slightly with the ability to discern detail. On conventional refractors smaller than 80 mm, this purple glow is almost unnoticeable. It begins to become intrusive at 4 and 5 inches (100 to 130 millimeters), but only for large instruments does it become objectionable. I saw it in a 6-inch f/15 refractor used as a guide telescope for the Schottland 16-inch Schmidt camera (King 1955, p. 370). Saturn had a crisp white-yellow disk surrounded by a bright purple blur.

Poorly made modern doublets show behavior that does not match the usual C-F color correction. A strong halo of red or greenish-blue surrounding the focused image is certainly a reason for concern. Such behavior is not normal.

Lesser amounts of chromatic aberration can be also be discerned by examining the fringes of the image just inside focus. The wavelength that focuses closest to the lens in a normal doublet is about 550 or 560 nm (yellow-green). If the place where the achromat folds the spectrum is too close to the red end, the inside-focus fringe is blue with perhaps a small green component. If the fold is too close to the blue end, the fringe is a scarlet red instead of magenta (Sidgwick 1955).

### 12.6.3   Star Test of Apochromats or Advanced Refractors

Coloration is far less noticeable in apochromats. Taylor claimed that the out-of-focus star disks in his photovisual lenses were virtually colorless. I have never inspected a Cooke photovisual lens, so I cannot provide confirmation. According to Sidgwick (1955, p. 201), a focused photovisual lens has a dazzling yellow-green disk with a purplish-red fringe. It should be pointed out that a weak red fringe appears on point sources even in reflectors, although it is difficult to observe. The diameter of the diffraction disk increases with long wavelengths, and the telescope is unable to pack red light into the small bundle.

My apochromatic refractor has a slight magenta fringe at a short distance inside focus and a green fringe at the same position outside focus. In focus, no color is obvious. This description is consistent with yellow or green focus nearest the objective and red or blue focus slightly farther away. A blurred blue-violet focus forms nowhere. Presumably, violet is folded back near the focus of other colors. Because violet is not bright, it can no longer be seen in the "noise" of the other strong colors. The location of the red focus is not far enough behind that of yellow-green to be distinctly noticeable.

The white appearance of a focused star image or the muting of color in views of the planet Venus (in comparison with a conventional doublet) should be a powerful indicator that an apochromat or advanced refractor is properly color-corrected. You should tolerate little spurious color in any modern triplet or fluorite-doublet design. Planetary images should not show easily discerned blurry colors.

### 12.6.4   Chromatic Effects in the Eye

Make certain you are not blaming the objective lens for color errors in your own eye. Most people do not realize that their eyes are not achromatic. In fact, the erroneous assumption that the human eye is achromatic led later scientists to question Newton's research on dispersion. In normal daylight vision, the eye-brain system is able to process out much of the color error encountered. Astronomy is no common activity, however, and the processing is subverted during observation. Taylor mentions how the apparent color correction of a telescope was upset with change of magnification and exit pupil.

The answer to this problem is to use the eye at a reduced pupil size. As the magnification of the telescope increases, it illuminates less of the eye's pupil. The eye's color correction improves with smaller pupil size for the same reason that refractors perform better at high focal ratio. Most perceived chromatic aberration is then produced in the telescope instead of the eye. Star test with a short focal length eyepiece.

### 12.6.5   The Eyepiece

An objective can present a perfectly acceptable image that is destroyed by imperfect achromatism in the eyepiece. One may be unjustly blaming the telescope's objective lens for an error that happens later in the optical train.

Fortunately, the modern general-purpose eyepiece is designed to work passably well even with a steep f/4 light cone. Most refractors that we would want to star test operate at f/9 and higher. At these mild focal ratios, compound eyepieces such as Orthoscopics or Plössls work superbly. Not unless they have been improperly made or assembled do they add significant chromatic aberration to the image. Still, they perform best when the star is in the center of the field. Do not make chromatic aberration judgments on decentered stars.

The easiest way of checking your eyepiece is to change to a different eyepiece and see if the color error goes away. Also, put the suspect eyepiece in a reflecting telescope and see if the color difficulty is still present.

### 12.7   Conclusions and Remedies

About the only optical problems discussed in this chapter that are changeable are those that deal with atmospheric effects or improper assembly of the lens cell. Most other color errors must be handled at the factory. You must be very cautious in blaming a perceived chromatic aberration on the instrument. Personally, I have never seen a quality refractor with grossly improper correction of chromatic aberration. I have heard of a few cases secondhand. Even department-store models seem to get color correction right although they botch nearly every mechanical feature on the instrument. I have seen fast richest-field refractors or large binoculars that had only marginal color correction, but specialty refractors must be judged to a different standard than the lunar-planetary models. Owners of these telescopes should realize that they have traded increased color error for a wider field.

Testing with a bad eyepiece presents the greatest opportunity for error. Be certain that the suspected chromatic aberration appears in many eyepieces, preferably not of the same type. Do not test with the Huygenian or Ramsden eyepieces that are often included with the telescope. If a Barlow is used, make certain that it is achromatic. Because of the high focal ratios of most refractors, some companies have been known to include simple-lens Barlows. Such a lens is usable, but it generates an incorrect color correction in the star test. Perform the test at high magnification to avoid color problems in your eye, and be absolutely sure that an unusual coloration in your light source is not shifting the results. Finally, test on multiple occasions before the final assessment is made.

# Chapter 13

# Roughness

This chapter discusses the diffraction effects caused by quasi-random or asymmetric errors polished into the surface of the glass. The circular rings break up into tiny speckles in focused images, and the out-of-focus disk shows non-circular detail. The reader should take four important points from this chapter:

1. Wavefront roughness usually follows a continuous spectrum at increasingly finer scales, which telescope makers arbitrarily divide into categories such as "dog-biscuit" or "microripple." However, such distinctions are more matters of nomenclature than descriptions of real phenomena.

2. Medium-scale roughness (primary ripple or dog-biscuit) errors are the ones which most severely damage the image because they don't divert light far from the core of the image. The scattered light is hence more condensed and brighter.

3. Roughness errors are difficult to distinguish from turbulence, and careful star-testing is required to avoid unfairly judging an instrument. Tolerance for roughness errors must be viewed in the context of likely turbulence errors.

4. Roughness at the scale of microripple is of interest only to makers of specialized instruments who have already reduced other forms of diffracted light to the vanishing point. Microripple of small amplitude has little relevance to general-purpose instruments.

## 13.1   Roughness Scales and Effects

Harsh methods of polishing and use of fast polishing compounds can lead to random or nonperiodic error that is not a circle of revolution. This so-called "surface roughness" is not generally viewed as a problem on the global scale, the way figuring errors are perceived, but it can be harmful to the image in its own way.

We must carefully define what is meant by surface scale before introducing the deformations of that surface. Think of the aperture as being expanded to the size of the United States. The spherical curvature of the Earth is analogous to the focusing curvature of the wavefront. In the aberration function plots, this curvature has been removed as a noninstructive universal constant. The map has been flattened on the average.

Figuring errors are large-scale deformations. An example is spherical overcorrection, which starts fairly level at the center of the aperture and rises to a peak at the 70% zone. The aberration function then falls rapidly until it reaches the edge. Similarly, the center of the U.S. starts fairly flat in the plains states, rises toward the Appalachian or Rocky Mountain ranges, and then falls rapidly toward the oceans.

No serious mapmaker would suggest that the U.S. topography could be completely represented by a simple model of two ridges with a flat area between. Nevertheless, we may usefully describe the coarsest features of the landscape with broad-brush concepts like *continental divide* and leave the narrower details for later. Describing the figuring errors of the optical surface as "spherical aberration" or "zonal defects" is that sort of large-scale reference. Here "scale" refers not to how high the aberration is but how *wide* it is, or rather how persistent the aberration is over long distances.

To improve the map, the landscape is refined by adding rivers or watersheds. Many of these features extend over areas the size of an entire state. On the mirror, we can decide to measure roughness with ruler divisions of around $1/10$ or $1/20$ of the aperture. These are "medium-scale" roughness errors. We could also map individual mountains or county-sized variations in the terrain and the analogous "small-scale" roughness errors. With sufficient magnification, the map could chart the position of boulders, plowed fields and ditches. Likewise, if we examine the optics on the molecular scale, we see a convoluted surface, but such errors are so much smaller than the wavelength of visual light that they cannot be sensed by ordinary means. The wavefront remains flat after encountering molecule-sized roughness.

Medium-scale roughness errors go by the colorful name "dog biscuit" and the less-colorful name "primary ripple." Their greatest width scale approximately matches the spaces between grooves on the polishing tool. These channels are always cut or cast into the polisher to provide space for the pitch to spread with pressure and to supply reserves of the finely-suspended polishing abrasive. The grooves are a necessary evil. If they are not cut into the lap, large-scale shape errors are generated that are even worse than moderate amounts of roughness.

Small-scale roughness errors, called "microripple," have spacings of about 1 to 2 mm. The cause of these errors is less obvious than primary ripple, but their origin is probably found in the choice and use of polishing materials. Cerium-oxide polishing compound seems to give rougher results than rouge. Waxy laps yield more rippled surfaces than pure pitch, and paper laps are worse than wax. At the basic level, however, non-uniformities in the glass itself seem to limit the smoothness. Texereau claims that the lap is able to attack the surface of the mirror through a combination of physical and chemical means, and that once begun, such errors are self-sustaining (Twyman 1988, pp. 578–584; Texereau 1984, pp. 88–91).

Certain fast-acting laps deliver a roughness with characteristic dimensions intermediate in scale between classic primary ripple and microripple, descriptively called "lemon-peel" surfaces. This appearance is rare in instruments intended for astronomical use, however. Usually, telescopes are polished on gentler materials.

We might expect the diffraction image from the roughness facets characteristic of primary ripple to be 5 to 20 times larger than the unaberrated image, but that simplified logic does not take into account the accidental correlations that occur when nearby scattering facets act in phase with one another. Antinodal bright areas and nodal dark regions will form. The net effect of mild primary ripple is to blow the scattered light into a knobby glow surrounding the image, which has its greatest brightness within a radius less than 5 times the Airy disk. Such scattered light can be a bad problem because it is condensed enough to easily see.

Let's compare that defect with the likely behavior of microripple. Texereau states that microripple is occasionally as bad as 6 nm on the wavefront and has an average spacing as small as 1 mm (Twyman 1988, p. 580). However, we are fortunate that the slope of each 1 mm facet is seldom correlated with the slopes from nearby facets, so the effective apertures of the facets only statistically combine. This 6 nm case is also the worst one; most wavefronts have microripple below 1 nm ($<1/500$ wavelength). Because of the small size and lack of correlation of the scattering surfaces, the diffraction pattern of scattered light from microripple is a shattered dim glow, quite similar to the aura that occurs with a turned-down edge. Microripple of small amplitude is hard to see with the Foucault knife-edge test. It requires specialized equipment to detect unambiguously.

When roughness is small, as it is for optics, it only affects the diffraction shape of the image in a minor way. It removes light from the focused image and shoves it out into a blotchy halo of small diameter for primary ripple and large diameter for microripple. The missing energy is calculated by seeing how much the central intensity is lessened.

The Strehl ratio of roughness can be calculated from an approximation (Born and Wolf 1980, p. 464). Here $i_s$ represents the Strehl ratio at best focus and $\sigma_{\mathrm{RMS}}$ is the root-mean-square deviation of the wavefront (in wavelengths) as measured from the reference sphere centered on best focus:

$$i_s \approx 1 - (2\pi\sigma_{\mathrm{RMS}})^2. \qquad (13.1)$$

For example, a $1/14.05$-wavelength RMS deviation yields a Strehl ratio of 0.8 (the Maréchal tolerance). A $1/20$-wavelength error typical of noticeable primary ripple gives a ratio of 0.9. A severe case of microripple might have a deviation as large as $1/100$ wavelength, so the intensity is reduced only to 0.996. Clearly, microripple has a very different character than primary ripple.

Another approximation to the Strehl ratio has been given by Mahajan (1982):

$$i_s \approx e^{-(2\pi\sigma_{\mathrm{RMS}})^2}. \qquad (13.2)$$

It gives a more accurate number than Eq. 13.1 at large aberration amplitudes. We can invert Eq. 13.2 for a $i_s = 0.8$ to define a "Mahajan tolerance" of about $1/13$ wavelength RMS. For small roughnesses, however, the difference between these approximations is negligible.

## 13.2   The Terminology of Roughness

We must distinguish the nomenclature from the reality of surface error. Roughness is typically modeled either as a *continuous* spectrum from large scale to small scale or as a discontinuous *composite scale* spectrum. The "spectrum" in this case is not composed of light intensities plotted versus colors, but magnitude of roughness versus width scales. A composite scale is something like huge swells of water on which are superimposed tiny wind-blown capillary waves—smooth undulations with wrinkles. The terminology of calling lap-sized roughness "primary ripple" and small roughness "microripple" originates from assuming that two separate causes generate composite-scale roughness.

I have seen mirrors that obviously obeyed this composite-scale model very well. They were covered with smooth, wavy roughness that displayed little of the smaller-scale roughness in between the primary ripple and microripple. More often, though, mirrors appear less and less rough at more diminishing scales, but there is no one scale at which the tester can say the roughness stops (an example appears in Fig. 13-1). Such names as "primary ripple" mean less on such surfaces because there is always a scale just below it. We might call it a "not-so-large ripple" scale, followed closely by an "even smaller ripple" scale. The model described below follows this continuous spectrum behavior instead of the composite-scale that the terminology is based on. The words will continue to be used because they are convenient and firmly lodged in the literature.

Another reason for using the artificial divisions of roughness into medium-scale versus small-scale is that they are typically found in different tests. The Foucault test is good down to a small-scale of roughness intermediate between primary and microripple, but then its sensitivity fails. The investigation of microripple requires a phase-interference test that deliberately suppresses sensitivity to large-scale error.

## 13.3 Medium-Scale Roughness, or Primary Ripple

The appearance of a mirror suffering from primary ripple is shown in the Foucault test photograph of Fig. 13-1. The roughness is only apparent in the center of the mirror at this knife setting. Ripple extends into the bright and dark regions, though it is less visible in these areas. The roughness is dimly seen as a random structuring with a set of superimposed grooves beginning in the center and extending outward.

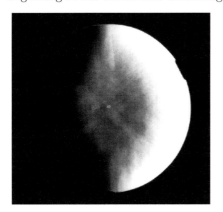 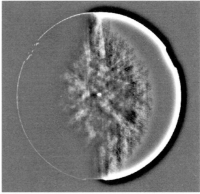

**Fig. 13-1.** *Roughness visible in the central zone of a mirror in the Foucault test. At right: contrast is improved by subtracting an unsharp-mask image.*

This 6-inch (150-mm) f/5 mirror was produced during the manufacturing boom at the last return of periodic comet Halley and is typical of the sloppy fabrication practices of the time. As bad as it looks, the roughness is estimated at only somewhere between $1/10$ or $1/20$ wavelength RMS (peak-to-valley roughness between $1/3$ and $1/5$-wavelength). Spherical aberration amounting to 1 wavelength overcorrection was also found during this bench test. Obviously, the spherical aberration was the worst failing.

Your eye also suffers from medium-scale roughness. Take aluminum foil and perforate it with a pin. Hold the foil about 8 to 15 cm in front of your eye and look through the pinhole at a frosted incandescent light bulb. Try to focus your eye on the lamp, not the pinhole, and cover the other eye. If you have punched the right size hole in the foil, you should see a mottled disk that roughly approximates the out-of-focus patterns seen in this book. The outside ring is perhaps the only one clearly delineated. The appearance may be cleared up slightly by placing a colored filter between the lamp and the pinhole.

As you blink, horizontal lines appear briefly on the defocused disk. You can see that some of the details change with every blink. They are probably caused by variations of the moisture thickness on the cornea. Depending on how bright the light is, you may also see some dim radial spikes outside the disk. These spikes may be caused by diffraction from the non-circular iris opening or streaks in the roughness.

The roughness is visible as coarseness in the expanded disk. This coarseness does not vary from blink to blink. The aberration is many wavelengths high, so the appearance of individual rings is obscured and confused. When I was 19, I had a fleck of metal removed from my cornea, and the evidence of the trauma can still be seen in the out-of-focus image. The roughness can originate from corneal defects, surface roughness in the eye lens, and non-uniformities in the refractive index of the eye lens.

The human eye is not even close to diffraction-limited. An eye with a 3-mm iris opening (typical during daylight) can theoretically resolve lines separated by 0.6 arcminutes, but a person who resolves lines only 1 arcminute apart is deemed to have excellent vision. How can we test telescopes to the diffraction limit through such an imperfect aperture?

In fact, the answer to this seeming paradox is quite simple. Angular errors in the instrument are magnified until they are bigger than errors in the eye. Once the separation between the finest possible details have been magnified beyond 5 arcminutes (i.e., $1/6$ the diameter of the Moon), aberrations in the telescope begin to dominate aberrations in the eye. A 1-inch aperture should resolve lines separated by 0.092 arcminutes, so sufficient image size is reached by $5/0.092 \cong 50$ power/inch (20 power/cm). Somewhere beyond this magnification, even perfect telescopic images begin to become fuzzy.

Ironically, some people boast about telescopes that can "withstand more than 100 power/inch" (40 per cm). What they don't realize is that they're not bragging about the telescopes. They are inadvertently admitting the poor quality of their own visual acuities. When using extremely high magnifications beyond 100/inch, the diffraction disk appears bigger than two-thirds the angular diameter of the full Moon.

### 13.3.1   The Aberration Function of Medium-Scale Roughness

To generate rough wavefronts, the fractal model described in the chapter on turbulence is again used, with certain modifications.

The first change is to suppress midpoint deviations for two iterations. This step ensures that the surfaces so generated will be uncorrelated at distances greater than $1/8$ to $1/4$ of the aperture. One doesn't expect that medium-scale roughness will persist over long distances, and by not allowing the surface to deviate until it is divided into a grid of 16 squares, this correlation scale is achieved. Only 16 points out of almost 13,000 are artificially clamped to zero, but the entire character of the surface is changed.

The other modification is to avoid quenching the roughness. Figure 13-1 shows fine detail over scales smaller than the tool spacing (presumably about $1/8$ of the diameter). In the case of turbulence it was desirable to suppress the deviation at small scale because no mechanism existed to produce it. Turbulence cells have a quasi-period of about 10 cm. Roughness in the glass, because it originates from many causes at a number of scales, will be modeled here to behave as a self-similar fractal.

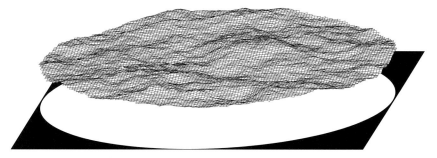

**Fig. 13-2.** *The aberration function of medium-scale roughness, also called "primary ripple" or "dog biscuit."*

Figure 13-2 shows an example aberration function of medium-scale roughness. The streaks visible in Fig. 13-1 are not represented in this algorithm. One expects such grooves to diffract light into low-contrast spikes at right angles to their extent (as a spider vane does). We must not overemphasize their importance, however. The visual perception system tries to create order in what we see. It is especially fond of straight lines and often creates a line where only a hint of one is actually present. Orion's Belt, for example, is curved a great deal. The eye imposes linearity because it *prefers* linearity.

## 13.3.2   Filtering Effects of Medium-Scale Roughness

Because the scale of roughness is much smaller than the whole aperture, one expects a brisk drop at low spatial frequencies, a condition similar to turned edge. The MTF thereafter should remain a fairly fixed fraction of the perfect MTF. Thus, the average degradation drops from unity to a constant at about the correlation length (Schroeder 1987, p. 208). We see in Fig. 13-3 that the previous guess of a correlation length of $1/4$ to $1/8$ of the aperture is a good one. The sagging of the curves seems to have reached a steady fraction of the perfect aperture's MTF at about that range.

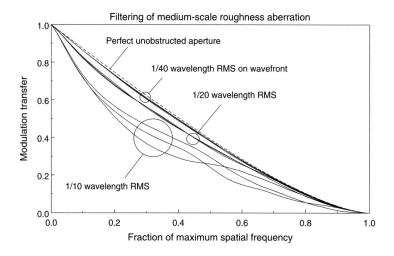

**Fig. 13-3.** *Filtration caused by primary ripple. Three amounts are shown: 0.1, 0.05, and 0.025 wavelengths RMS wavefront deviation.*

Roughness aberration is nonsymmetric, so three curves are plotted for target patterns with bars oriented up-down, left-right, and at a 45° angle. Because these curves represent a single realization of the rough surface rather than an average over many such surfaces, the MTF wiggles somewhat. These curves are examples of the variations that can be expected from changes in the MTF-target orientation or from slightly different surfaces.

The degradation is severe for 0.1 wavelength RMS wavefronts, but it improves rapidly for smaller roughnesses. The quality is acceptable for wavefront roughnesses less than 0.05 wavelength RMS. Some manufacturers guarantee optics that smooth, but they always give the specification on the surface rather than the wavefront. Read claims carefully.

Also shown is the smooth wavefront with RMS deviation of only $1/40$ wavelength ($1/80$ wavelength on a mirror surface). If any reasonable care is taken, all astronomical optics can be made this smooth. Global wavefront aberrations are difficult to reduce below $1/28$ wavelength RMS ($1/8$ wavelength peak-to-valley), but optics can easily be smoothed until the wavefront roughness is less than $1/40$ wavelength RMS deviation.

### 13.3.3 Star Test on Medium-Scale Roughness

Two focus runs appear in Fig. 13-4 and Fig. 13-5. The first is an image sequence of an otherwise perfect $1/40$-wavelength RMS roughness wavefront. Even though the wavefront is very good, the roughness is detectable in the out-of-focus images. Figure 13-5 doubles the aberration and uses a different fractally-derived wavefront. This $1/20$-wavelength RMS aperture is acceptable in the MTF chart, yet it seriously distorts out-of-focus images. Fortunately, it seems to tuck away the messiness visible out-of-focus to yield a fairly crisp pattern while in focus. If this pattern were turbulence, it would be at least a 9 on the 1–10 Pickering seeing scale.

We go approximately 8 wavelengths on either side of focus (Table 5-1). If the wavefront has primary ripple close to $1/40$ wavelength RMS, the effects of roughness are very delicate and hard to detect. At $1/20$ wavelength RMS (about the limit of what you should tolerate), you will see it all too plainly.

Often, you must test for roughness alongside some spherical aberration. Roughness is easier to see on the soft-edged side of focus. The dim outer portions of the disk flare into a twisted, asterisk-like pattern. Don't concentrate on the roughness until you have determined that spherical aberration is acceptable. Spherical correction errors are much more damaging to high resolution images than roughness errors because their width scale is so large.

### 13.3.4 Roughness and Turbulence

Turbulence closely resembles roughness, so it interferes strongly with the star test for that aberration. Thus, roughness is nearly impossible to check under real skies using an actual star. Nights where the air is absolutely still are so rare that they will never coincide with a deliberately-planned star test. Besides, star tests are the last thing the observer wants to do on nights of exceptional steadiness.

An artificial source is often crucial to test for roughness. Also, testers cannot check for primary ripple anytime and anywhere. They must try for a serendipitous combination of time and place that results in a tranquil test-

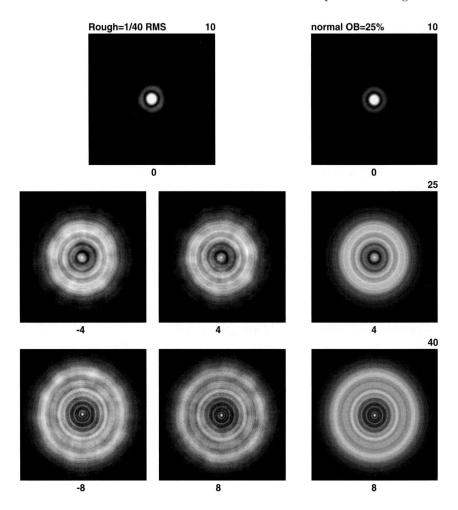

**Fig. 13-4.** *Medium-scale roughness of $1/40$ wavelength RMS with defocusing aberration from −8 to +8 wavelengths. Obstruction is 25% and the perfect image is seen in the right column.*

ing path. Maybe the necessary conditions will occur during a night when the temperature is not dropping too rapidly. The likeliest good tests are conducted on a windless evening or a very early morning over grass. The artificial source test goes best when the flashlight and sphere are set up in the bright period after sunset but before twilight has ended. Use the Sun to illuminate the sphere in the early morning. If these times are difficult to arrange, test for roughness with the artificial source at night. (See Hufnagel

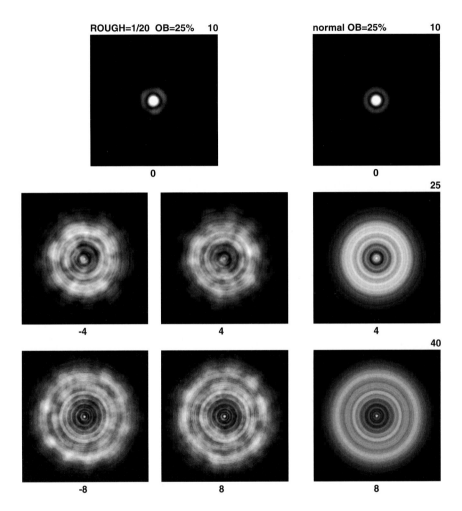

**Fig. 13-5.** *Another primary ripple wavefront, this time having a statistical deviation of $1/20$ wavelength RMS, is focused from $-8$ to $+8$ wavelengths. The smooth wavefront is to the right.*

1993, pp. 6–12.)

Also, you must be realistic in your expectations. Roughness is only important if it is a reasonable fraction of the similar turbulence aberration. Thus, roughness is judged to be objectionable only if it appears during the nights that turbulence affects the telescope least. If the image is flickering a small amount when one sets up the test, the result is not useless.

See if the fixed roughness pattern is visible even against the relatively light turbulence in front of an artificial source. If you cannot discern a fixed roughness pattern under these excellent conditions, then you may be assured that during actual use the roughness is affecting the image little.

The scale must also slide a little to accommodate local conditions. If seeing is abysmal during 99% of the nights at your location, perhaps roughness is less important. In locations with good seeing, roughness standards must be tighter.

If roughness is still grossly objectionable even after taking these mitigating conditions into account, the optics must be refigured.

## 13.4   Small-Scale Roughness, or Microripple

The original concern over microripple stems from efforts early in the 20th century to observe the solar atmosphere all of the time, not just during solar eclipses. The solar corona is a thin, high-temperature gas that extends out several solar diameters. Observations during eclipses were excellent, but resembled infrequent snapshots. Scientists wanted a method to view the inner corona daily and to monitor its changes. The corona is brighter than the full Moon, but it can be lost next to the hellish intensity of the Sun.

To make a telescope capable of blocking out parasitic scattered light requires more advanced methods than the empirical baffling recipes generally used by astronomers. André Couder stated that the intensity of the corona 5 arcminutes from an occluded solar image is only about 1 millionth as strong as the light intensity streaming from the unblocked Sun. Even nonuniformities in the glass of his coronagraph lens scattered light only a little less intense. He estimated the scattering from the atmosphere, even on a clear mountaintop, was about half as intense as the corona, and the scattering from the most carefully cleaned lens was equally bright (quoted by Twyman 1988, p. 585). Clearly, contrast was already suffering badly from unavoidable effects, and little room was left for scattering by microripple. The severe $1/100$ wavelength RMS microripple example mentioned above by Texereau would be unacceptable. It scatters 0.4% of the energy striking the aperture, more than a thousand times too bright.

Texereau also describes a finely polished surface with microripple approximately 0.05 nm RMS deviation, or about $1/11{,}000$ wavelength. This value inserted into Eq. 13.1 results in an intensity reduced $(2\pi/11{,}000)^2$ from 1, or only $3 \times 10^{-7}$. This tiny amount of scattered light would be even less intense by the time it was considered at an angle of 5 arcminutes. Such a surface is sufficiently smooth to be used in a coronagraph (Texereau 1984, p. 88).

Optics exhibiting the primary ripple of Fig. 13-1 demand little or no attention to the relatively subtle effect of microripple. In fact, the fractal model of medium-scale roughness automatically includes a moderate amount of microripple (about $1/1{,}000$ wavelength RMS), but the presence of coarser-scale roughness dominates the lesser scale.

Nevertheless, we want to investigate what happens when primary ripple is stripped away and all that is left is small-scale roughness. Microripple is often blamed for low contrast. Can this mysterious roughness scale be responsible for so many optical worries?

### 13.4.1 The Aberration Function of Small-Scale Roughness

The fractal algorithm was not used in the microripple model, because we want to remove medium-scale features and concentrate on small-scale effects alone. A pseudo-random number generator was used to assign heights to the $128 \times 128$ pupil grid. Because asymmetry was expected, tending toward flat tops with sharper grooves, a square root was taken of this starting surface, and the result was normalized. The surface is shown in Fig. 13-6.

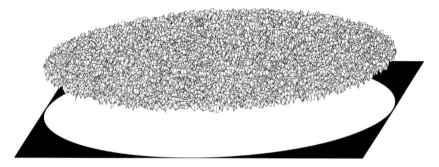

**Fig. 13-6.** *A modeled microripple surface with amplitude expanded greatly.*

### 13.4.2 Filtering of Small-Scale Roughness

Consider what was said above concerning correlation length. Because the microripple has a very tiny correlation length (less than a millimeter or so), we should expect a precipitous drop in the modulation transfer function, followed by a constant degradation. These effects are illustrated in Fig. 13-7. MTF drops quickly and then remains a more or less constant fraction of the perfect value.

In fact, microripple as large as $1/10$ wavelength RMS is an unlikely event, even though it appears on the graph. It is shown only to make the fast initial drop more apparent. Texereau gave a worst-case amount of only $1/100$ wavelength. We can see by the behavior of the MTF graphs that

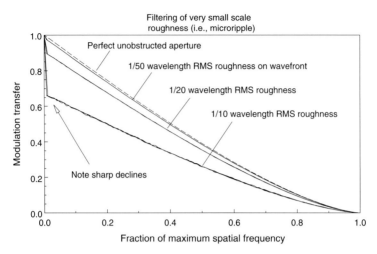

**Fig. 13-7.** *Various MTF curves characteristic of microripple. The aberrations appearing here are exaggerated to show the shape.*

$\frac{1}{100}$ *wavelength of microripple would be indistinguishable from a perfect aperture in most dark-field observing situations.* Calculated images differed little from perfection, so no star test diagrams of microripple appear here.

### 13.4.3   The Great Unknown

So why do we hear all sorts of warnings about the debilitating effects of microripple? Microripple is one of those myths of telescope making that feeds on folk wisdom and hearsay. Part of the trouble is the difficulty of measuring it. Texereau describes a technique (originated by Lyot) that requires an attenuating phase plate, a specialized device that delays and weakens the propagation of the unscattered wavefront. Since the strength of microripple cannot be measured easily, it gets the blame for any unidentified optical difficulty.

Also, published descriptions of the construction of unusual instruments such as coronagraphs (where microripple *does* matter) tend to frighten readers. People believe that microripple may affect more prosaic forms of ordinary observing. The light diffracted from a slightly turned far edge is vastly stronger than that coming from microripple. Nearly every telescope with an unmasked edge has much more diffuse light than the scattering caused by the microripple roughness.

Extended objects suffer far greater degradation from obstructions like spider vanes, mirror clips, and tiny screws projecting from the side of the secondary holder than from microripple. For example, spiders deflect more light than any likely case of small-scale roughness. A spider with 4 vanes 0.5 mm thick on a 200-mm aperture diffracts 0.5% of the incident energy, slightly more than Texereau's $1/100$-wavelength worst case microripple.

A root-mean-square microripple error of 0.5 nm (about $1/1000$-wavelength) results in a Strehl-ratio decrease of 0.00004. If this missing light is distributed over the field of interest, it results in a signal-to-noise ratio on extended objects that can be as bad as 44 dB. This value is between the 30 dB maximum defined in Chapter 9 for dirty optics and the 55 dB SNR of good magnetic tape.

For most dark-field observing, however, microripple is not very harmful. For example, 1 mm width-scale roughness scatters light into a halo about 100 arcseconds wide. Maybe 10% of that energy will cover a 20-arcsecond image of Mars. The rest of the stray light is beyond the planet's limb where it doesn't contaminate the image. Thus, the SNR improves to 54 dB, a very large value indeed. An analogy to a 50 dB signal-to-noise ratio is the darkening of the image of the Sun as viewed through a safe solar filter. If the signal were the unfiltered solar image, the noise caused by $1/1000$-wavelength microripple would be about as strong as the filtered Sun. If you require an instrument capable of discerning dim details next to a bright source of interference, you may well need to worry about microripple. Small-scale, low-amplitude roughness is not a threat for most observers.

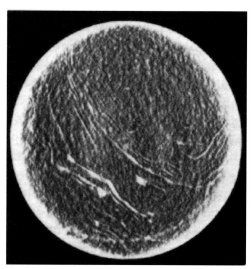

**Fig. 13-8.** *A testing technique originated by Lyot reveals microripple and veins of differing hardness on the glass. (From* How to Make a Telescope *by Jean Texereau, Copyright ©1984 by Willmann-Bell, Inc. and used with permission.)*

# Chapter 14

# Astigmatism

Astigmatism is the tendency of an objective to focus at two distances. Each focal position is stretched, one at a right angle to the other. An average focus is found between them, with the image forming a crosslike pattern. Because of the stretching at the angles of the cross, as well as the inability to locate a unique focus, contrast of high-spatial frequency information is sharply lessened. This chapter will discuss a number of points:

1. Astigmatism has many separate causes, and most can be cured at moderate or no expense.

2. Unambiguously locating the source of astigmatism takes careful logic (and to be honest, a small amount of luck).

3. Small amounts of astigmatism are detected by gently rocking the focus about the position of best focus.

4. The way to determine whether the telescope has too much astigmatism is to try to detect non-circularity of the image at a calibrated focus setting.

## 14.1 Astigmatism in Eyes and Telescope Optics

Astigmatism means *not stigmatic,* or *not focusing to a spot.* In the widest possible definition, all of the nonsymmetric aberrations discussed in this book are astigmatic. The symmetric aberrations may produce fuzzy spots, but at least they are round.

This type of aberration was originally defined by Ludwig von Seidel and modified by Fritz Zernike (Born and Wolf 1980, p. 470). Astigmatism divides focus into two stubby lines separated by a short distance along the direction of eyepiece travel. The lines are at right angles to one another. A sort of "best focus" is seen at the halfway point between them, where the illumination pattern takes the shape of a cross.

Astigmatism is frequently corrected in human vision.[1] The *cylinder* numbers in the eyeglass prescription are adjustments for astigmatism. This aberration is usually caused by a deformation of the cornea, or the transparent outer covering of the eye. Astigmatism could result from a tighter "stretch" of the cornea in one direction than in the other, as well as a misshapen eyeball. The aberration can be temporarily corrected in some cases by pulling one corner of the eyelid.

For example, my right eye has a cylinder power of 2 diopters[2] at an axis of 90° and my left eye has a power of 2.5 diopters at 88°. Because I also have significant focusing correction, I see point sources stretched up in one eye and flattened in the other. The approximate 90° axis is probably no accident; the stretch direction may be related to the muscle attachment points of my eye or to the shape of the orbital cavities in my head.

The simplest example of an astigmatic lens is a cylinder with no curvature in one direction and significant curvature in the other. Truncated chords of cylinders are often used in reading magnifiers. By putting the magnifier right against the page, one can suppress the poor focusing properties of the lens and stretch tiny letters in one direction.

Truly cylindrical lenses or mirrors are almost never used on purpose and never happen accidentally. The most common form is a hybrid of spherical and cylindrical shapes. In fact, one can subtract the spherical focusing power of a lens entirely and be left with a purely astigmatic form.

A cylindrical lens that won't focus in any axis is modeled as part of a torus. A torus is shaped like a doughnut. The particular form that is most interesting here has a hole in it with exactly the same diameter as the torus' cross section. A drawing of such a doughnut appears in Fig. 14-1, with half of the torus chopped away to reveal the interesting region. Consider the tiny circle drawn on the inside of the hole. When lifted away from the rest of the torus, that circular piece has the same surface shape of an astigmatic lens with no focusing power (the other side of the lens is flat). The curve goes into the paper along the up-down direction and out of the paper to the left or right. Imagine looking down on a saddle shape,

<hr>

[1] A more common problem fixed in eyeglasses are the *spherical* corrections, which are modifications of the focusing power of the eyes. "Spherical" to an optometrist refers to the $A_2\rho^2$ focusing term of the expansion of Eq. 10.2. The words "spherical aberration correction" used by telescope makers designates the $A_4\rho^4$ term of that expansion.

[2] A diopter is the reciprocal of the focal length in meters. The typical 2-meter focal length of a small telescope produces a focusing power of only 0.5 diopters.

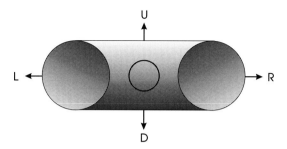

**Fig. 14-1.** *A tiny circle on the inside of a torus is the purest form of the astigmatic deformation.*

with the left-right directions toward the pommel and seat, and up-down toward either stirrup.

Astigmatic surfaces can be modeled as combinations of purely spherical (i.e., focusing) surfaces and nonfocusing toroidal surfaces. If we move the tiny circle of Fig. 14-1 to the outside of the doughnut, its surface no longer resembles a saddle. Instead, it looks like one of these hybrid surfaces. It has lower astigmatic power than before, with some spherical curvature mixed in. In the astigmatism of a real lens, the converging wavefront doesn't truly have a saddle shape. The shape is produced only after the spherical focusing component is subtracted away.

## 14.2 Causes of Astigmatism

Astigmatism in telescopes is a symptom of several optical problems, some of which are listed here:

1. Misalignment (often mixed with coma).

2. Poor support of the optics' weight, causing pressure directed along an axis (the "potato chip" sag).

3. A supposedly flat diagonal or right-angle prism that is actually slightly spherical (a surprisingly common problem).

4. A slight cylindrical deformation ground or polished into the glass (a very tiny amount is found in most mirrors and lenses).

5. Poorly annealed glass (often appears in "porthole" mirrors or other thick pieces that were made with another application in mind).

6. Uncompensated astigmatism in the observer's eye.

The most disastrous of these causes are number 4, true astigmatism ground or polished into the surface, and number 5, unrelieved stresses contained in the glass itself. Saving money by using undocumented glass for the mirror substrate is a risk that many makers are willing to accept, and they often get away with it. The astigmatism that is derived from the other sources, however, is no less objectionable. Luckily, these causes are easily repaired.

In the days when all mirrors were small and thick compared with their diameter, astigmatism was comparatively rare. Even halfhearted adherence to the optical shop practice of rotating the tool with respect to the mirror usually kept astigmatism dormant. Only when stresses were frozen into the mirror disk itself (cause #5) did astigmatism appear.[3]

Cause #4 is more common now that large, thin mirrors are being figured. Even careful opticians can polish cylindrical curves into such a flexible surface. If conditions that result in astigmatism appear, they are usually a function of how the mirror was supported during grinding or polishing and are therefore persistent. Astigmatism, if it appears at all in such mirrors, is usually severe.

Discovering the cause of observed astigmatism to determine possible strategies for its elimination takes methodical but straightforward detective work. The process will be described in section 14.5.

## 14.3   Aberration Function of Astigmatism

The term added to the wavefront aberration function to account for astigmatism alone is (Born and Wolf 1980, p. 470)

$$W_{\text{astig}}(\rho, \theta) = A_2^{astig} \rho^2 \left( \cos^2 \theta - \frac{1}{2} \right). \tag{14.1}$$

Here $A_2^{\text{astig}}$ is the coefficient giving the amplitude of the astigmatism, $\rho$ is the distance from the axis, and $\theta$ is the angle from the axis of astigmatism. The constant $1/2$ subtracted from the $\cos^2 \theta$ term is the needed focus shift to produce a Zernike best-focus aberration. Below, the astigmatism axis is conveniently placed at $0°$, but it can occur at any angle. $W_{\text{astig}}$ is graphed in Fig. 14-2.

For example, if $A_2^{\text{astig}}$ is $1/4$ wavelength, then $W_{\text{astig}}$ goes from $+1/8$ wavelength to $-1/8$ wavelength. This definition is slightly different from the usual one for primary astigmatism. Coefficient $A_2^{\text{astig}}$ is the total peak-to-valley aberration and is the number that compares most closely with the Rayleigh tolerance.

---

[3]If disk itself was at fault, Russell Porter gave a succinct, though final, solution: "Seek out a good hard, solid hydrant. Hurl the mirror as fiercely as possible at said hydrant. Walk home." (Ingalls 1976).

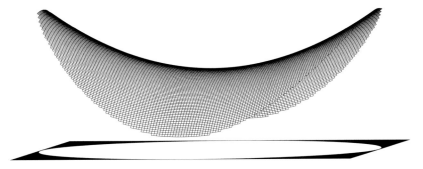

**Fig. 14-2.** *The saddle-shaped aberration function of astigmatism just after it has passed through the aperture.*

Eq. 14.1 has two interesting features. The first is the way the astigmatism scales with distance from the axis. It has the same power, $\rho^2$, as defocusing aberration, so one may interpret astigmatism as a pathological form of defocusing. Also, at a defocusing aberration of $A_2 = \pm(1/2)A_2^{\text{astig}}$, the aberration becomes flat along one line, with the line for the "+" value oriented at right angles to the line for the "−" value. This fact demonstrates that an optimum focal point exists for each axis of the mirror and that these optimum foci are on either side of conventional focus. The actual best focus position is a compromise between these axes.

The division of focal regions is best seen in Fig. 14-3, where the same longitudinal slice through focus is viewed first from the side and then from the top. The views are mirror opposites of one another. The approximate lines of brightest focus are the three-lobed wing structures, only one of which appears in each diagram. The little bright lozenge that appears fore or aft of the wing is just the other wing viewed end-on. If these slices could be perceived in three dimensions, one would see a pair of illuminated regions vaguely resembling boomerangs at right angles to each other, overlapping nose-to-nose.

As the astigmatism gets worse, the bright region looks less like a wing and more like a long bar. The two bars separate and move apart. In the diagram, the bright regions separate and become more like lines.

The best focus diffraction pattern pinches the rings into two bars for small aberrations (see Fig. 14-4). For larger amounts (many wavelengths) of astigmatism, best focus (if any focus could be called "best") resembles a square-woven basket. At 1.5 wavelengths of aberration, an on-axis dip in intensity or a nodal minimum exists. By defocusing to ±0.75 wavelengths, we see the wings of Fig. 14-3 as they would appear face-on in

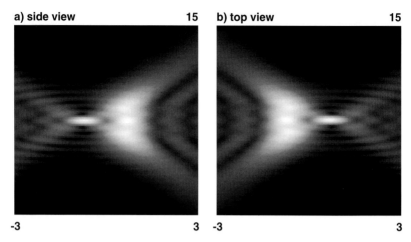

**Fig. 14-3.** *Two slice patterns depicting 1.5 wavelengths of astigmatism. The up-down dimension of each frame is 15 angle units (1.22 = Airy radius). Defocus is between −3 and 3 wavelengths. Best focus is at the center.*

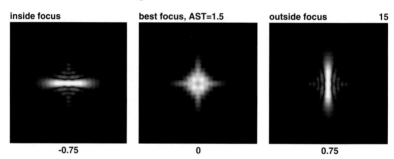

**Fig. 14-4.** *Strong astigmatism (1.5 wavelengths total aberration): inside focus, best focus, outside focus.*

the eyepiece.

Another interesting feature of Eq. 14.1 is that the toroidal shape is approximated by a parabolic radial dependence. Like spherical aberration, there are higher order terms to this expansion as well, but they are customarily ignored.

## 14.4  Filtering of Astigmatism

Since astigmatism is not circularly symmetric, the transfer function depends on how the MTF bar target is oriented. Hence, Fig. 14-5 shows each

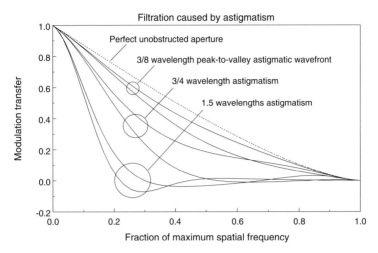

**Fig. 14-5.** *Modulation transfer functions for astigmatism at best focus. Three amounts are shown:* 3/8 *wavelength,* 3/4 *wavelength, 1.5 wavelengths. An aberration of* 3/8 *wavelength is just outside the Maréchal limit (0.8 Strehl ratio). In each pair, the lower curve is for MTF bars oriented along the axes of astigmatism. The higher curve is for bars at* 45°.

aberration amount as two lines, with all intermediate MTF curves approximately between them. Clearly, astigmatism is profoundly harmful at 1.5 wavelengths. The 0.8 Strehl ratio occurs at a little less than 3/8 wavelength peak-to-valley.

Because it affects the aperture on the same scale as defocusing, astigmatism is primarily an intermediate-to-high spatial frequency error. It affects the transfer of contrast only mildly at low spatial frequencies. The transfer function of astigmatism doesn't fall as quickly with increased spatial frequency as the MTF for primary spherical aberration or obstruction. Look at its performance at middle spatial frequency, however. The lowest curve even for the marginally acceptable 3/8-wavelength range degrades the MTF to an average of 70% the perfect value.

The degradation bottoms out on the lower curve of the 3/4-wavelength MTF at about 0.5 of the maximum spatial frequency. For a 200-mm aperture, details with spacing of about 1.2 arcseconds and less would be the most severely damaged. Because it attacks high spatial frequencies, astigmatism reserves its worst behavior for lunar-planetary observation. This aberration may partially account for the poor reputation of thin-mirror Newtonians for high-magnification observation.

## 14.5    Star-Test Patterns

Star-test focus runs appear in the next two figures. The aberration amount in Fig. 14-6 is $3/4$ wavelength. It is shown as it would appear with 20% obstruction. Figure 14-7 shows effects of $3/8$ wavelength of unobstructed astigmatism. The signature of astigmatism is the oppositely directed oval appearance on either side of focus. Recall that these patterns are calculated with an astigmatism axis aligned with the square. In real observing, astigmatism is not required to sit upright. It can be seen at any angle. As defocus is increased, the pattern becomes less elliptical. Defocusing is kept small in these figures because astigmatism most severely affects high spatial frequencies and is most readily detected close to focus.

In fact, the most useful method to detect astigmatism is to focus a dimmer star and then rock the eyepiece back and forth across focus. The astigmatism stretches the image first one way and then the other, and the aberration is immediately apparent. A focused image is supposed to appear as a cross, but you may have trouble seeing the diffraction disk at all in the telescopes for which astigmatism is likely. More common are apertures that just show a hint of the pattern, as in Fig. 14-7.

If ellipticity is seen, turn to Table 5-1 and determine how far you must move the eyepiece to defocus 4 wavelengths. For a focal ratio of f/6, the amount is only 0.025 inches or 0.63 mm. Defocus this far and carefully inspect the image of a dim star. If the pattern is distinctly elliptical, the telescope has too much astigmatism. Ideally, astigmatism is difficult to detect at 2 wavelengths defocus.

However, do not be surprised if most telescopes suffer from a trace amount of this aberration, if only because of the ever-present force of gravity. Few instruments have none.

## 14.6    Identification in Newtonian Reflectors

Just because the instrument suffers from astigmatism doesn't necessarily mean that the problem is ground into the glass. Finding astigmatic error is easy; identifying its source is more difficult.

First of all, determine if your own eye is causing the astigmatism. Simply using your other eye to look through the telescope often does not help (see my prescription above), so that's not the way to tell. You can try rotating your head with respect to the eyepiece and see if the astigmatic axis follows, but changes caused by such slight rotations are difficult to perceive.

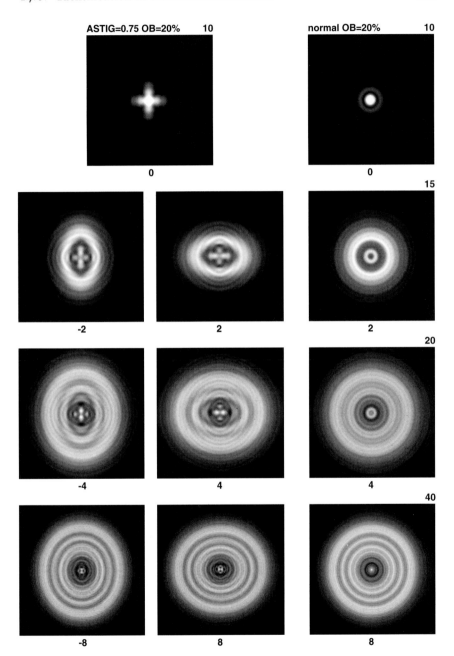

**Fig. 14-6.** *Focus run of* ³/₄*-wavelength astigmatism. The normal aperture is in the right column. Obstruction is 20%. Ellipticity is still clear at 8-wavelengths defocus.*

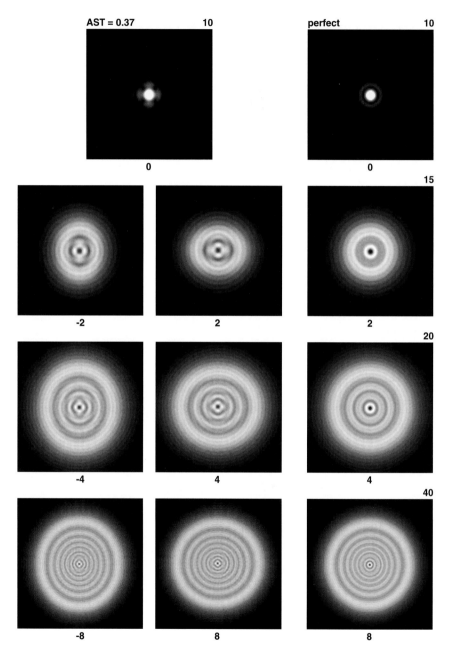

**Fig. 14-7.** *Unobstructed aperture with ³⁄₈-wavelength total astigmatism. The right column depicts a perfect aperture. Stretching is visible at 4 wavelengths defocus, but is hard to see at 8 wavelengths.*

The best way to determine if the problem is in your eye is to increase the magnification. You will make the astigmatism easier to see if it is contained in the telescope, and diminish its strength if it is contained in your eye. Few eyes are so bad that they will show strong astigmatism if the exit pupil of the telescope is set below 1 mm. The bundle of light exiting the telescope decreases in cross-sectional area with higher power, and the illuminated area of misshapen cornea is reduced significantly. As the exit pupil approaches a pinhole, your eyes perform better.

At this point, spin the eyepiece. The astigmatism axis should remain fixed. If it follows the rotation, the eyepiece is astigmatic.

The next thing to investigate is the angle along which astigmatism seems to compress or stretch the image. In refractors or Schmidt-Cassegrains, the angle is obvious. For Newtonians, you can perform the same trick used in the alignment chapter. By defocusing a long way and poking your hand halfway into the optical path, you can determine the direction of stretching. Be suspicious of the main mirror cell if the astigmatism axis is oriented along the horizon or elevation direction (that is, in the gravity axis). Suspect the diagonal cell or the diagonal itself if the astigmatism seems to be aligned with respect to the tube (in the diagonal-tilt axis).

Unfortunately, these two situations sometimes occur together, especially for large altazimuth Newtonians with a level eyepiece. Therefore, we must change the deformation for one mirror or the other. The first thing to try (especially if you're doing a level-telescope artificial source test) is to point the telescope at a star near zenith and see if the astigmatism is still visible. If the main mirror is riding on a single edge point, this step will redistribute the weight of the mirror and hence its compression. Perhaps the pattern will still be bad, but at least it will be different. It might, for example, transform into a three-sided pattern. If the image is unaffected, shake the telescope slightly and try again.

If no change is seen, main mirror warping may yet be the problem. In the case of a mirror glued into its cell, one adhesive pad may be unduly straining the mirror, and the tension might have little to do with the mirror's weight.

The worst possibility is that the mirror actually has an anomalous curvature in the glass. To determine if that problem afflicts your telescope, try a 120° rotation of the mirror. Realign the telescope and test again on a star near zenith. The error should also rotate if it is contained in the mirror.

*The image rotates.* Ask yourself if the mirror performed well in the past, and only recently has performed poorly. If so, the weight of evidence seems to indicate that the mounting has failed or the mirror has become chipped or cracked.

Disassemble the whole mirror cell, inspect the mirror, and carefully reassemble the cell. Make certain that the mirror is adequately held but is nowhere pinched. For mirrors glued to a flat metal plate, make certain that you do not overly tighten this plate into place.

If the telescope is still astigmatic after these corrective measures or if it has always performed badly, then consider the possibility that the aberration is either ground into the glass or the mirror substrate material was poorly annealed.

*The image doesn't rotate.* When a 120° rotation does not affect the axis of astigmatism, then your attention must turn to the diagonal. Again, ask yourself if it performed well up to a recent date, then suddenly turned bad. Or have images always been marginal, and you are just now investigating with the star-test techniques presented here?

If the loss of quality has been abrupt, then the diagonal mounting is probably at fault. Take it out and look it over. Have you recently taken it apart for cleaning? Have you recently readjusted it?

Many Newtonian diagonal holders use cotton wadding behind the diagonal. Often, too much cotton stuffs the holder and causes tension on the mirror. Use only enough cotton behind the diagonal to hold it into place.

Some diagonal holders have a split-cylinder construction. During reassembly, carefully widen the slit enough to give the diagonal mirror room. Make sure that a screw is not protruding from the base to strike the mirror in its back side, and be certain that the tip of the diagonal does not touch the base.

If all these mounting changes do not help, perhaps the diagonal has a spherical curvature polished into its surface. Because this sphere is at a 45° angle, the effect on the image turns to astigmatism.

You can check this poor performance by removing the diagonal holder and rigging it on a separate support (a photographic tripod is ideal). First, perform a straight star test on an inexpensive 50 or 60 mm refractor using an artificial source. Verify that the image is nicely circular. These department-store refractors are often optically good, and one should be kept for this purpose even if it is never used for observing. Then, do the star test again, looking at approximately 45° through the diagonal.[4] If the diagonal has curvature, you will see that the refractor has developed a sudden case of astigmatism.

You can also check the operation of star diagonals or right-angle prisms using this auxiliary telescope technique. You may rely on any mirror satisfying such a check because the test demands equal path length over the whole surface of the right-angle bend. This condition is probably harsher

---

[4]Pointing this combination can be frustrating, but you will eventually succeed.

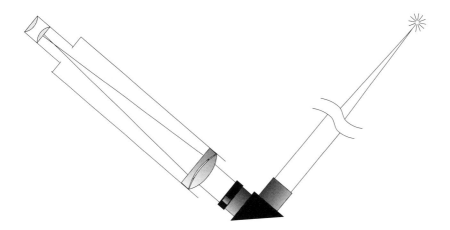

**Fig. 14-8.** *A sensitive test of diagonal mirrors and star diagonals.*

than actual operation demands. In normal use the converging light cone leaves much of the surface dark, but during the test the whole path is equally lit.

## 14.7   Refractors or Schmidt-Cassegrains

Except for instructions concerning the diagonal, the comments and instructions dealing with Newtonian reflectors above are still useful. First, remove the right-angle prism or mirror if you are using one. Many (if not most) such devices have poor optical quality, and the problem may be cured by this simple expedient.

If astigmatism is seen in a refractor, one possible cause is poor alignment. Enough surfaces are present in such telescopes that designers, if they so choose, can strip coma away from off-axis images. Only astigmatism is left. Try to realign using instructions in Chapter 6.

The secondary is not strongly tilted in Cassegrain-style reflectors, as it was for the Newtonians described above. Thus, a spherical error in the secondary will not show itself as astigmatism. Astigmatism must come from misshapen or severely strained optics. One likely source is the secondary holder itself. Some secondary mirrors aren't sufficiently isolated from the adjustment plate at their bases. Distortions in that plate can be transmitted to the mirror and show up as astigmatism (or worse) in the image.

The secondary mirror of a Schmidt-Cassegrain adjusts by the turning of set screws with a hex-head wrench. Because of the mechanical advantage of such a tool, you can unknowingly put huge tensions (500 pounds or more) on the secondary cell. The secondary is the only mirror to adjust in Schmidt-Cassegrains, so if you can't eliminate astigmatism by reducing forces in the secondary holder, you must return the instrument to the maker for servicing.

## 14.8   Remedies

Nothing can be done about astigmatism in the glass except to refigure or replace the optics. Perhaps the maker will agree to refigure them for you, since the optics either left the factory with astigmatism or developed it later because of improperly annealed glass.

Luckily, astigmatism is most often the result of improperly assembled mirror cells and secondary holders. Increasingly, mirrors are held in cells by the technique of gluing them to a plate instead of the more benign method of holding them loosely by clips. The thin plates buckle and transmit their warped shape to the optics through forces applied by the adhesive pad.

We tend to judge everything by familiar uses, and in this case what we know is tightening bolts in, for example, an automobile. Everyday vibrations would quickly shake an automobile to pieces if the screws weren't tight. However, telescopes are delicate. The worst vibrations they are likely to encounter is a gentle, infrequent jiggling during transport. They don't turn at 2000 RPM like an internal combustion engine but shift position perhaps 40 times in a night. They are scientific instruments. Tighten screws firmly but gently.

# Chapter 15

# Accumulated Optical Problems

## 15.1 Breaking the Camel's Back

What you have been shown thus far is how the individual aberrations and transmission variations can affect the image. More important, however, is the way minor problems add up. "The wobbly stack" of Fig. 3-1 shows how many errors accumulate as a collection of filters. Even if each filter is relatively unimportant, the total filtration could render the image fuzzy and indistinct.

The concept of modulation transfer outlined in Chapter 3 presented a single standard around which we could rally. By defining optical quality as the ability of the system to preserve contrast in an image, many disparate optical problems were compared on an equal footing.

As each optical problem was discussed, it was assumed that the single error was the only difficulty. Of course, this is nonsense. Like wolves, optical problems travel in packs. The expression "maximum tolerable" was used in earlier chapters to indicate the worst amount of a single error that can be endured. Unfortunately, any further loss of imaging quality, whether it was derived from that particular error or not, causes the MTF curve to sag even lower.

For an aperture troubled by acceptable amounts of several errors, let's calculate the ability to preserve contrast as each successive optical problem is piled on. This will show, as no individual aberration section could, the deterioration of optical quality as an accumulation of small weights. Eventually, the modulation transfer function collapses under the load. Ironically, we will see that the inadequacy of imaging performance in our example is not caused by any one error on the glass. Instead, poor imaging generally results from the summed effects of several errors, including poor telescope alignment and the unavoidable deterioration of atmospheric conditions.

The optical problems of Table 15-1 are sequentially added to a perfect aperture. The example pupil is not unusual and may even be considered better than normal. The total errors in the first column do not add up straightforwardly, so the root-mean-square deviation is shown as it accumulates in the last column. The amounts of cell pinching and misalignment seem excessive, but these errors do not compare well with the $1/4$-wavelength Rayleigh criterion. Because they are more limited in area than correction mistakes, they have to have a higher total value to result in the same degradation. All of these errors are about equally bad, and none would significantly damage optical quality by itself.

Table 15-1
Aggregate errors in wavelengths

|                  | Total of each | Peak-to-valley error | Cumulative RMS error |
|------------------|:---:|:---:|:---:|
| 25% Obstruction  | –   | –   | –   |
| Undercorrection  | 0.20 | 0.20 | 0.054 |
| Cell pinching    | 0.29 | 0.40 | 0.077 |
| Misalignment     | 0.30 | 0.53 | 0.094 |
| Turbulence       | 0.27 | 0.70 | 0.117 |

Note that this aperture is not affected by a turned edge, zones, astigmatism, or surface roughness. In fact, it would bench test very nicely, with only $1/5$-wavelength undercorrection error. Warping is an important aberration here, so we might think of this aperture as one of the thin-mirror Newtonians common today. The value of misalignment is consistent. These fast instruments are difficult to keep collimated and many of them routinely are used in a state of poor alignment. A misalignment aberration of 0.3 wavelengths, when appearing alone, still reduces the contrast less than $1/4$ wavelength of spherical aberration. The RMS deviation in the last column points out how some of the aberrations cancel others. For example, the misalignment appearing alone would affect the RMS deviation by a little less than 0.07 wavelengths.

The stacked MTF curves appear in Fig. 15-1. Only one curve for each asymmetrical aberration is shown, all for the same orientation of the target bars. Each optical error degrades the image slightly, some seeming to be stronger at some spatial frequencies than others. In fact, the particular mix appearing in this example appears to be complementary. The spherical aberration wipes out contrast at lower spatial frequencies (around 0.2 maximum) while the misalignment acts more strongly at medium spatial frequencies (0.5 maximum). The boxes represent an otherwise perfect aperture that has a defocusing aberration of 0.4 wavelengths. This single aberration follows the lower-limit envelope fairly well.

Surprisingly, this diagram represents the typical operating condition for a large astronomical telescope. The choice of aberration amounts in

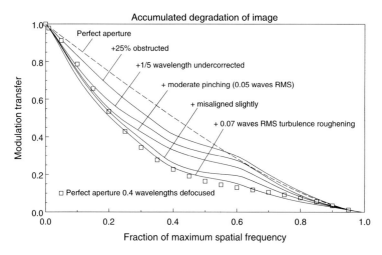

**Fig. 15-1.** *Filtering of a realistic aperture. The curves show the filtration as the aberrations are successively added.*

the example has been especially generous to air turbulence. According to material presented earlier, the chosen amount of turbulence would rate a high 8 to low 9 on Pickering's "seeing" scale.

Star tests are shown in Fig. 15-2 as these optical problems added one-by-one. Each difficulty is not too much worse than the frame above, but the bottom row is considerably poorer than the first row.

Peter Ceravolo has made a well-calibrated set of 6-inch (150-mm) f/8 mirrors having peak-to-valley correction errors of 1, $1/2$, $1/4$, and $1/10$ wavelength. When he set them up side-by-side and had observers rate them, he noticed that people had no trouble telling the 1 and $1/2$-wavelength correction errors from the better pair, but had a hard time distinguishing the $1/4$-wavelength mirror and the nearly perfect one (Ceravolo *et al.* 1992).

Based on the calculated example above, we can speculate on the reasons for this failure to discriminate a nearly perfect mirror from a barely acceptable one. Ceravolo's telescopes were probably less troubled by misalignment, pinched optics, or obstruction than by turbulence. Terence Dickinson rated seeing at 7 out of 10 in one such session. When we consult the turbulence material in Chapter 7, we can estimate that a "seeing" of 7 induces an aberration somewhere near 0.10 wavelengths RMS. Recall that $1/4$ wavelength of correction error is about 0.075 wavelengths RMS. The lack of a visible performance difference between the better mirrors could have occurred because the contrast degradation was dominated by the seeing. Not until the spherical aberration became big enough to compare to the turbulence-generated roughness was the difference easy to perceive.

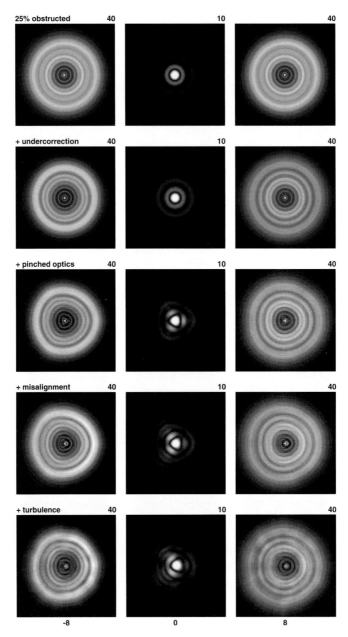

**Fig. 15-2.** *The images of the aberrations in Fig. 15-1 are shown as each additional difficulty is added.*

Figure 15-3 shows focused examples of these correction errors with the turbulence aberration added (assuming no other aberrations contribute). A 20% obstruction is reasonable for a 150-mm f/8 Newtonian.

Place this figure at some distance from your eyes and try to perceive the difference between $1/10$-wavelength and $1/4$-wavelength image frames. Keep in mind that the turbulence patterns continuously change. The modulation transfer curves appear in Fig. 15-4. Turbulence is sufficient to corrupt the excellent optics of the $1/10$-wavelength mirror and it dominates the correction error of the $1/4$-wavelength mirror. Only the lower quality mirrors are so poor that spherical aberration overpowers turbulence.

## 15.2 Fixing the Telescope

In the absence of hard information, people tend to concentrate on one of the telescope's suspected optical difficulties and blame it for everything. Mirror-making enthusiasts, for example, go to extraordinary lengths to figure ultra-precise optical surfaces. They know optical fabrication, so they see all error in terms of improperly shaped surfaces. People who assemble their telescopes from prefabricated parts deal exclusively with telescope design. Some zealously reduce the size of the secondary obstruction. Others attempt to reduce the spider obstruction or at least mask it by bending the vanes. A few become specialists in the arcane tricks of baffling or try to seal the tubes of their reflectors with optical windows. Many suspect their telescope isn't adequately collimated and focus their primary attention on alignment.

The lesson of Fig. 15-1 is that no optical problem is all-important nor can any problem be neglected entirely. Each difficulty deserves an appropriate response, with the important word being *appropriate.* Each suspected error deserves some attention, but no error must be emphasized to the exclusion of others. More to the point, no problem should be emphasized so much that its cure *damages* good operating characteristics of the telescope.

Also, we must think about the type of observing as well as the errors. Specialized observing situations exist where a little spider diffraction, microripple, or a few flecks of dust make a difference. In other cases, they don't matter much at all. Deal only with real threats.

If you mask your mirror to reduce a turned edge, be sure also to carefully baffle the instrument as well. After all, the image doesn't care about the source of the spurious light. One of the most neglected steps is a careful baffling of the final focuser tube, either by a series of shallow rings or by threading. (One clever manufacturer achieves this baffling by fitting a coiled

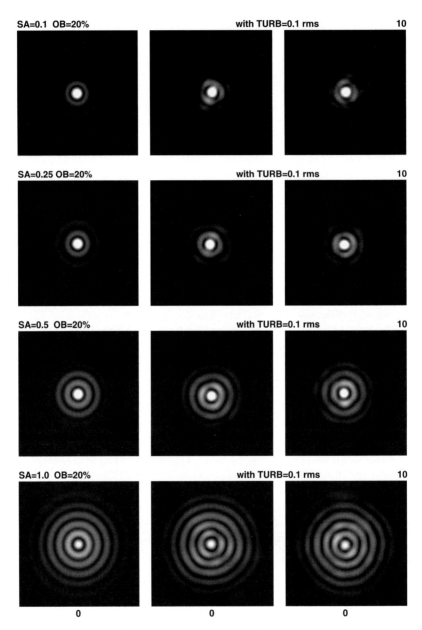

**Fig. 15-3.** *A model of Ceravolo's four mirrors if they are used in the presence of atmospheric turbulence errors amounting to 0.1 wavelength RMS. Obstruction was arbitrarily chosen to be 20%. The aberrations caused by surface errors alone are in the left column. The other columns contain examples of fractally-derived turbulent wavefronts added to the correction errors.*

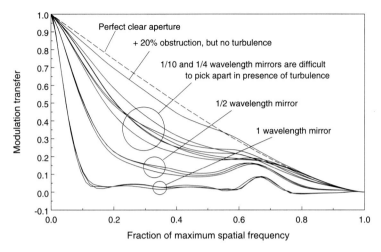

**Fig. 15-4.** *The MTF curves of spherical aberration coupled with turbulence-induced roughness of 0.1 wavelength RMS.*

spring inside the tube.)

Pay attention to everything visible from the inside of the focuser. Can a bright star just out of the field of view contaminate the image with internal reflections? Is your Newtonian tube long enough to prevent distant street lights from adding glow to the image?

If each of the degradations appearing in Fig. 15-1 is cut in half, you can derive an enormously improved image. Certainly, alignment tops the list of offenders, but if the telescope is aligned, consider the job only partly finished. Secondary size is important, but some of the small sizes suggested in the literature (10% to 15% of the aperture) can be too demanding. By reducing the secondary obstruction to 20% or below, you have climbed well up on the curve of diminishing returns. The important thing is that you have addressed each problem in turn. If each MTF degradation is boosted slightly, the net gain can be appreciable.

A solution to a lower MTF that may not be obvious to some readers— and to others may seem like cheating—is to obtain a larger telescope. Recall that the maximum spatial frequency (in units of cycles/angle) is $D/\lambda$. Hence, if Fig. 15-1 depicts the response of a 400 mm (16 inch) reflector, we can see that it delivers contrast about as well as a *perfect* unobstructed aperture one-third to half its size. That means it's behaving about as well as the finest 6-inch unobstructed telescope.[1] In fact, a 16-inch reflector

---

[1]Differences caused by the atmospheric turbulence scale, changes in eyepiece performance at lower focal ratios, and brighter images mean that performance won't be precisely duplicated.

possessing only those aberrations depicted in Fig. 15-1 would be judged an excellent telescope *for its size*. Therefore, if we are troubled by the performance of a small telescope, we can accept similar degradations in a larger aperture and still come out ahead (Zmek 1993). Using such a steamroller method to cure errors may not be subtle, but it's effective. Anything that results in a better image is legitimate.

Many issues having nothing to do with design or optical quality affect the performance of the telescope. For example, ask yourself if you have properly dealt with obvious things like obtaining a smoothly operating focuser before you ever consider obscure items like minimizing obstruction.

Some instruments are so shaky that one touch on the knob sends the image into wild gyrations. Such telescopes cannot be focused using common intuitive hand-eye coordination. Other telescopes are solid enough, but have focusers so tight and hard to turn that an observer is forced to wrestle with them. Some focusers are lubricated with a particularly heavy grease that stiffens in the cold.

No amount of optical perfection can improve a telescope that cannot be focused. No matter how much you have reduced the obstruction, carefully aligned the optics, or baffled the tube, the image of a poorly focused instrument is still substandard. Figure 15-1 demonstrates this principle in a backhanded manner. The little boxes were intended to show how simple defocusing mimics the aggregate curve, but the implied message is that defocusing *alone* is enough to destroy the image.

Telescopes are a mature technology. Severe modifications are probably mistakes. Yet a careful tweak here and there, as long as it's not excessive, can ensure that your telescope operates as well as it possibly can. It will probably even work better than you would have believed before you started.

## 15.3  Errors on the Glass

Errors polished into the glass are permanent. Things like spherical aberration, turned-down edge, or ground-in astigmatism cannot be adjusted out, nor can the user just wait, as in atmospheric or cooling effects. The telescope will never be able to perform adequately.

Glass errors demand sober thought. Say you have inexpensively obtained a fast, thin-mirror altazimuth reflector, a "light bucket" having low to medium magnifications as the primary purpose. You cannot possibly expect crisp Airy disks and clearly defined diffraction rings. Few would want to pay for the optician's time needed to obtain such perfection in a large instrument, and few living under typical skies could often make use of such perfection. An optician cannot give an optical surface a great deal of singular attention without charging an enormous amount of money for the service. The time required to figure mirrors to the diffraction limit increases explosively with aperture or low focal ratio. Large and fast mirrors have both in abundance. This large telescope will not give razor-sharp planetary views, but it should at least perform well on the objects it was meant to observe.

If you have obtained a general-purpose telescope of moderate focal ratio and moderate aperture, however, you have a right to expect reasonable performance whenever seeing allows it. Before complaining to a manufacturer, star test the telescope again under different conditions. Make absolutely certain that the telescope is aligned and that the error doesn't originate with the eyepiece. Determine which optical component produced the error. If at all possible, try to see a star test on a good instrument before you judge a telescope as bad. Either stop down the offending instrument with an off-axis mask or perform the star test on a small or slow telescope likelier to give a nearly perfect result. Don't fully trust spherical aberration estimates gathered under rapidly changing temperature conditions.

If, at the end of all these checks, you are still convinced that the telescope has unacceptable optics, contact the manufacturer. Don't waste time discussing your optical suspicions unless you are very sure. Telescope makers can draw on reserves of confusing jargon unavailable to you. Unless you are very knowledgeable, such terminology will soon have you gasping like a landed fish. In your complaint, merely indicate that the telescope is bad. Clearly and carefully explain that the instrument does not focus to a tight spot and say that you are not pleased with the product.

Becoming angry in your dealings with makers serves no purpose and may be contrary to your interests. Always follow phone calls with written correspondence. Few manufacturers knowingly offer poorly made telescopes. Most will work with you until you receive satisfaction.

## 15.4 Testing Other Telescopes

Once you become familiar with star testing, nothing prevents you from evaluating every instrument you come across. Such practice will help you to develop an eye for different aberrations. Sooner or later, an alert star tester will see every type of optical difficulty discussed in this book and some that are not discussed. You are encouraged in this effort to broaden your experience.

Keep the test results to yourself, though. Considerations of courtesy aside, such opinions could be wrong. You generally know nothing of the history of the instrument. You don't know if it is cool or warm. You have not had a chance to align it first, so you need to mentally subtract a significant alignment error from the pattern. Furthermore, one-shot tests are anecdotal and do not allow for follow-up testing. Remember, you were told to test your own telescope again and again. What makes you think you can evaluate someone else's from a glance in the eyepiece?

If you are asked for your opinion, give it along with a comment about the considerable uncertainties. Don't present the result as a pronouncement from heaven. Carefully explain how you developed the evaluation. If others don't know the star test, teach it to them. After all, I hope you realize by now that star testing is not that mysterious.

## 15.5    When Everything Goes Right

I don't want to leave you with a fatalistic interpretation of the star test. Once taught how to evaluate telescopes, people tend to be overly critical of their instruments. Nothing pleases them. It seems that the illusion of reality has been stripped away—and with it the wonder.

Here is an example of this loss of illusion: Years ago, a universal flaw in old motion pictures was pointed out to me. Just before the end of a reel, markers in the form of punched holes appear twice as an aid to projectionists. If punched in the negative, the holes are inverted to dark spots. Because most films are compressed horizontally, these marks appear as flattened ovals, one at about 10 seconds and another just before the reel changes. The second projector is always started at a point when the frame is dark or abruptly changes brightness.

I had never seen this tiny flaw before and I never fail to see it now. I almost wish I had never been told. This place where the bones of the technology poke through invariably jolts me from the film's comforting illusion and reminds me that I am just watching a movie.

Similarly, once optical phenomena are familiar, you will see them everywhere. Glasses wearers will be unable to walk in drizzle at night without noticing the interference bands in a refracted sparkle of light on the lenses. Looking upward into a clear blue sky, you will occasionally notice floaters in your eye surrounded by tiny diffraction rings. You'll see the ominous signature of chromatic aberration in every rainbow.

I hope that you will not become unnaturally sensitive to the flaws in your telescope. I know individuals who own telescopes having abominable optics, yet they continually conduct productive and frequent observing sessions. I have known other owners who complained about telescopes that were little removed from perfection. They hardly ever spent time under the stars but were always adjusting and modifying their light-starved instruments. It seems that the attitude of the telescope user is the final filter in the wobbly stack and often becomes the worst form of degradation. The star test enables more realistic images. It is not meant to turn a happy observer into a sad one or to spoil the glorious illusion that a telescope produces.

Astronomical telescopes can weave delightful images, and I would serve readers badly if I were to leave them with a sense of disappointment to spoil the magic of starlight. I want to describe something I saw with my own eyes when everything went right—when much of the filtration dropped away and the optics were unimpeded.

It was one of those rare times when the temperature had been virtually constant all day. One evening, my observing group set up a 16-inch f/5.6 Newtonian telescope. It had a 3-inch thickness mirror that often had trouble cooling down, but that whole day it had been near ambient temperature. The evening was wonderfully steady. It was one of those infrequent nights when there seemed to be no upper limit to the useful magnification. We aligned the instrument and turned to Jupiter, then at about 45° elevation.

The shadow of a moon was crossing Jupiter's disk. It stood out crisp and distinct against the planet's brilliance. The gray disk of the moon itself was clearly visible as it transited the planet. So many whorls and crenelations were visible on the surface, that neither hours of sketching nor my limited artistry could have captured them. I wasn't looking through a telescope so much as I was being projected beyond one. I had passed through the eyepiece.

I have had similar experiences rarely but often enough to make it all worthwhile. Once I saw Cassini's division visible on the whole lit circle of Saturn's rings. The crepe ring was easily visible; it looked filmy against the darkness. Another time, at 350 power, I saw globular cluster M15 resolved clear across the core, each star visible as a tiny sparkle of light.

I wonder how many of the billions of human beings who have ever walked the earth have seen these things. I feel fortunate and humbled to have done so myself.

On these special nights, I did not see the telescope as a filter. I believed the image was real. And that is the point of all of this labor. We learn to judge the magnitude of optical errors to help the instrument fulfill its purpose. We do so for those brief moments when we can forget that we are looking through a telescope—when we can feel the quiet majesty of the sky.

# Appendix A

# Other Tests

The 1930s were boom years for amateur telescope making in the United States, primarily through the popularization efforts of individuals such as Russell Porter and Albert Ingalls. Estimates have been made that up to 250,000 telescopes were constructed during the years before World War II. In a way, it was the only option. The Depression was raging, and established optical shops specialized in making expensive refractors or contracting for professional instruments. If you wanted a reasonably priced telescope in those times, you had to make it yourself.

Soon, a few amateurs turned "pro," making instruments of the type other amateurs wanted and could afford to buy. Slowly, as number of such manufacturers increased, the character of amateur astronomy changed. No longer was grinding glass a rite of passage for entrance into the astronomical world. The advent of commercial Schmidt-Cassegrain catadioptric telescopes around 1970 completed the transformation. Telescopes are now consumer items.

In the old days, nearly everyone had some familiarity (if not expertise) with the knife-edge test and a general acquaintance with the concepts behind bench-testing. Few modern amateur astronomers have been directly involved in making their own instruments. Amateurs have heard about bench tests but have only looked through testers at a convention display. Most amateur telescope makers today deal with the mechanical design and construction of their telescopes, not the optics.

Thus, much of the material below will be new to many people. It may seem that I deal curtly and summarily with the various optical shop tests appearing here. This abruptness is not my intention. The tests below can be entertaining and give new insights into optical quality. Each one is so different from the rest that it offers a fresh perspective into the aberrations on the wavefront. Most of my criticisms are not about the tests themselves, but their improper use.

However, I do want to point out that these tests are not recommended if all you want to know is whether or not your telescope is a good one. They are all interesting, and some are phenomenally sensitive, but they aren't the most direct path to knowing if your telescope can work well. The star test is that path.

For the purpose of completeness, these tests are described below, along with brief lists of difficulties for novices or unanticipated expenses. These reasons for not recommending them are varied, but most of them boil down to the following:

1. Most of these tests are useful during optical *fabrication* of individual optical pieces, not *evaluation* of finished telescopes.

2. Many of these tests involve the purchase or manufacture of accessory hardware, some of which can be very expensive.

3. Often, they require complicated data reduction or difficult theoretical knowledge.

4. Most are oriented toward one type of surface and require multiple tests or additional optics if they are to be applied to the whole instrument.

Readers are encouraged to find out more about one or more of the following testing techniques. Each one of them could fill (and perhaps deserves) its own book, just as this one has been devoted to the star test. You can spend a lifetime discovering the details concerning any of them.

## A.1   The Foucault Test

Jean Bernard Léon Foucault was an all-purpose scientist. He is best known for demonstrating the rotation of the earth by precession of the axis of a pendulum and measuring the speed of light. He also took the first daguerrotype photograph of sunspots, thus initiating astrophotography. Foucault made an early metal-on-glass telescope mirror. Finally, he invented a sensitive test of optics at their center of curvature.

Imagine a reflective sphere 6 meters in diameter. Clearly, light radiating from a point at the center of that sphere and diverging outward would strike every portion of the sphere at the same time. It would then reflect and converge to be perfectly imaged as a point on the source that emitted it originally.

Although it would be a beautiful thing to behold, a reflective sphere 6 meters in diameter has few uses. If only one tiny portion of that sphere were silvered, the reflective part would be a weakly concave area. The non-reflective portions could then be trimmed off. Let's say the remainder is a 10-inch (250-mm) f/6 (1500-mm) mirror that we wish to test.

Some method of reading the optical quality must be devised before it can be said that a true test is being done. The first problem is that a source of light at the center of the sphere, an illuminated pinhole for example, is imaged back on top of itself. The imaged light is unavailable to the optician. Foucault solved this problem by offsetting the source slightly. The image point in this case is found across the center of curvature at a distance about equal to the offset. As long as the distance between the pinhole and image is kept small, the test only is slightly affected by astigmatism.

The second problem is coming up with a method of probing the image point for incorrect focusing. One could inspect it with an eyepiece and thus have a variant of the star test, but this method was already known at the time of Foucault. The pinhole inspection procedure does not readily yield numbers useful to plan the next polishing step. Inspection with an eyepiece also demands an extremely small source; in the 250-mm mirror above, the pinhole should be less than $16\mu$m (0.0006 inches) across. This restriction was especially severe in Foucault's time because portable light sources were based on flame and were hence quite weak, diffuse, and difficult to focus on a pinhole.

Foucault's clever solution was to introduce an occluding edge into the beam near the imaging point. This test goes by the popular name "Foucault's knife-edge test" although the method does not depend on the sharpness of the blade. The knife is slowly introduced near focus. In the simplest configuration, the tester's eye is placed close to the knife and peers past it at the mirror. If the knife is between the mirror and the image point, the dark shadow of the knife appears to darken from the same side of the mirror as the knife. Outside focus, the darkness appears to cross the mirror from the reverse side.

One need not use a pinhole source at all. A short slit can serve equally well as long as the knife is parallel to its image. This way, the illumination can be increased hundreds of times.

The knife is moved toward and away from the mirror until focus is located. If the focused point is struck precisely, the shadow on the mirror does not exhibit the direction of knife motion. A knife setting for which non-directional behavior is found proves the mirror must be part of a sphere. It dims evenly before darkening entirely. The Foucault test of a spherical mirror is a true null test—the reflection blanks out. See Fig. A-1.

If any high or low places on the mirror exist, no mirror-knife separation can be found at which the mirror darkens uniformly. The test superficially resembles the shadows cast from a lamp shining from the side of the mirror

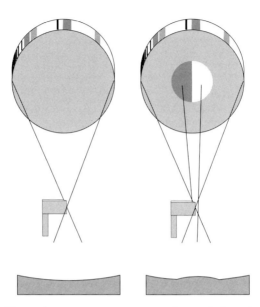

**Fig. A-1.** *Two Foucault test setups, one is perfect and the other shows a slight hill in the mirror's profile (the aberration is exaggerated).*

opposite the knife. The hill acts as a protrusion on the apparently flat surface. One side is very bright, and the other side is very dark. The elevated region is shown perched on a neutral-gray plane. Of course, this side-lighting concept should be viewed as a convenient delusion. The "hills" cast no shadows, and the entire appearance of the display can be changed merely by moving the knife along the axis of the mirror. In the figure, you can pull the knife back until the center bump is uniformly gray and appears to be sitting in a huge cupped depression.

Foucault's genius was that he did not rest once he found this sensitive test for spherical mirrors. He modified his new test to figure paraboloids used as the primary optical element of Newtonian telescopes. The problem with testing paraboloids at their "center of curvature" is that a parabola is not a circle and a single center of curvature is not defined on its surface. You can squint your eyes and convince yourself that the shallow dish is a sphere to first order, but a perfect paraboloid shouldn't null.

The behavior of light rays near the center of curvature of a paraboloid can be straightforwardly calculated, however. They converge along the horn-shaped caustic defined by an overcorrected surface. The caustic is a region in which ray optics strictly breaks down, but for the purpose of the purely geometric Foucault test, one pretends that it does not.

Jean Texereau drew a very informative diagram of this behavior, which is reprinted in Fig. A-2 (Texereau 1984). The caustic appears best in the ray diagram at the bottom left, where part of it is blocked by the knife. The appearance of the Foucault test at various knife positions is depicted on the right side by stippled drawings. The length of this ray-crossing region (which appears as a black bar at the tip of the knife) is related to the correction of the mirror. For a sphere at its center of curvature the length, of course, is zero. For a paraboloid it is

$$LA = \frac{D^2}{4R} \tag{A.1}$$

where $R$ is the approximate radius of curvature of the mirror and $D$ is its diameter. $LA$ means *longitudinal aberration,* the stretch of the black bar in the diagram. For a hyperboloid, $LA$ is a larger number, and for a prolate spheroid it is smaller.

Foucault reasoned that if an optical worker measured the shift between situations A and C and kept changing the shape of the mirror until that shift was at or a little less than $D^2/4R$, then the paraboloid was being closely approximated. Previously, mirror making had been the province of high art and not a small amount of guesswork. Foucault had reduced the procedure of mirror testing to finding the centers of curvature of the center zone (A) and the edge zone (C) and subtracting them. (See Suiter 1988.)

Examples of these situations photographed on a real mirror appear in Fig. A-3. You can also see a tiny central button zone. Because of its location in the shadow of the diagonal, it would not harm the images.

The contours seemingly shown by the imaginary side lamp have apparent amplitudes of something like 3 to 6 mm for a 150-mm f/8 paraboloid. Since this paraboloid departs from a sphere by about $1/8$ wavelength, we can calculate a synthetic magnification of errors that amounts to about 4 mm/0.00007 mm or 60,000.

This development, coupled with the technology for depositing metal films on glass, set the stage for the huge reflectors of the 20th century. Foucault is the godfather of the massive instruments we use today.

Foucault's knife-edge test is sensitive and proven, but it is not recommended as a final evaluation, for several reasons:

1. The test requires some practice. One must be skilled in setting up, aligning, and interpreting the Foucault test.

2. It does not allow testing of the convex elements of compound optical systems without expensive additional hardware. Except for an auto-collimation test against a huge optical flat, one must disassemble the telescope and test individual pieces, some of which may not be easy to remove.

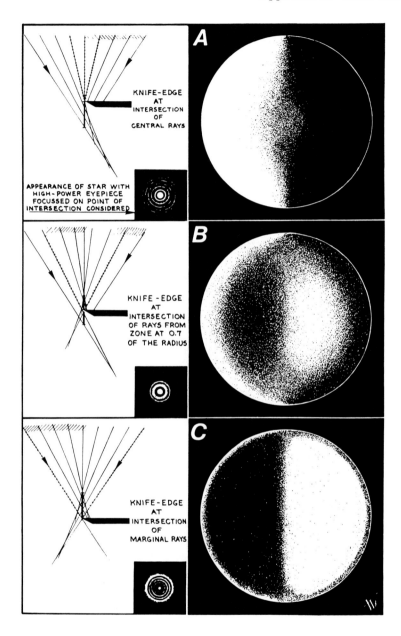

**Fig. A-2.** *A drawing of three knife locations and the resulting appearance of a parabolic mirror in the Foucault test. From* How to Make a Telescope *by Jean Texereau, Copyright ©1984 by Willmann-Bell, Inc.*

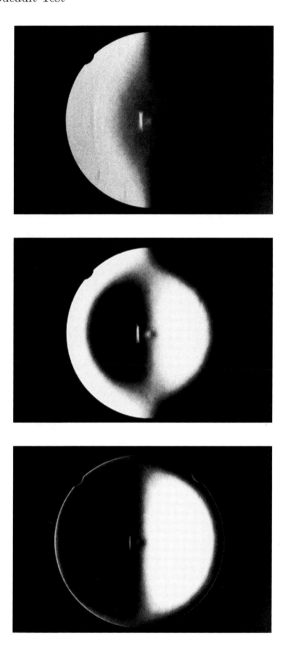

**Fig. A-3.** *Photographs of the three cases of Fig. A-2 on a paraboloidal mirror. Bright streaks are spurious reflections of the slit. (Photographs by William Herbert of Columbus, Ohio.)*

3. In its more sophisticated forms, it requires a tiresome and easily bungled mathematical reduction procedure. Computers can help with this calculation, but such computations can be mishandled at the input stage.

4. It requires that an elaborate knife edge tester be constructed. Simpler testers could be made when people only tested long-focus Newtonian mirrors, but fast instruments give little room for error. Very good motion platforms—called kinematic stages—and compact source/knife assemblies must be built or purchased.

Variants of the Foucault test include the caustic test and the wire test. All are more or less bothered by these same difficulties.

One other use of the knife edge test would be applicable to all forms of optics if it were more convenient. Using a knife edge at the focus of a star recovers the conditions that led to the gray, flat appearance of a sphere at the center of curvature. This method is easiest for owners of an excellent clock drive and a heavy, unshakable mounting, because they can follow the brightest stars. Some sort of method for gradually introducing the knife into the focused beam is also necessary because this variant of the Foucault test is extremely touchy.

Since few telescopes are likely to perfectly null, those wanting to use a knife-edge at focus should provide their testing setup with a method to measure the length of focus shift from a situation resembling A in Fig A-2 to situation C. In a typical test, this focus shift should be below 100 $\mu$m (0.004 inch). Using the artificial star described in Chapter 5 eases the mounting, clock drive, and illumination problems, but some sort of measurement screw must still be placed on the focuser.

## A.2   The Hartmann Test

This test, developed by J. Hartmann around the year 1900, is used most often to check the surface of very large observatory instruments. A screen is centered over the objective lens or mirror. Carefully sized and placed holes are cut into this screen. Then the telescope is pointed at a distant star or artificial source at the center of curvature.

Two photographic plates are then exposed, one inside of focus and the other outside. After they are developed, they are carefully measured. If the test is successful, the images of the holes are identifiable, resolved, and not so large that their positions are uncertain. Two pictures aren't really necessary when the positions of the holes over the mirror are very accurately known, but caution dictates a second photograph.

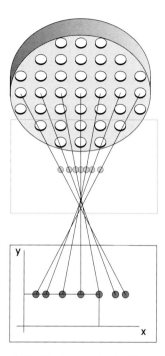

**Fig. A-4.** *Configuration of the Hartmann test. The rectangles represent photo-graphic plates with the intersection of dot-pair lines hovering between them. The measurement coordinates are indicated on one plate.*

Finally, the corresponding dots in the two pictures are connected mathematically. Once the intersections of the dot pairs are known, they are entered into expressions that convert longitudinal aberrations to wavefront error, provided that the surface is deformed smoothly. See Fig. A-4 for a diagram depicting the manner in which the Hartmann test is used to measure aberration. A two-hole version of the Hartmann arrangement is occasionally used today as a focusing aid (Suiter 1987).

This method is not recommended for first-time testers for the following reasons:

1. These photographs are best taken on glass plates. The region of interest near focus is small and photographic film is flexible. Both plates and equipment to handle them are expensive.

2. The two plates should be held precisely perpendicular to the optical axis and each other during exposure.

3. The measurements of dot positions are typically made with a plate measuring engine, which looks like a microscope or a microfiche reader

on a milling-machine bed. Although they are common enough in professional observatories, they are not available to the rest of us.

4. The mathematical reductions are of about the same complexity as advanced versions of the Foucault test, but because of the number of connected dots, many more calculations must be done. This data analysis may be a very tiresome chore. (See Danjon and Couder 1935 for an early reduction procedure that led to the procedure appearing in Texereau 1984.)

## A.3   Resolution of Double Stars

While determining the resolving power of a telescope is not a complete optical test, many people treat it as such. Thus, it deserves mention here. This method of evaluating telescope images became popular during the 19th century, when double stars were the subject of very active research. Observers who were primarily interested in the clean separation of two stars began to judge the performance of their telescopes entirely by this characteristic.

Certainly, a telescope that fails to show double stars close to the expected resolution is displaying one of the symptoms of poor optics, but other types of equally bothersome optical difficulties do not betray themselves this way. Spherical aberration of $1/4$ wavelength insignificantly damages the telescope's ability to split stars. (See the encircled energy plot in the chapter on spherical aberration.) However, on planetary detail requiring only moderate resolution, optics with correction errors present distinctly fuzzy images.

Figure A-5a displays the various criteria of resolution. The first is called the Rayleigh criterion, which is not to be confused with the $1/4$-wavelength Rayleigh limit of wavefront error. The Rayleigh resolution criterion is met when the separation of the two objects is precisely at the radius of the theoretical Airy disk. In other words, the second star is placed on the valley between the first star's central disk and the first diffraction ring.

The degree to which the Rayleigh criterion divides the stars varies with details of the diffracting aperture. Different obstructions and aberrations result in differing depths of the "saddle" between the stars. For a perfect circular aperture with no obstruction and no aberrations, the dip between the stars is to about 70% of the brightest intensity.

The second criterion was stated by double star observer W.R. Dawes in 1867 (Sidgwick 1955). It applies only to unobstructed apertures dividing equal stars. In the Dawes criterion, the separation is a little less than 85% of the separation defined in the Rayleigh criterion. Fig. A-5a illustrates it

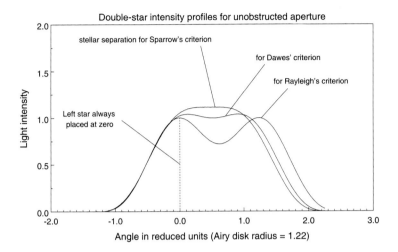

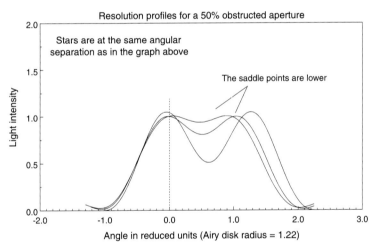

**Fig. A-5.** *Resolution of equal brightness stars in two instruments: Top a) a perfect circular aperture; Bottom b) the same stars as seen in the same instrument with a 50% central obstruction. The huge secondary mirror actually improves resolution.*

as the intensity curve with the small intensity drop between the stars. This drop is only about $1/30$ magnitude less than the maximum intensity. When doubles are this tight, their lack of roundness contributes as much or more to distinguishing duality than the intensity drop between them.

The third and narrowest separation is called Sparrow's criterion, which is defined as that separation that results in a flat isthmus between the stars.

The Sparrow criterion is adjusted for obstructed and aberrated apertures until it always gives that flat region between the stars. Thus, it is always uniquely defined and always delivers the same behavior, but its exact separation varies with details of the aperture.

Sparrow's criterion for unobstructed apertures has stars separated by about 92% of Dawes' criterion or about 77% of Rayleigh's separation. In the perfect, unobstructed aperture's MTF chart of Fig. 3-6, the Sparrow criterion is found at a spatial frequency off the graph at $1.06S_{max}$. This placement doesn't mean the resolution is illusory. Some double-star observers have approached or even exceeded this value. Stars are point objects, while the MTF target consists of bars. Points can be resolved by using the shape of the image as the only discriminator.

Figure A-5b depicts one of the most disturbing aspects of using double stars as test objects. The summed diffraction patterns of two stars seen in a 50% obstructed aperture is calculated with the same stellar separations as were used in the unobstructed aperture of Fig. A-5a. For all three curves, equal separations deliver stronger dips in intensity between the stars. To recover the behaviors of Fig. A-5a, the stars must be pushed closer together. In short, the 50% obstructed aperture resolves better.

Double-star resolution doesn't tell us much about other types of observing performance,[1] particularly in that case where the 50% blocked aperture will fail badly. Planetary images are greatly degraded by such severe obstruction. Blocking the aperture kicks a large fraction of the light outside the central spot into distant portions of the point image. Resolution of a nearby star is little affected, because the star is close to the center of the image and the light diffracted by the obstruction is largely beyond it.

If the desired object were a small, low-contrast crater on the Moon, the whole image is the sum of all light scattered from light patches around the crater as well as the image of the crater. Much of this spurious light is joined together to fog the interesting image. The scattering from any single diffuse spot is not enough to seriously damage the image by itself, but the combined effect of all of them worsens contrast considerably.

Blocking the aperture by a 50% central obstruction helps some double stars resolve, but the same obstruction leads to severe image degradation of planetary detail. You can easily verify this result yourself. Look at the Moon or a planet some night with and without a large paper obstruction in front of the aperture. Unless the telescope's obstruction is high already, the artificially blocked aperture will appear much worse.

Using the resolution of double stars as the sole criterion of optical quality, the astronomer is demanding that the judgement favor high spatial

---

[1]Dawes himself was well aware of this difficulty, even though his name is attached firmly to the misuse of this test as an indicator of optical quality.

frequencies. In the case of obstructed apertures, the spatial frequency response has been robbed of some of its intermediate frequency strength to achieve better contrast at higher frequencies.

Double stars as test objects present other difficulties. Variability is associated with the sky and with the stars themselves. Ideally, one should use equal-brightness white stars separated at the diffraction limit and demand that they be high in the sky. Few stars conveniently arrange themselves this way. Usually, the test must be done with unequal brightness stars separated by a distance close to your instrument's Dawes or Rayleigh criterion but not precisely at it. One of the stars may be tinged with blue or red, and they may be at a low altitude, which produces unfortunate atmospheric dispersion into rainbow-like spectra. "Seeing" will constrict the number of nights on which double star tests can be attempted, particularly for large instruments.

Artificial double stars can be used to test resolution, but they cannot cure the basic inadequacies of the evaluation technique. Because very high magnification must be used, ground turbulence must be low. By bringing the source close to the telescope, one writer avoided the problem of turbulence. In this case, the source was only about 10 meters away (Maurer 1991). However, such a close distance makes such a test an unreliable check for aberrations (see Chapter 5).

Atmospheric problems also trouble the star test, but because the stars are considered singly, you have more freedom to choose one at high altitude. Since the star test involves inspecting the much larger defocused stellar disk, it does not always require that seeing be perfect.

For the above reasons, the double star resolution test is not recommended as an all-purpose test. In brief summation:

1. Resolution tests are interesting to those who are concerned with double stars. Resolution is of little use as a general indicator of telescope performance because it favors high spatial frequencies.

2. Suitable target stars are difficult to find. Artificial sources have their own pitfalls.

3. Seeing must be superb before the double-star resolution test yields interesting results.

## A.4  Geometric Ronchi Test

A test is attractive if it doesn't require a great deal of data reduction or interpretation. One such test involves placing a coarse periodic grating of dark and transparent bars near stellar focus of the instrument. An example frequency of such a grating is 100 lines/inch (4 lines/mm), with a corresponding period of 0.01 inch (0.25 mm). This method was investigated by Vasco Ronchi around 1923 and thus carries the name the *Ronchi test*.

Interpretation, at least when we assume that light is comprised of rays, is simple. Supposedly, light has originated from a point source very far away (like a star). If the star is correctly imaged, it should be focused to a single point. Starlight passes through a grid of straight, opaque bars, which remove the light rays that strike them. The perceived pattern on the mirror is just the shadows of those vertical bars.

If the optics have aberrations associated with them, the light from different zonal radii is not diverted toward a single focus. In the case of spherical aberration, various axis crossing points are distributed near the region of the caustic. Because the grating lies at various distances from these points, the spacings of the grating projected on the aperture seem to vary from radius to radius. In the case of undercorrection, this effect is portrayed in Fig. A-6.

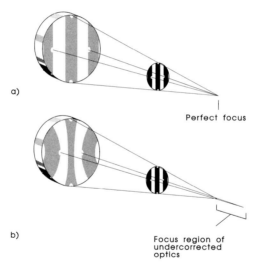

**Fig. A-6.** *A Ronchi ruling is placed near the focus of a star and examined without an eyepiece. a) If the rays are all directed to a common focus, the optics are perfect. b) If the lines distort, they indicate aberrations. The Ronchi grating need not be confined to the tiny circle. Any stripes outside the illuminated portion of the light cone do not contribute.*

If the grating is 100 lines/inch and the aperture has a focal ratio of f/8, the 2.5 periods (or "lines") shown in the illuminated part of the grating would be about 0.2 inches inside focus and only 0.025 inches in diameter.

It seems as if the Ronchi test is the final answer, a clear and unambiguous null test. Unfortunately, it doesn't always work that way.

A 10-inch f/6 mirror came to my attention in 1980. In spite of the fact that it gave soft images, it passed the Ronchi test using a grating of 100 lines/inch. It failed the star test in a stunning manner, however. When removed from the tube and bench tested with a more elaborate variation of the Foucault test, it showed a $1/2$-wavelength undercorrection.

Still, it had passed the Ronchi test at focus. Something was wrong, either with one of the tests or the mirror. Consider the aberrated Ronchi drawing of Fig. A-6 again. The distortion of the pattern seen against the mirror is caused by the change in focus distance as measured from the grating. As depicted, the focus difference (or the longitudinal aberration) is about a third of the distance from the grating to the average point of focus, causing severely distorted Ronchi lines projected on the mirror. The density of lines at the center of the aperture is much higher than at the edge. One might call this curvature a "33% distortion." If the region of focus is a much smaller fraction of the distance to the grating, distortions can be appreciably lower. For optics of conventional focal ratios and diameters, this low-distortion condition is true much of the time.

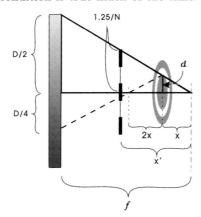

**Fig. A-7.** *A similar-triangles setup used to estimate the Ronchi curvatures. The particular crossing points chosen here would be characteristic of overcorrection, but the derivation in the text would not be affected if they were reversed.*

One can easily calculate the length of the focus region for optics diverting light to the edge of the diffraction disk. If we draw the similar triangles of Fig. A-7, the outside triangle has edges of height $D/2$ (half the aperture) and base $f$. The triangle outside of focus has height $d$ and base $x$, with $d$ being the radius of the diffraction disk. The radius of the Airy disk is (1.22)(wavelength)(focal ratio), or $1.22\lambda F$. We can use similar triangles to show that $x = 2.44\lambda F^2$. Because we must regard a finite-sized region to estimate the number of lines showing, the density of lines at the edge is compared with the density of lines at a point roughly halfway out the radius of the mirror. The dashed line, because it has only half the slope, can cross over at about twice the distance $x$ from the point of focus.[2]

If light from the edge is deflected to cross the axis at more than $3x$ from light at the 50%-radius zone, it begins to miss the diffraction disk entirely and signs of severe optical degradation become visible.

The vertical dashed line depicts a grating located between the aperture and the region of focus. It has the same 2.5 lines as Fig. A-6, measured for the outside zone. Above the center, 1.25 lines are showing (a "line" is a complete on-off cycle, or a period). The height of this little triangle is therefore $1.25/N$, where $N$ is the number of lines per inch (or mm) of the grating. The base length of this triangle is left unknown and is called $x'$. The big triangle is the same as before. Using similar triangles again, one can show that $x' = 2.5F/N$.

To calculate the distortion, we estimate the tolerable focus shift divided by the distance to the grating, or

$$\text{Distortion} = \frac{3x}{x'} = 3\frac{2.44\lambda F^2}{2.5(F/N)} = \frac{3(2.44)\lambda FN}{2.5}. \tag{A.2}$$

Merely by identifying 2.5 as the number of lines of the grating that are intercepted (called $n$),

$$\text{Distortion} \cong \frac{7.5\lambda FN}{n}. \tag{A.3}$$

For f/6 optics with a 100 line/inch grating, taking as the wavelength the yellow-green color that the human eye likes best, the maximum tolerable distortion with 2.5 lines showing is about 0.04.

Anyone who has ever used one of these gratings knows that the sharpness of Fig. A-6 present an unrealistic view of what is happening. The actual shadows are fuzzy and indistinct. A 4% bowing of the lines in the presence of this fuzziness is nearly impossible to see. Figure A-8 depicts the actual pattern that results from a $1/4$ wavelength of undercorrection, still without the blurring at the edges of the lines.[3]

---

[2] The Airy disk in this diagram is greatly exaggerated in size. Hence, the crossing point of the dotted line appears nowhere near $2x$ from focus. However, in real situations with very small Airy disks, an inner crossing distance twice that of the edge is an excellent approximation.

[3] This pattern does not use the approximation in Eq. A.3 but is more accurately calculated using an adaptation of the method of Prugna (1991) to include correction error.

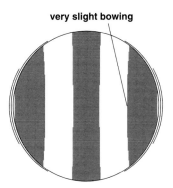

**very slight bowing**

**Fig. A-8.** *The Ronchi distortion expected of a ¼-wavelength undercorrected f/6 telescope when a 100 line/inch grating is placed near focus and the telescope is directed toward a star. The thin exterior lines are the borders of the first- and second-order interference.*

An arbitrary cutoff can be imposed. This limit is somewhat artificial, but let's set it conservatively at 8%. If we can't set up a test with at least an 8% maximum bowing of the lines, we are not testing the optics with anything close to the kind of precision necessary. One suspects the actual cutoff should be higher, but for the purpose of argument, let's give the geometric Ronchi test the benefit of doubt.

Examination of Eq. A.3 reveals how the Ronchi test could recover enough sensitivity to barely achieve the limit. If the grating were moved closer to focus, reducing the number of lines seen on the aperture to 1.25, this mirror will have lines that bow 8%. If the number of lines is increased to 200/inch, the pattern will also distort 8%.

These solutions contain inherent problems. Although the geometric Ronchi test is derived with a ray approximation in mind, the real world doesn't care about the designer's thinking. It follows wave physics. Interference between the gaps on the grating result in superimposed offset artifacts called *diffraction-order images.* These side images make the edges of the bars less certain, obscure behavior at the true edge, and generally muddle the view. They grow less important as fewer and fewer lines are strongly illuminated, but they can't be eliminated entirely because the outer portions of the image remain dimly lit.

White-light diffraction expresses itself as a blur at the edge of the lines, so if a line is expanded by moving the grating closer (the first solution), the blur is increased as well. Increasing the frequency of the lines (the second solution) doubles the angles at which the higher-order images appear, making the edges even more difficult to see. The brute force methods of either moving the grating to show fewer lines or using a finer grating are limited in their ability to improve sensitivity.

Again consulting Eq. A.3, distortion increases when testing optics of high focal ratio. At f/12, we have reached the 8% arbitrary limit with no other changes. The test has not suddenly become more sensitive, but the tolerances are wider with slow optics. For high focal ratios, the Ronchi test can indeed discriminate the difference between bad and good systems.

An additional method doubles sensitivity. A Ronchi null test is conducted not on a distant star but a point source at the focus. Light exits the instrument in the reverse direction, bounces against a full-aperture optical flat, and travels back through the instrument in the reverse direction. It is intercepted near focus by a Ronchi grating. This *autocollimation mode* doubles the aberration because the optics have been traversed twice. A well-known Schmidt-Cassegrain manufacturer tests telescopes in this fashion. Because the aberrations are doubled, and the f/10 focal ratio is high to begin with, we can see that this manufacturer's test is an adequately sensitive one. The problem for ordinary individuals is the same as it is for all autocollimation tests—huge optical flats are expensive.

What about a Ronchi test at the center of curvature? Several amateur authors have suggested that the geometric Ronchi test can be successful in a bench test of paraboloids at the center of curvature (Mobsby 1974; Terebizh 1990; Prugna 1991 and Schultz 1980). The problem with most of these tests is that they never calculate the sensitivity of their methods. The way of properly showing sensitivity is to compute the shape of a pattern for both perfect optics and optics which display a $1/4$ wavelength of correction error. One must demonstrate that the two patterns are sufficiently different that a distinction can be made.

In Fig. A-9, an example pattern of a perfect 16-inch f/4.5 mirror is calculated together with the pattern of the same mirror if it were a full $1/2$ wavelength undercorrected. Both are calculated as viewed in a 150 line/inch grating. The Ronchi screen is set at slightly different locations that present similar appearances near the mirror's center. One pattern is for a mirror better than any optical surface has ever been made. The other pattern is for a mirror of little or marginal usefulness in an astronomical instrument. Figure A-10 is a photograph of precisely this situation. The photograph shows, as no theoretical argument ever could, the difficulties of the geometric Ronchi test at the center of curvature.

The problem with the Ronchi test conducted at the center of curvature is that it is swamped by the overcorrection of aspherical mirrors operated far from their natural focus at infinity. The Ronchi screen is so obviously responding to something that one forgets that the difference between the response to a bad mirror and a good mirror may be slight. The under-

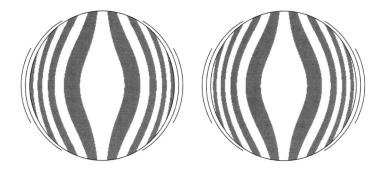

**a) 1/2 wavelength undercorrected**          **b) perfect**

**Fig. A-9.** *Theoretical patterns are generated for a Ronchi ruling of 150 lines/inch placed slightly inside the center focus of a 16-inch f/4.5 mirror: a) if the mirror is 1/2 wavelength undercorrected; b) if the mirror is perfect. Distances: a) −0.06 inches and b) −0.05 inches.*

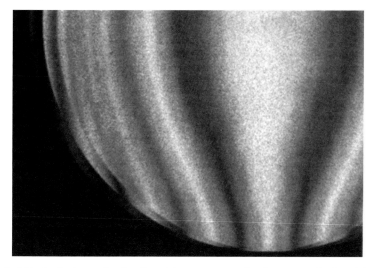

**Fig. A-10.** *A photograph of a Ronchi test on a real mirror as calculated in Fig. A-9. Is the mirror perfect or terrible? The mirror was Foucault-tested and found to be 1/8 wavelength undercorrected. The Foucault patterns appear in Fig. A-3. (Photograph by William Herbert.)*

corrected prolate spheroid, the perfect paraboloid, and the overcorrected hyperboloid *all* look badly overcorrected at the center of curvature. All but the highest focal ratios show this condition.

For the 16-inch f/4.5 mirror at the center of curvature, the length of the blurry focus region is about 0.444 inches (11.3 mm). That's what the

Ronchi screen is acting on. However, the length of that region is 0.428 inches if the mirror is undercorrected right at the $^1/_4$-wavelength Rayleigh limit or 0.460 inches if it is overcorrected. This difference of 0.016 inches is slight, only a tiny adjustment of those grossly distorted Ronchi patterns.

Sensitivity could be recovered by using a kinematic measurement platform and matching a *number* of theoretical patterns, all the time being careful to record the longitudinal motion of the Ronchi screen (as in Prugna 1991). Unfortunately, the test is almost never undertaken in this manner, probably because it so closely resembles the Foucault test that the user was trying to avoid in the first place.

Professional optical workers have dealt with the sensitivity of the Ronchi test. Cornejo and Malacara (1970) write:

> The Ronchi test is a very powerful test for spherical as well as aspherical mirrors. However, this test is of an accuracy limited by diffraction to a value such that the resulting surface can be used to form images, *but not for wavefronts to be analyzed interferometrically.* [Italics added.]

In other words, the test can generate surfaces accurate enough for use in cameras or other coarse imaging devices but not surfaces that are so precise that they can be tested with an interferometer. Such accuracy is demanded in astronomical telescopes.

Ronchi himself commented on the accuracy of the geometric test that carries his name (Ronchi 1964). In an excellent review article he says,

> As long as the grating employed had a very low frequency, like the ones that we had used at first and that had also been used by other authors treating the same argument, the geometric reasoning corresponded quite well with the results of the experiments and measurements; *but at the same time the method did not lead to results as fine as desired.* It was evident that in order to increase this sensitivity it would be necessary to use gratings of the highest frequency possible, but then the results decidedly deviated from those predicted from geometrical reasoning. [Italics added.]

Here Ronchi describes his justification for abandoning the geometric test in the 1920s. He goes on to describe the techniques to use the overlap between diffraction orders as an interferometric test. The evaluation is made by the complicated interpretation of two equally-aberrated wavefronts somewhat displaced from one another. In this true wave-optics Ronchi test, the separation of the shadows is not determined by geometry but by the interference of light.

The geometrical Ronchi test has some uses, however. It is an excellent way of seeing sharp zones. It can detect seriously defective optics—curvature at stellar focus is often enough to reject an instrument out of hand. It is a good way of testing camera optics or any optics used far from the diffraction limit. But this test has a variable sensitivity that has been unappreciated or ignored by many advocates.

Readers may notice that if a checkerboard grid of squares replaced the Ronchi ruling, the Ronchi test would have a superficial resemblance to the Hartmann test. The corners of the squares would be equivalent to the hole positions. Yet no complaint was made about the Hartmann test's sensitivity. The critical difference is that the Hartmann screen is rigidly fixed on the aperture instead of floating somewhere near the focus. Plates are exposed and data are taken with high-precision measuring devices. Systematic errors are reduced by making plate measurements of dot positions from multiple directions. These raw measurements are followed by a sophisticated mathematical reduction procedure.

Many amateurs, particularly those who promote the use of the geometric Ronchi test at the center of curvature for aspherical optics, present the test as the simple comparison of patterns. They have stripped the mathematics away, and with it goes the error-detection ability of the test. The siren song of the geometric Ronchi test is that people can just look at a pattern and avoid the difficulty of measurement. Unfortunately, the measurements contain the sensitivity.

In summation, the geometric Ronchi test is not recommended for telescope evaluators for the following reasons:

1. The sensitivity of the test is variable and depends on the focal ratio of the tested optical system and the frequency of the grating used. Also, results vary depending on whether the test is done at the focus or the center of curvature. Certain combinations are very sensitive; other combinations are fatally insensitive.

2. When conducted at the center of curvature, the geometric Ronchi test is commonly used as a simple comparison of patterns, but the bending of such patterns can differ little from the patterns with unacceptable correction errors.

3. It requires a sufficient acquaintance with the theory of the test so that a "worst case" unacceptable pattern can be calculated. Before declaring tested optics to have passed, one must have an appreciation of what failure looks like. A good place to start is to calculate the anticipated test pattern with and without $1/4$ wavelength of low-order spherical aberration on the wavefront.

## A.5　Interferometry

Many types of interferometers are used to test telescopes. Little purpose is served in dwelling on each of them here. Most of them require expensive auxiliary equipment, so the likelihood is small that one of these methods will be used by an individual who wants merely to test a single telescope. An example interferometer will serve to demonstrate the technique, a method that appears at first glance to require less equipment than most of the others.

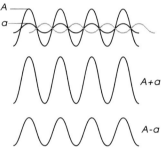

**Fig. A-11.** *The principle of interference.*

### A.5.1　How Do Interferometers Work?

Light is a wave, and two waves with the same frequency add together by summing amplitudes $A$ and $a$. If the waves are moving in opposite directions, the result is a standing wave, like a guitar string. If the waves are moving in the same direction, the result is a wave that can have an amplitude as much as $A+a$ or as little as $A-a$, depending on the respective phases. (See Fig. A-11.) This wave is the result of *interference.*

One would seldom expect two waves to line up in direction well enough to see visible, reasonably stationary, interference effects in nature. Indeed, this effect is almost unknown using diffuse white-light sources. The exception can be found in the case of thin films.

With thin films, an incident light beam is reflected twice in quick succession by two very nearly parallel surfaces. The most common way of achieving parallel surfaces in nature is with liquids. Thus, our first experience with thin-film interference is usually found in the colors of a soap bubble. Thin-film interference also occurs in some insect wings, bird feathers, and mollusk shells. It even has a name that was coined before physical understanding was achieved, *iridescence,* after Iris, ancient goddess of the rainbow.

The color in a soap bubble is caused by the reflection from the outside of the bubble interfering with the reflection from the inside. (If you want to try an experiment, the colors are easier to see on a soap film still held in the loop.) The strength of the reflection from the air-to-soapy-water interface is about the same as the strength from the soapy-water-to-air interface, so the soap bubble interference should have high contrast. A color is favored at those frequencies for which one reflection is out of phase with the other by an even multiple of the color's wavelength.

What happens to those colors for which the conditions aren't favorable? A wave contains energy, and that energy doesn't go away when the wave is canceled. If one path has been blocked, it goes in another direction. The light passes straight through.

The reason we see colors at all is because soap bubbles are so thin. If the surfaces had two reflections with a phase delay amounting to 1000 wavelengths of blue light, it would be 999 wavelengths of not-so-blue light, 998 even-less-blue, and so forth. So many frequencies would be favored that the reflected light would be colorless again. The spectral response would resemble a pocket comb, with many selected frequencies jutting up. However, our eyes are not sensitive to such fine structure and we would see only white light.

We also don't see bubble colors in ordinary windows for the same reason. In fact, this color effect is only seen at a certain stage of the ephemeral life of a bubble. A fresh soap film is thick, so one sees many frequencies adding together to a rough approximation of white. As it evaporates, it passes through an iridescent stage where the colors depend on the local thickness. Stripes of red, yellow, green, blue, and purple appear briefly. Then comes a stage when all colors of reflection are equally discouraged. The bubble is colored a pale white or a white tinged with yellow once again.

The bubble is still behaving as a barrier when it appears pale yellow, but soon it will get so thin that the wavelength of light is incapable of sensing the interface at all. If the bubble is long-lived, careful inspection will reveal an area of the film where it is actually invisible. The layer is so thin that it cannot materially impede the forward progress of the wave.

If, instead of using white light, we illuminate a fresh film with one color only, what would we see? As the film dries up, it goes from invisible to visible at any given location, depending on whether that wavelength is favored to reflect. The bubble looks tattered and frayed depending on how fast it is drying at a certain location, and onlookers are able to tell it is still whole only by looking at the edges.

The interference principles exemplified in a soap bubble can help us to understand how interferometers work. If we can generate one perfect wavefront, or at least a known wavefront, we can use it to interfere with the unknown wavefront of our telescopes. If the wavefronts are identical, the interference will be the same over the whole aperture.

A simple example is given to illustrate the ideas behind this principle. Let's say we wish to test a flat used for a diagonal mirror. We set it up in the configuration of Fig. A-12 with a known optical flat, illuminate it from above with fairly pure yellow-green light, and get far enough away in a vertical direction so that perspective does not cause any effects of its own.[4] Here the thin film is not glass or soapy water, but the wedge of trapped air.

If the diagonal is flat and the blocks (actually, thin strips of paper) are of the same thickness, one would detect a uniform brightness depending on the relative phases of the two reflections. Such precision is almost impossible to achieve by luck alone. More likely one will see, as in Fig. A-12a, a thin film of air amounting to $N$ wavelengths on one side to $N + n$ wavelengths on the other. If we follow the course of light as it passes through the glass and reflects off the two layers, we see that the two reflections have a phase difference of $2N$ wavelengths on the short side of the wedge and $2N + 2n$ wavelengths on the other side (to within a constant). One can subtract the $2N$ phase difference since it is the same over the whole piece and concentrate on the $2n$. From the discussion with soap bubbles above, the expectation is that light stripes should appear at the locations where the interfering phases appear separated by 0, 1 wave, 2 waves, etc. and dark bars should appear where the phases are separated by $1/2$ wave, $3/2$ wave, $5/2$ wave, etc. Because the phase difference results from reflection, which doubles the distances light propagates, a bar occurs for every increase of a half wavelength in the separation of the plates. Furthermore, the bars should be straight, as in Fig. A-12b, because the separation varies only in the direction of offset.

If the diagonal is not flat, however, the bars curve as in Fig. A-12c. We may easily view the dark bars (called "fringes") as contours of the tested piece separated by a half wavelength of light. By stretching a dark thread across the test setup, we can even estimate the amount of curvature. This case is out of line by not quite half a fringe so the tested piece is smoothly curved by a little less than $1/4$ wavelength.

This test can easily be generalized to other shapes. If the known surface is a convex paraboloid, a Newtonian telescope maker just needs to test and polish until the bars are straight. The truth is, no one works this way because all of the pieces made would need to have precisely the same focal

---

[4]In practice, such a test is conducted with a mild condensing lens just above the two pieces (Fizeau's interferometer). Such an arrangement concentrates the returning light and rectifies the incident diffuse beam so that the optician can draw close.

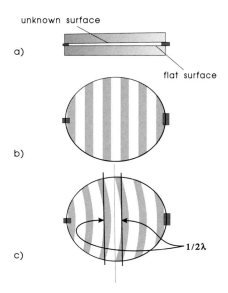

**Fig. A-12.** *Interference from a thin film of air is used to test the quality of a flat surface.*

length (for no good reason). An optician needs a powerful incentive before incurring the expense of a curved testing piece. A camera manufacturer who may have a tight tolerance on thousands of spherical parts has a valid justification to make one. A telescope tester has easier roads to follow.

Most easily interpreted interferometer tests have one feature in common. They always start with a single beam divided into two parts. One becomes the "reference" beam, and the other beam is transmitted through the optics. The reference wavefront must be conditioned into the same converging shape as it would attain had it passed through perfect optics. Finally, the beams must be brought together with only a few wavelengths of tilt. After all of these diversions, the two beams should have roughly the same amplitude in order to provide good contrast between the bright fringes and the dark ones. For example, if the lower surface were aluminized in the example above, the fringes would be very weak. One interfering beam would originate from the transparent glass (maybe 4% – 5% reflectivity) and the other would bounce strongly off the aluminum coating (92% reflectivity). The coating should be removed to use interferometry in this case.

Another condition that must be maintained is approximately equal path length. The light source ultimately consists of a molecular or atomic transition, with a finite line width, implying through the Heisenberg indeterminacy principle, a localization of the light beam. A typical stream electromagnetic energy originating from a single transition is a wave packet about

0.5 m long. If the beam is split, half to enter a compact "perfect" conditioner (where it is immediately returned) and the other half continuing on to the optics, then these two path lengths must not differ by more than 0.5 m if the two beams are to successfully interfere. This situation is eased considerably by using a laser, which has a longer coherence length.

### A.5.2    The Point-Diffraction Interferometer

An interferometric test generally requires extra equipment of the highest quality. However, an elegant solution was invented by R.N. Smartt and John Strong (1972) and announced by them at an Optical Society of America conference. This method requires the manufacture of a sophisticated mask, but presumably an isolated worker may still attempt the test because of its low cost. Telescope testing was reported by Smartt and W.H. Steel (1975), and the evaluation of unknown wavefronts has been mentioned by others (Allred and Mills 1989; Mallick 1978). This technique has also appeared in popular literature (Delvo 1985).

The aberrated beam of a telescope is imaged into a blurry spot bigger than the diffraction disk of a perfect aperture but still small enough to be close to the proper size. The aberration is preserved through the focus but only if the whole wavefront is allowed to contribute. If an opaque mask with a tiny hole is placed somewhere near the focus, the transmitted beam passing through that hole diverges spherically, no matter where the hole is located. That perfect wavefront occurs because individual portions of the wavefront are each behaving perfectly. The sum of all these spots at the plane of focus behaves imperfectly because they are mutually out of phase. Another way of thinking about it is to use a filtration argument. So much spatial information has been filtered out of the image passing through the tiny hole that the emerging signal can't help but be clean.

As this tiny hole is increased in size, the wavefront produced by it remains approximately spherical until the hole is about the size of a perfect diffraction disk. Then, sensibly, it begins to degrade into the actual wavefront.

This process is very interesting but is still of no help because nothing interferes with this perfect wavefront. If the mask is taken away, the original wavefront is present but no perfect wavefront exists with which it can interfere. If, however, the opaque mask is made slightly transparent, it is possible to cause the perfect wavefront escaping through the hole to interfere with the greatly diminished original wavefront.

A point-diffraction interferometer is sketched in Fig. A-13. The original

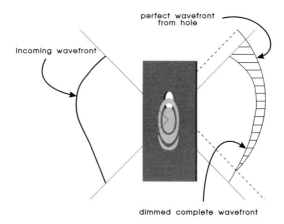

perfect wavefront
from hole

Incoming wavefront

dimmed complete wavefront

**Fig. A-13.** *The point-diffraction interferometer.*

wavefront and the wavefront escaping through the hole differ by the lined region. If a few visible fringes are desired, the hole must be offset until the sphere is tilted with respect to the darkened, complete wavefront by a few wavelengths. The hole is moved to the outer parts of the image, and the perfectly spherical wavefront emerging from this decentered hole becomes very dark. Transmission of the mask must be set low in order to obtain high-contrast fringes.

The first disadvantage of this test is that most of the light is cut off. This problem can be overcome by darkening the room and allowing your eyes to adapt or by using long-exposure photography. The second difficulty involves mask making. The maximum radius of the hole is a fixed function of the focal ratio, $d = 1.22\lambda F$, so that number is no problem. But the transmission of the mask must vary from 0.005 to 0.05 depending on the severity of the aberration and how much tilt is desired.

Most users prefer to avoid cutting the hole. Instead, they make it part of the filtering operation. The filter can be made from a mostly exposed piece of fine-grained photographic film. The holes are made by shading the film with tiny microspheres during the exposure step, as in Delvo's article, or these spheres can shade a glass slide during partial aluminizing. Smartt and Steel also describe an adjustable transmission mask comprised of two polarizing layers, one of which is punctured. To tune such a mask, they turn the unpierced polarizer until high-contrast fringes are seen. This polarizer is immersed in a liquid having the same index of refraction as the mounting plastic of polarizing material.

Although this test typically uses a laser and is performed in a bench-test autocollimation mode, the common-path arrangement does not demand the use of monochromatic light. Autocollimation is also not required. Smartt and Steel describe a test conducted at the focus of a large telescope on the image of a star. The test required excellent seeing, a stable mounting, and probably (although they didn't say) extraordinary patience.

In Delvo's article, the difficulty of making these masks has been reduced. Drops of liquid mercury are smashed into a high-resolution photographic plate, covering it with tiny mercury spheres.[5] Unfortunately, such clever fabrication methods can't cure the test's most severe problem, which is pinhole alignment. The mask must be placed to within a few dozen micrometers from the center of the pattern. A kinematic stage is required if the user wants to avoid excruciating effort, preferably a stage with three axes.

To review, the difficulties of the point-diffraction interferometer test are as follows:

1. This test image is very dim.

2. The number of visible fringes and the contrast of the interference pattern are coupled together because the brightness of the spot drops away as it is decentered.

3. Convenient operation requires an expensive kinematic stage.

4. At the center of curvature, non-spherical mirror testing is difficult because the fringes are no longer straight. Test-reduction software is available, but its profitable use still demands great care and effort.

5. The most convenient configuration requires a full-diameter autocollimation flat.

## A.6   The Null Test

This test is actually a subset of many others. Briefly stated, a null test involves a testing configuration in which the perfect result is simple and requires no further reduction. Thus, the Foucault test is emphatically *not* a null test when a paraboloid is tested at the center of curvature, but a knife edge placed at the focus of a distant source or a star *is* a null test. If the optics are well figured, the whole surface will dim uniformly. Likewise, the point-diffraction interferometer used at the focus of a star is a null test. If the optics are perfect, the fringes are straight. The Ronchi test at the focus of a star behaves similarly; optics that pass the test show straight shadows of the bars on the aperture. If a full aperture autocollimation flat

---

[5]Mercury is toxic and exposure to it is cumulative. Be careful.

is used, many of the tests in this chapter become null tests. Even the star test qualifies.

Here, the words "null test" are limited to mean those bench tests for which the spherical aberration of a properly figured surface is undone by putting the opposite spherical aberration in the beam emerging from the source. The Dall null test will be used as an example because it is common in the amateur literature, but there are many null testing devices, some superior to the Dall tester.

The Dall null tester looks like a Foucault tester, except that the source pinhole is behind a small plano-convex lens. This lens puts an equal and opposite amount of spherical aberration onto the beam that would normally diverge spherically from the pinhole. A good paraboloidal mirror bends the wavefront back into a converging sphere. When the knife enters the image of the pinhole, it does not produce the distorted Foucault patterns of Figs. A-2 or A-3. It blanks out, just as if it were testing a sphere.

Null testers are not inherently flawed, in spite of the poor reputation they received during the Hubble Space Telescope fiasco. However, many problems make the Dall null test difficult, including the following:

1. The tester lens must be of impeccable quality. It must have a good edge and surface accuracy of approximately the precision that the tester hopes to find. A poor lens cannot be used to test a good mirror.

2. The wavelength is no longer free; null testing should not be done in white light. Calculations of the proper pinhole-lens separation depend critically on the index of refraction of the lens and will be valid for one color only. To use this test, one must have full information on the refractive properties of the lens. A color filter should be placed between the lamp and the pinhole to restrict the bandwidth of the light employed.

3. The lens-pinhole distance must be very precisely set or the test does not null for perfect optics but for overcorrected or uncorrected wavefronts. (Testing on the Hubble telescope failed for a similar reason.)

4. The axis of the pinhole-lens assembly must be very carefully aligned on the center of the mirror.

5. The Dall null test has zonal spherical aberration that results in improper curvature when fast mirrors are made to conform to the testing apparatus. It is not an accurate null (Buchroeder 1994).

# Appendix B

# Calculation Methods

To generate the photograph-like patterns, modulation transfer functions, and other miscellaneous graphs in this book, it was necessary to use the Huygens-Fresnel principle in the context of Fourier optics. What follows is intended only as a sketch of the concepts used here. For more insight, consult the references mentioned below. The most readable is Joseph W. Goodman's *Introduction to Fourier Optics* (Goodman 1968) or Eugene Hecht's text *Optics* (Hecht 1987).

APERTURE, one of the programs mentioned in this appendix, has been released as an optional software accompaniment to this volume. This program allows the calculation of the axially-symmetric patterns seen in the text, including spherical aberration, central obstruction, zones, turned edge, apodized apertures, and others. While this program is not necessary to appreciate the points made in earlier chapters, the realities of publishing limit the number of images that can appear here. APERTURE allows one the luxury of exploring the fine details of some of the most interesting diffraction behavior.

## B.1  Diffraction Concepts

Chapter 4 presented a simplistic introduction to some of the ideas behind diffraction and the Huygens-Fresnel principle. For the purpose of discussion, we assumed every point on the wavefront re-radiates the wave. That convenient fiction has some difficulties, however. If each point is allowed to radiate in every direction equally, the aperture would arbitrarily reflect back into space some of the energy that reached it.

Reflection at the aperture is not observed, nor is it seen at any point on the wavefront. Waves don't suddenly reverse direction unless they encounter a change in the medium. The wave sum also doesn't deliver the correct answer when integrated over a situation with no aperture, just a source of light and a receiver. The integral is over a complete sphere, and the radiators at right angles between the source and receiver have too strong a weight.

Fresnel realized that these were impediments, so he made certain approximations. His model was not derived from first principles, which probably helps explain the intense scrutiny by such worthies as Poisson. In the early 19th century, even the physical process that produces light was not yet understood.

Later research of Gustav Kirchhoff produced a version of the Huygens-Fresnel theory derived from first principles. His result, called the Fresnel-Kirchhoff diffraction formula, no longer requires that the rearward direction be ignored, though it demands a few conditions:

1. Light is modeled as a scalar wave. Polarization is not included. The model is oblivious to the vector nature of light.

2. The field values near the aperture are the same as they would be in the absence of the aperture (weighted by a simple trigonometric function).

3. The distance from the aperture is sufficient to ensure that no bound or evanescent fields are present.

One consequence of the second condition is the simultaneous specification of both the field values on the aperture in addition to their derivatives. The time-harmonic form of the wave equation[1] is a second-order differential equation for which the normal method of solution is to set either the value of the field on the boundaries or the derivative of that field. It is unusual that Kirchhoff gave both.

With its overspecified boundaries, we must regard Kirchhoff's solution as an approximation. This approximation will not affect results if the aperture does not have a lot of structure. We may rightly suspect that the Fresnel-Kirchhoff equation will be less accurate for devices like high-resolution diffraction gratings. For gently sloped optics, with most of the area many wavelengths from all edges, the approximation does not cause much trouble. More detail concerning these criticisms is available in Baker and Copson (1950).

A modified form of the Fresnel-Kirchhoff formula (using variables de-

---

[1] This formulation is called the *Helmholtz equation.*

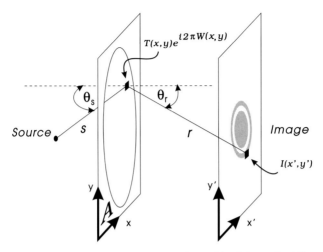

**Fig. B-1.** *Variables appearing in the Fresnel-Kirchhoff formula. The aperture is in surface A.*

fined in Fig. B-1) is

$$U(x', y') = \frac{1}{N} \int \int_A T(x, y) e^{i2\pi W(x,y)} \frac{e^{i2\pi(r+s)/\lambda}}{rs} \left( \frac{\cos\theta_s + \cos\theta_r}{2} \right) dx\,dy.$$
(B.1)

Here, $N$ is an arbitrary normalization and the time dependence has been suppressed. $U(x', y')$ is the value of the field at the image location $(x', y')$. (Uniform transmission versions of the formula are derived in Hecht 1987, pp. 461–462; Goodman 1968, pp. 37–41; Born and Wolf 1980, pp. 378–380.) The integral may be performed over the entire surface $A$, but the integrand is non-zero only inside the aperture pupil.

The term $T(x, y)e^{i2\pi W(x,y)}$ is called the *pupil function* and is merely a complex number in circular notation. The transmission coefficient $T(x, y)$ is its modulus[2] and the function $W(x, y)$ (in wavelengths) implies the phase. $W(x, y)$ contains aberrations like turbulence, pinched optics, defocusing, astigmatism, etc. The cosine term in brackets is the *inclination* or *obliquity factor*. This function will eliminate nonphysical backward propagation. If we place the source far away, then $\theta_s$ is 0 and $\cos\theta_s$ is 1. Set $\theta_r$ to 180°, as it would be for backward propagation, and the inclination factor vanishes.

In writing Eq. B.1, another approximation has been implicitly made. The aberration function $W(x, y)$ affects the angles in the inclination factor slightly, and the equation doesn't contain this effect anywhere. For all practical purposes, this change in angle is extremely small. Typically, the

---

[2] *Modulus* is the absolute value of a complex number.

worst wavefront tilts in this book are 30 wavelengths over 100 mm, or about
0.01°. Equation B.1 also contains an assumption of linearity.

Key elements in the Fresnel-Kirchhoff formula are the two factors $e^{ikr}/r$
and $e^{iks}/s$ ($k = 2\pi/\lambda$). Here, Huygens' principle of re-radiating elemental
points is written in mathematical form. Each of these expressions is the
time-independent part of a spherical wave function. The denominator will
cause the intensity to obey the inverse square law of light (twice as far, one-
fourth as bright). The numerator will ensure that the Fresnel zones will be
properly painted on the aperture. The "$s$" spherical wave represents the
propagation of the wave from the source to a point on the aperture. It is
then reborn as the "$r$" spherical wave, which propagates to the receiving
point.

The intensity is related to the energy, so it cannot be complex-valued.
It is calculated from the field above as follows:

$$I(x',y') = U(x',y')U^*(x',y') = |U(x',y')|^2. \tag{B.2}$$

Once the integral has been performed over the whole open aperture, Eq.
B.2 says that the intensity is known for only *one point* in the image space.
To find it at any other location, we must change the values of $x'$ and $y'$ and
evaluate the field integral again. To completely map out an entire image
this way requires (to say the least) a great deal of time.

Another name for the expression $I(x',y')$ is the *point-spread function,*
or PSF. The PSF determines how diffraction, obstructions, and aberrations
degrade a perfectly sharp point source of light into a fuzzy disk. In the case
of perfect optics filtered only by a finite circular aperture, the PSF follows
the familiar Airy disk pattern.

## B.2    The Fraunhofer and Fresnel Approximations

We can simplify Eq. B.1 by noticing some symmetries and by casting
the problem in another coordinate system. First, we place the source at
a distant on-axis location so that $s$ is a very large constant. Then we can
pull the $e^{iks}/s$ wave function constant out of the integral and bury it in the
normalization constant. Because we are using a focusing lens or mirror, we
pretend the receiver point is also very distant by "unbending" the wavefront (Born and Wolf 1980, pp. 382–386). In the Fraunhofer approximation
(which is what this unbending is called), the important quantities are no
longer the distances but the off-axis angles from the center of the aperture
to the distant sensor.

This approximation is written as (Hecht 1987, p. 494)

$$U(\phi_{x'}, \phi_{y'}) = \frac{1}{N'} \int \int_A T(x, y) e^{i2\pi W(x,y)} e^{i(k \sin \phi_x \, x + k \sin \phi_y \, y)} dx \, dy. \quad \text{(B.3)}$$

While not superficially looking much simpler than Eq. B.1, the Fraunhofer approximation has done away with those very messy distances $r$ and $s$ (or at least they are now neatly tucked away). The angle $\phi_x$ is the angle to the image point in the $x$-direction, while $\phi_y$ is the angle toward the image point in the $y$-direction. The second exponential in the integrand is just the phase difference induced by the tilt angle to the image location being calculated. This term does the same thing as picking up the corner of a table and asking how much higher the table is all along its surface. Over the leg still touching the floor, the extra height is zero. At the lifted corner, it has its full value. Everywhere over the aperture, this "tilt" aberration may be easily calculated. For all cases of interest here, $\sin \phi$ is very close to $\phi$, which makes it even simpler.

In the Fraunhofer approximation, the inclination factor is ignored because of the very tiny deflections of the wavefront from its spherically converging path. $N'$ is the new normalization constant.

The Fraunhofer formula is not supposed to apply to non-zero values of defocusing aberration. However, the next term of the expansion of Eq. B.1 used in deriving the Fraunhofer approximation is just this defocusing. Including this term changes the integral to the Fresnel approximation. However, an external defocusing cannot be imposed on the Fresnel approximation—that step would doubly count the defocusing. It is tidier to encapsulate all such terms into the pupil function, which is then applied to the skeletal Fraunhofer formula.

The light touch of small amounts of defocusing can perhaps be gauged by the focus shift in Table 5-1 divided by the focal length of the instrument (which is the same as the fractional change in the sagitta of the wavefront). For example, at 12 wavelengths defocusing aberration on an 8-inch (200-mm) f/6 telescope, $\Delta f / f = 0.0016$, a very tiny fraction.

The star test of a focused aperture does not precisely reproduce at equal distances inside and outside of focus, but the difference is small. For example, a 200-mm f/6 telescope defocused by 1.9 mm is listed in Table 5-1 as having a defocusing aberration of 12 wavelengths. A careful calculation shows that 1.9-mm inside focus has a more precise aberration of 12.02 wavelengths. On the outside, an equal eyepiece motion becomes 11.98 wavelengths defocusing aberration. If we were to adjust the focuser until the aberration were precisely 12 wavelengths, then the image inside focus would be ever-so-slightly smaller and brighter, and the image on the outside of focus would be incrementally bigger and dimmer. Thus, the effect is manifested as a magnification difference. Perhaps if we were to defocus very precisely with a measurement screw, we could barely detect such changes, but most star testers will never notice the difference. We must simply ensure that the fraction $\Delta f/f$ is small (Bachynski and Bekefi 1957; Li 1982; Erkkila and Rogers 1981).

## B.3    Image Calculations for Symmetric Apertures

Further simplification of the Fraunhofer approximation results if the pupil function is circularly symmetric. If the integral in Eq. B.2 is rewritten in circular coordinates, the angle integral can be performed to yield

$$U(r') = \frac{1}{N''} \int_{\rho=0}^{1} T(\rho) e^{i2\pi W(\rho)} \rho \, J_0(\rho \pi D r'/f\lambda) d\rho, \qquad \text{(B.4)}$$

where $\rho$ is the normalized radial coordinate of the aperture, $r'$ is the radial coordinate on the focal plane, $J_0$ is the zeroth-order Bessel function, and $N''$ is another normalization constant (Luneburg 1964, p. 345; Schroeder 1987, pp. 181–182).

In this book, all circularly-symmetric images were calculated using this simplification. The particular algorithm used divided the radius into $N_\rho$ equally-spaced points (typically 300–500) and calculated the intensity sum

$$I(\varphi) = \frac{4}{N_\rho^2} \left| \sum_{j=0}^{N_\rho} T_j e^{i2\pi(W_j + W_d)} \left(\frac{j}{N_\rho}\right) J_0\left(\frac{\varphi \pi j}{N_\rho}\right) \right|^2. \qquad \text{(B.5)}$$

Here the value $\varphi$ is the reduced image angle $D\theta/\lambda$, where $\theta$ is the true angle, $D$ is the diameter of the aperture, and $\lambda$ is the wavelength. (This angle conveniently reaches the edge of the Airy disk for a uniform circular aperture at 1.22.) $W_d$ is the defocusing aberration $A_2(j/N_\rho)^2$ (defined in Chapter 10) in wavelengths, and $W_j$ contains the rest of the aberrations. $T_j$ is just the transmission coefficient at a sampled radial point $j$. $J_0$ is calculated using a subroutine adapted from *Numerical Recipes* (Press *et al.* 1986).

It was straightforward also to keep track of the encircled energy of the image as $\varphi$ was increased. Because Eq. B.5 is a radial sum, the intensity of the outer portions of the image had to be weighted for the increased perimeter. The normalized encircled energy increment is approximately

$$\Delta EE(\varphi) \approx \frac{\Delta \varphi \pi^2 \varphi I(\varphi)}{2\epsilon_{TR}}, \qquad \text{(B.6)}$$

where $\Delta\varphi$ is the jumpsize in image angle and $\epsilon_{TR}$ is the total energy fraction that enters the system. If the obstruction is 50%, $\epsilon_{TR}$ is 0.75, and the encircled energy increases enough so that it reaches unity far beyond the Airy disk.

Actually, if the encircled energy is accumulated in the simple-minded manner of Eq. B.6, results are poor. The energy in focused images sharply increases just as the circle radius starts to open. Errors made here can be large. The program used Simpson's rule integration with a sophisticated starter.

The modulation transfer function (MTF) was not calculated for circularly symmetric apertures in its more straightforward form as an autocorrelation (see below). Such a calculation is too slow. Instead, once $I(\varphi)$ had been carried out far beyond the Airy disk, it could be used to infer the transfer function. The image is merely the convolution of a perfect sinusoidal target with the point spread function. For spatial frequency $\nu$, the integral is (as adapted from Schroeder 1987, p. 204)

$$\mathrm{MTF}(\nu) = \frac{1}{M_0} \int_0^\infty I(\varphi) J_0(2\pi\varphi\nu)\varphi \, d\varphi. \tag{B.7}$$

The number $M_0$ is a normalization at zero spatial frequency.

A problem with this calculation is not apparent from casual inspection. The upper limit of the integral assumes that the intensity is known out to an arbitrarily high angle. We can calculate the intensity out to any angle, of course, but there must be energy beyond that angle that we know nothing about. High angles are represented by very low spatial frequencies. Thus, at first glance it would seem that this energy would be automatically taken into account by forcing the normalization $M_0$ to be the integral evaluated at $\nu = 0$.

This approximation throws a wrench into the works. A modulation transfer function calculated this way does have the proper value (i.e., 1) at a spatial frequency of 0, but at higher spatial frequencies, the calculated transfer function is too high. The inescapable conclusion is that the truncation of the angle causes a numerically diminished MTF at low spatial frequencies. In other words, if we have not gathered that distant energy in our intensity calculation, we had better not take tally of it in Eq. B.7. Therefore, the computational algorithm is slightly modified:

$$\mathrm{MTF}(\nu) = \frac{EE(\varphi_{\max})}{\mathrm{MTF}(0)} \sum_{m=0}^{N_\varphi} I(m) \left( \frac{m\varphi_{\max}}{N_\varphi} \right) J_0 \left( \frac{2\pi m\varphi_{\max}\nu}{N_\varphi} \right). \tag{B.8}$$

Here $\mathrm{MTF}(0)$ is just the sum done for $\nu = 0$, and $m$ is the summation index. $EE(\varphi_{\max})$ is the fractional encircled energy as far as the point-spread function integral is done. $N_\varphi$ is the number of angles in the intensity summation. The effect on the MTF is to induce a small downward curl at low spatial frequencies. In most of the figures appearing in this book, the intensity function was carried out to angles where the lower part of the MTF could be approximated by a straight line to the known intercept of unity at the origin. Usually, the encircled energy at the most distant angle of a focused pattern exceeded 99%.

## B.4    Image Calculations for Nonsymmetric Apertures

Although the field calculations of Eq. B.4 are long, they are a great deal shorter than the double integral required for a nonsymmetric pupil function. Others have noted that generating these patterns is tedious (Allred and Mills 1989); before computer time became inexpensive, they were not often attempted at all. Each aperture is modeled by a square grid of $129 \times 129$ points, with points farther than 64 from the center set to zero. Within the aperture are 12,853 points. The image plane is a grid of $129 \times 129$ points as well. The integral in Eq. B.3 must be done for each of these 16,641 image locations. For each nonsymmetric image frame in this book, the integrand of Eq. B.3 needed to be evaluated over 210 million times.

The image plane may be mapped out in one grand sweep using another technique. If a two-dimensional discrete Fourier transform were taken of the complex pupil function, the result would be (after rearrangement and further processing) a complete image. The fast Fourier transform (FFT) is useful to reduce the computational load (Brigham 1988).

This procedure involves considerable computation itself. In this book the angle $\varphi$ was sampled at $D\theta/\lambda$ values as small as 0.05 or 0.1. To achieve a grid with such fine spacing, the pupil function array would have to be blank-padded (filled with zeroes) out to $1024 \times 1024$ or $2048 \times 2048$. The storage of just this single-precision array takes 8 to 32 megabytes. Much of the speed advantage of the FFT would be gobbled up by the relatively slow disk-access times to virtual memory (large RAM sizes were not common when this program was designed). One software company offered a two-dimensional FFT routine that could turn around a complex $1024 \times 1024$ array in a few minutes. However, this routine did not use the disk as virtual memory during the benchmark test; the array was held entirely in fast electronic memory.

Once such an FFT is finished calculating, the array has to be reorganized and the image intensity extracted. All 8 megabytes need not be kept, but the additional processing to sample and compress the image would take more computer time. In the end, it was decided that the extra effort required to process the image by simple integration of Eq. B.3 was not a severe burden, and was more than compensated by the complete transparency of the code.

The algorithm that was used at the core of the program was a discrete version of Eqs. B.2 and B.3. It had the form

$$I_{m,n} = \frac{1}{N^2} \left| \sum_{t,u=-64}^{64} T_{t,u} e^{i2\pi(W_{t,u}+W_d)} e^{i\pi\varphi_{\max}(mt+nu)/64^2} \right|^2, \qquad (B.9)$$

where $W_d$ is the defocusing aberration, $W_d = A_2(t^2 + u^2)/64^2$ and values $W_{t,u}$ contain the rest of the aberrations. $N$ here is the number of pupil points, i.e., 12,853. This sum is done for each image point in a grid that runs indices $m$ and $n$ from $-64$ to 64.

Asymmetric pupils have complex transfer functions. The full description of the performance of asymmetric apertures is called the *optical transfer function* (OTF) and has the following form:

$$\text{OTF}(\nu) = \text{MTF}(\nu)e^{i\Psi(\nu)}. \qquad (B.10)$$

The imaginary exponent $\Psi(\nu)$ is the *phase transfer function*. For small aberrations the real part of the OTF is much larger than the imaginary portion. Thus, phase is commonly neglected. The modulus $\text{MTF}(\nu)$ is the quantity usually equated with the optical quality of the system.

The effect of a small imaginary part of the OTF on the bar pattern image is to shift it sideways a tiny amount but not enough to reverse it completely. Reversal is adequately handled by a negative MTF.[3]

Clearly, we cannot use the circularly symmetric formulation of Eq. B.7 to calculate the OTF of an asymmetric pupil. Instead, we may use a tidy formulation described well in a number of places (Born and Wolf 1980, p. 485; Parrent and Thompson 1969, p. 22; Luneburg 1964, p. 356). The OTF is calculated as the autocorrelation of the pupil function:

$$\text{OTF}(\nu_x, \nu_y) = \frac{\int\int P(x,y)P^*(x-2\nu_x, y-2\nu_y)dx\,dy}{\int\int |P(x,y)|^2 dx\,dy}, \qquad (B.11)$$

where the integral is taken over the aperture plane. Here $P$ is a shorthand notation for the pupil function defined in the text following Eq. B.1. The aperture coordinates are defined so that the perimeter is at $x^2 + y^2 = 1$, and the spatial frequency fractions are similarly normalized. One can envision the integral above as the overlap between the pupil function and the pupil function moved sideways by the spatial frequency fractions as in Fig. B-2. For non-aberrated pupils, the OTF is the dark area divided by the uncovered area of the whole aperture.

---

[3]The MTF as defined in Eq. B.10 is always positive, but the sign component of the phase transfer function is sometimes appended to the MTF when the OTF is mostly real. The resulting "MTF" is smoother and tells more about the optical performance.

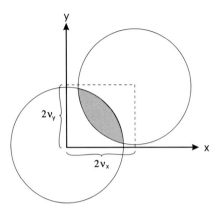

**Fig. B-2.** *The MTF as the overlap with a shifted pupil.*

The actual algorithm took into account the sampling of the aperture on a rectangular grid. Since the offsets have to land on sampled positions, the OTF was calculated only for integer offsets along the $x$ and $y$ directions and a 45° offset with equal shifts. The algorithm for a shift in only the $x$ direction was

$$\text{OTF}(\nu_x) = \frac{\sum_{t=s}^{64} \sum_{u=-64}^{64} T_{tu} e^{i2\pi W_{tu}} T_{t-s,u} e^{-i2\pi W_{t-s,u}}}{\sum_{t,u=-64}^{64} T_{tu}^2} \tag{B.12}$$

where indices $s$ (for "shift"), $u$, $s$, and $t$ run from $-64$ to $64$ and $\nu_x = (s+64)/128$. The maximum spatial frequency corresponds to $\nu_x = 1$. Here the pupil array is measured from its center.

Encircled energy can be defined for an asymmetric aperture, but no such calculations appear in this book.

## B.5   The Programs

### B.5.1   Symmetric Pupil Function

If the pupil could be described in both amplitude and phase by a figure of revolution, diffraction patterns were calculated using the self-contained program APERTURE. This program allows the user to specify both the transmission and the aberration as a function of radius. After selecting a value of the defocusing aberration, APERTURE calculates the point spread function (PSF) and the encircled energy. Once the PSF has been calculated far enough away from the central diffraction disk, the modulation transfer function can be generated.

APERTURE is relatively fast. If the radius is divided into 300 sampled points, it can deliver the 200 calculations comprising a typical in-focus PSF in less than a minute using a 25 MHz 386/7. It then shows the image in shades of gray on a VGA screen.

At this point another program, POSTDR, can be invoked. POSTDR translates the intensity file into a $128 \times 128$ halftone image using the PostScript[TM] page-description language. POSTDR allows one to adjust the contrast and brightness of the picture to fit within the limited dynamic range of printing paper.

## B.5.2 Asymmetric Pupil Function

The structure of the program is divided into two tasks. The first program, PUPIL, generates a beginning pupil function. Typically, this pupil function file is calculated to represent a focused and unobstructed telescope. It also possesses a standard aberration value, such as 1 wavelength RMS. This file is then fed to the diffraction pattern program ASYMM. One applies additional obstruction and defocusing on the pupil function and an aberration multiplier as well. ASYMM then generates the image intensity file.

Because ASYMM was designed to do the tedious direct integration of Eq. B.3, it was written with a 32-bit FORTRAN optimizing compiler and uses a DOS extender during execution. It runs in 9.6 hours on a 25 MHz 386/7 and 2.3 hours on a 486DX50.[4]

The modulation transfer function is calculated from the pupil function file using a separate routine named MTF. It generates a file with the OTF's of the three bar directions in sequence. The MTF is readily derived from these complex values.

The longitudinal slice patterns through focus are calculated with a variation of ASYMM.

## B.6 Verification of Numerical Procedure

As you may expect, the actual implementation of the algorithms is very messy compared to the sparse presentation above. Three methods were used to check that the coding was properly done:

1. Checks between APERTURE and ASYMM for circularly-symmetric apertures,

2. Comparison with an exact procedure, and

3. Reproduction of complicated patterns appearing in literature.

---

[4] ASYMM is fragmented and requires a great deal of experience to execute reliably. It would require a great deal of rewriting to be run by general users. It will not be released.

### B.6.1    Comparison of APERTURE and ASYMM

Two dissimilar procedures were used to generate diffraction patterns in the symmetric and asymmetric programs. Even though both programs have a pedigree that traces back to Eq. B.3, very little resemblance between them can be easily seen. They use different routines and are written in different languages. We can calculate the same situations using these two separate procedures and verify that the answers are indeed the same.

Taking a circularly-symmetric pupil and cranking it through the slow, direct-integration program ASYMM, one should obtain the same answer as APERTURE does. Tests were done for a number of pupils, and good comparisons resulted. Two such images appear in Fig. B-3; the point spread functions appear in Fig. B-4.

The pictures are virtually identical except for a slight azimuthal structuring of the ASYMM output. A possible reason for this image difference is discussed below in section B.8.

Had these programs generated markedly different patterns, we would not have known whether either was correct. But because two quite dissimilar routines generate the same answer, they are either coded correctly or an unlikely accident has occurred—an error that exhibits itself identically in both procedures. Lacking evidence to the contrary, we will assume that they are correct for now and proceed with other checks.

This verification does not support the original theory contained in Eq. B.3. It merely says that the programs seem to be calculating Eq. B.3 correctly. A partial confirmation of the theory has been performed experimentally, but diffraction patterns from real apertures are exceedingly compact. Hence, their brightnesses are difficult to measure quantitatively (Taylor and Thompson 1958, Burch 1985).

### B.6.2    A Numerical Comparison with an Analytic Solution

Any numerical procedure should reproduce the simple systems for which the answer is known analytically. Unfortunately, few diffraction problems have been solved in closed form. From our point of view, an analytic theory of a circular aperture containing at least one aberration would be acceptable.

A solution to an otherwise perfect circular aperture with defocusing aberration appears in Chapter 8 of Born and Wolf. It involves what are called the *Lommel functions* to perform a version of the integral in Eq. B.4

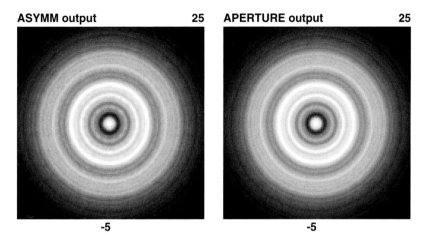

**Fig. B-3.** *Comparison images of* APERTURE *and* ASYMM *on* $+\frac{1}{4}$*-wavelength spherical aberration of a 25% obstructed pupil.*

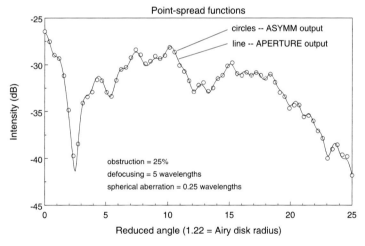

**Fig. B-4.** *Point-spread functions that were used to generate the previous figure along one radius.*

(Born and Wolf 1980, pp. 438–439). Two solutions are each written as an infinite series having its own region of applicability, one inside geometric shadow and one outside of it. These series were programmed into a MathCad[TM] document and each was graphed in the region where it was supposed to work (not shown). Results were indistinguishable from the results of APERTURE. The tests went up to 12 wavelengths defocusing aberration and were limited to Bessel functions up to order 80.

Again this verification is reassuring, but incomplete. It tests the defocusing component of the aberration function (which appears in a separate term of both algorithms) but leaves the other aberrations alone. However, the central loops of ASYMM and APERTURE do not distinguish between defocusing and other aberrations. If a mistake were being made, it would have to be in the preparatory statements of both programs. Furthermore, any supposed error would have to leave the defocusing aberration untarnished in both procedures.

### B.6.3   Comparison with Published Patterns

Perhaps the most severe test of the approximation here was the comparison of patterns generated by ASYMM with published contour plots for coma and astigmatism. The coma contour plots were figured analytically by R. Kingslake (1948), but they are most commonly available as reprinted in Born and Wolf (6th ed., 1980). The astigmatism contour plot was published by Nienhuis and Nijboer (1949).

The expressions for aberration differ somewhat from the primary aberrations used to derive these contour plots, but if we trace through the details, we find that 3.2 and 6.4 wavelengths of primary coma translate to 2.13 and 4.27 wavelengths of peak-to-valley coma aberration as defined at Zernike diffraction focus. In other words, coma as defined here is $2/3$ the coefficient appearing in Born and Wolf. Likewise, the amount of astigmatism used there was 0.64 wavelengths, which translates to 1.28 wavelengths peak-to-valley astigmatism. The patterns as drawn by ASYMM appear in Fig. B-5. They match the overall shapes of the contour plots very well (axes were relabeled in Born and Wolf pp. 478, 480).

### B.7   Numerical Limitations on Programs

Although APERTURE is also a numerical model, it is ASYMM which has the greatest opportunity to fail. Experience showed that the 129 points on the aperture's diameter had difficulty simulating defocusing aberration exceeding 10 wavelengths. Along each diameter under such conditions, a minimum of about 5 samples occur within a Fresnel zone. The errors have a chance to average to zero only because many such diameters are added together statistically.

ASYMM simulates an aperture with an approximate circular pattern 64 points in radius. These points are distributed in a rectangular pattern. The edge of such a sampled aperture is necessarily ragged. We can perhaps

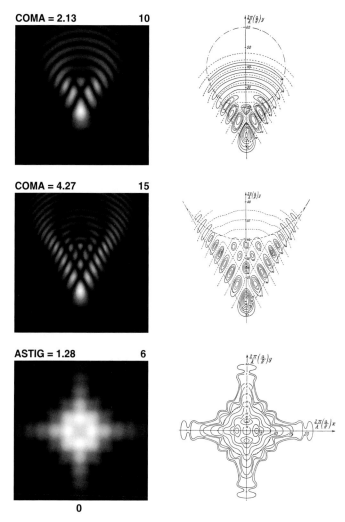

**Fig. B-5.** *Reproduction of coma and astigmatism image patterns. Left images are not at the same scale as the contour plots to the right. (Coma contours appear with permission of R. Kingslake and the astigmatism contour appears courtesy of Elsevier Science Publishing.)*

estimate how much error is induced by inspecting Fig. B-6, which shows the differences between APERTURE and ASYMM on a defocused unaberrated aperture expanded until the errors are obvious. Because APERTURE can be set to sum over a finer one-dimensional grid (here it is 500 points), it suf-

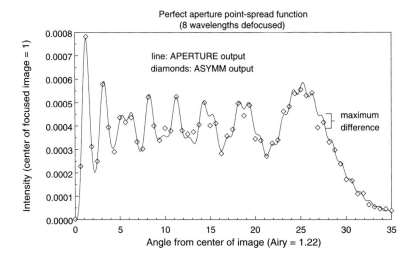

**Fig. B-6.** *Limited sample-size errors in* `ASYMM`.

fers less corruption. The model has smooth edges in `APERTURE` because the angular integral is done analytically.

The maximum difference is about 0.000075, or 1 part in 13,300. Thus, we are seeing less than 1 erroneous sample of the 12,853 points on the aperture contributing to the intensity.

Think about the way those ragged edges are working for a moment. If the point is farther from the center than a radius of unity, the model ignores it. Each point represents a square area around its feet. Thus, if this little tile is more than halfway outside the radius, its contribution is neglected. If it extends less than halfway outside the boundary, its full contribution is counted, even for the area that stretches outside. A $1/13,000$ error is a very small mistake and is perhaps better than the program deserves. One suspects that errors as large as 4 parts in 13,000 appear occasionally. Such an error would be 0.0003 or $-35$ dB. Since this intensity is about that of an image defocused 9 wavelengths, we should anticipate that the accuracy beyond defocus values of 8 to 10 wavelengths is lessened.

In practical use, `ASYMM` did not fail from rough pupil edges. Figure B-7 shows a comparison between two perfect images, each defocused by 8 wavelengths. One was produced with `ASYMM` and the other with `APERTURE`. They were both printed at extremely low contrast to show the feathery appearance induced by the coarse edges of the `ASYMM` pupil. This spurious detail was much dimmer than $-35$ dB. In all real cases, contrast was high enough so that such wrinkling was nearly invisible.

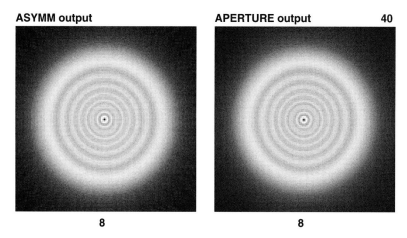

**Fig. B-7.** *Extremely low-contrast image patterns showing tiny errors in* ASYMM *calculation.*

The final problem with the sparsely sampled pupil of ASYMM is grating interference. If the phase shift between adjacent contributing elements is one wavelength, they once again act as if they are in phase. For our 128-point diameter pupil, this condition occurs at $D\theta/\lambda = 128$.

This effect is an artifact of pretending that the wonderfully smooth surface could be represented by a $129 \times 129$ square grid of points. In FFT terminology, we can call such a phenomenon "aliasing." It is an effect of changing the continuous Fourier transform to a discretely sampled one.

If we haven't defocused far enough to divert significant light to distant portions of the image space, no trouble results. In other words, the image and the twin image (way over at a reduced angle of 128) aren't interfering because they don't throw much light that far from their centers. Nevertheless, a limit exists as to how far the image can be defocused until interference becomes severe. We must know that limit so that it can be intelligently avoided.

Figure B-8 shows the pattern out to $D\theta/\lambda = 128$ for three cases: defocusing aberrations of 8, 12, and 16 wavelengths. Clearly, 16 wavelengths is too far, and 12 is questionable because of dark gray tendrils between the images. Only the frame depicting 8 wavelengths seems to show the diffraction disks as truly isolated.

We should only expect the images to be free of interference if we can fit a whole defocused disk into the darkness between the images. The geometric radius of an image in reduced angle is 4 times the number of wavelengths of defocus. This result may be derived by considering Eq. 5.1,

**grating interference**                                                                        **128**

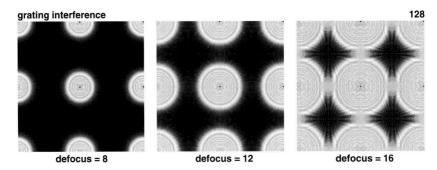

|  defocus = 8  |  defocus = 12  |  defocus = 16  |

**Fig. B-8.** *Interference between side-order images in* ASYMM. *Note that the reduced angle is very large at 128.*

$$f - f' = 8F^2 \Delta n \lambda,$$

where $F$ is the focal ratio and $\Delta n$ is the number of wavelengths of focusing difference. We can calculate the geometric radius of the image:

$$\text{radius} = \frac{(D/2)(f - f')}{f} = \frac{f - f'}{2F} = \frac{8F^2 \Delta n \lambda}{2F} = (4\Delta n)F\lambda. \qquad (\text{B.13})$$

Since the radius of the Airy disk is $1.22F\lambda$, we can identify $F\lambda$ as the conversion factor from reduced angle to radius. Thus $4\Delta n$ is the value of the reduced angle at the edge of geometric shadow. In the present case, 8 wavelengths defocusing aberration means the geometric shadow starts at a reduced angle of $4 \times 8 = 32$, or 26.2 times the radius of the Airy disk.

Eight wavelengths should be barely enough to fit a whole disk between the disk and the interference order centered at a reduced angle of 128. A geometric radius would appear at the center and edge with a diameter in the middle: $32 + 64 + 32 = 128$. Of course, the image appears to be somewhat smaller than the geometric radius. A whole disk would drop between the two with a tiny bit of rattle.

Occasionally, ASYMM was asked to calculate an image 10 wavelengths out-of-focus. Some interference from the side order was noticeable in a few cases, but the damage was not severe.

All patterns with a defocusing aberration beyond 10 wavelengths were calculated only with the program APERTURE, which is far less sensitive to sampling error.

## B.8   Difficulties in Printing

The dynamic range of book reproduction is not nearly the same as the dynamic range of the human eye. When the eye receives the wrong light level, it adjusts. Paper can't do that. The halftone process divides gray scales into dot patterns. An ideal dynamic range for such a process allows a gray scale with 256 levels of intensity.[5]

Clearly, the most desirable way of proceeding would be to use an unchanging scale for the printing process. This procedure is impossible with only 256 levels. We saw above that much interesting detail appears with an intensity of 0.0001, particularly with large values of defocusing aberration. Thus, no uniform scale can cover both in-focus images (intensity = 1) and defocused images (intensity $\cong$ 0.0001). We would need a gray scale with 10,000 intensity levels. Also, an image that is self-luminous and one that is reflective have subtle differences. Real stars are viewed in a dark field, with the eye's variable sensitivity tracking the lowered intensity of a defocused image. Images on paper must be lit by a lamp. When paper images get darker, the eye does not follow. The bright corners of the paper are still in the field of view, and the extra illumination subverts the tracking.

Coupled with this problem are the non-linearities associated with printing. Often the dark end of the scale is darker than anticipated through the mechanism of ink spot spreading. The brightest parts of the image are too bright because very small isolated dots fail to pick up any ink at all. The net result is an increase in contrast and a decrease in dynamic range.

We have no choice but to arbitrarily follow the decreased range of a roughly linear printing scale. In the images throughout this book, the brightness of the frame varies considerably. Focused images are compact; they seem to be drawn with just a spot of white coloring. On the other hand, defocused images are rendered much brighter than they actually appear when viewed through the telescope. Both contrast and brightness are under subjective control.

When you look at any image in this book, concentrate on the shape rather than the absolute brightness. The illumination of such an image is the least significant (and most deceptive) of its properties.

---

[5]300 dots-per-inch laser printers theoretically are limited to 30 distinct shadings if they use a $1/56$-inch halftone grid. Most achieve half that in practice.

# Appendix C

# Minor Axis and Offset Derivation

Ralph Dakin published exact expressions for minor axis and offset in *Sky and Telescope* years ago, but these expressions are arranged for convenience of calculation rather than exposition. Hence, the equations are a little mysterious and subject to error when published in secondary sources. This situation was not helped by an unfortunate typographical error in the original article. The mistake was corrected a few months later, but the repair was often missed and incorrect expressions progressed further in amateur literature (Dakin 1962, *erratum* 1963).

These quantities are not difficult to derive, and something can be learned from seeing the analytic geometry logic, so they are derived anew here. The formulas that follow are superficially different than Dakin's expressions, but they produce the same answers. The differences probably are caused by the way the coordinate systems are set up. Such modifications often lead to ostensibly different formulas.

## C.1  Derivation

Figure C-1 displays an "unfolded" Newtonian and defines various quantities useful in this derivation. These variables are $f$, the focal length; $D$, the diameter of the mirror; $s$, the sagitta (or depth) of the mirror; $T$, the distance from the focal plane to the center of the tube; and $L$, the diameter of the fully-illuminated region at the focal plane. In this derivation, I will determine the values of the minor (short) axis of the diagonal and the sideways or down offset of its center. The coordinate system is defined with its origin at the center of the focal plane. The $x$-axis extends through the center of the mirror, and the $y$-axis extends laterally away from the optical axis.

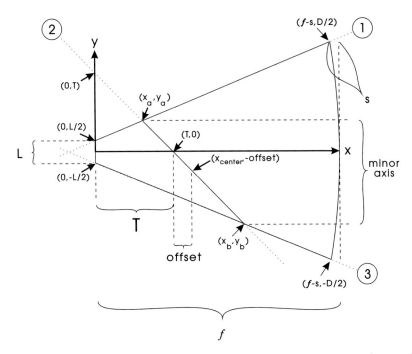

**Fig. C-1.** *The coordinate system and quantities of interest in sizing and properly placing the Newtonian diagonal.*

Three lines of Fig. C-1 are significant. Lines #1 and #3 follow the edges of the fully-illuminated field to the edges of the mirror. Line #2 is directed along the surface of the diagonal. We know it is at 45° and therefore strikes the two axes at the indicated points having coordinates $(0, T)$ and $(T, 0)$. Similarly, we know the coordinates of two points along each of the lines #1 and #3, and we can use this knowledge to obtain the defining equation of those lines as well.

Once the equations of the lines are known, the points of intersection at the far edges of the diagonal can be calculated. These intersections have coordinates $(x_a, y_a)$ and $(x_b, y_b)$. These points are all that are required to derive both the minor axis and the offset. The minor axis is

$$\text{MA} = y_a - y_b, \tag{C.1}$$

and the offset is

$$\text{Offset} = x_\text{center} - T = \frac{x_a + x_b}{2} - T. \tag{C.2}$$

Lines have the general form $y = mx + b$, where $b$ is the $y$-intercept and $m$ is the slope. Line #2 is the easiest to determine, and by inspection one can assign it the equation

$$y_2 = -x_2 + T. \tag{C.3}$$

Line #1 has a $y$-intercept of $L/2$, and the slope can be obtained by inserting the known coordinates of the point at the upper corner of the mirror:

$$\frac{D}{2} = m_1(f - s) + \frac{L}{2}. \tag{C.4}$$

Thus,

$$y_1 = \frac{D - L}{2(f - s)}x_1 + \frac{L}{2}.$$

Similarly, the equation of line #3 becomes

$$y_3 = -\frac{D - L}{2(f - s)}x_3 - \frac{L}{2}. \tag{C.5}$$

We can rename the quantity $(D - L)/2(f - s) \equiv n$. All three equations can be summarized as

$$y_1 = nx_1 + \frac{L}{2}, \quad y_2 = -x_2 + T, \quad y_3 = -nx_3 - \frac{L}{2}. \tag{C.6}$$

By setting $y_1 = y_2$, we can determine the coordinate $x_a$ as

$$x_a = \frac{T - (L/2)}{1 + n}, \tag{C.7}$$

and we insert that expression back into the line #2 equation to derive $y_a$:

$$y_a = -\frac{T - (L/2)}{1 + n} + T. \tag{C.8}$$

Similarly, the coordinates of the other intersection point are

$$x_b = \frac{T + (L/2)}{1 - n} \quad \text{and} \quad y_b = -\frac{T + (L/2)}{1 - n} + T. \tag{C.9}$$

The expression for the minor axis (Eq. C.1) is just the difference between the two $y$-values:

$$\text{MA} = \frac{T + (L/2)}{1 - n} - \frac{T - (L/2)}{1 + n} \quad \text{or} \quad \text{MA} = \frac{L + 2nT}{1 - n^2}. \tag{C.10}$$

The offset (Eq. C.2) is only a little more complicated:

$$\text{Offset} = \frac{1}{2}\left(\frac{T - (L/2)}{1 + n} + \frac{T + (L/2)}{1 - n}\right) - T \quad \text{or} \quad \text{Offset} = \frac{T + (nL/2)}{1 - n^2} - T.$$

$$\tag{C.11}$$

The final expressions of Eqs. C.10 and C.11 are exact. They only require an expression for the sagitta. A parabola of focus $f$ is determined by the equation $x = f - (y^2/4f)$, and the exact sagitta is obtained by evaluating the shift in $x$ on axis and at the $y$-value of the edge, $D/2$:

$$s = \frac{D^2}{16f}. \tag{C.12}$$

Please note that Eq. C.12 is not the same as the wavefront sagitta that will be calculated in Appendix E, but the surface sagitta, which is half as large.

## C.2   Test Case

Before proceeding further, it would be prudent to check these expressions against Dakin's results. One such calculation appears in Appendix G of Texereau (1984). With

$$
\begin{aligned}
s &= 0.0833333 \text{ inches,} \\
n &= 0.0789913 \text{ inches,} \\
T &= 6.3 \text{ inches, and} \\
L &= 0.43 \text{ inches,}
\end{aligned}
$$

one readily calculates (from Eq. C.10) that MA $= 1.43423950$ inches. This number compares well with the result of 1.43423955 using Dakin's formulas as reprinted in Texereau. Offset $= 0.056646217$ inches there, and 0.056646220 here. The slight differences are caused by numerical truncation error. (The calculations in Texereau were carried out to more decimal places for comparison.)

## C.3   Approximations

The nearly exact expressions are not that difficult to evaluate with the common availability of calculators and computers. Spreadsheet programs are especially handy for calculations such as these, but some people may want the more compact form of an approximation.

Notice that in Eqs. C.10 and C.11, the factor $1/(1 - n^2)$ can be approximated by $1 + n^2$. With most mirrors, the quantity $(D - L)/2(f - s) \equiv n$ is very close to $(D - L)/2f$. Capital $F$ is the focal ratio, so

$$\text{Offset} = \frac{T + (nL/2)}{1 - n^2} - T = (T + nL/2)(1 + n^2 \ldots) - T \cong \frac{T}{4F^2} + \frac{L}{4F}\left(1 - \frac{2T}{f}\right), \tag{C.13}$$

where the smallest terms have been ignored.

The same expansion could be done with the equation for MA, again ignoring exceptionally tiny terms, to obtain the answer

$$\text{MA} \cong L + \left( \frac{D - L}{f} \right) T. \tag{C.14}$$

The test case above was recalculated with Eqs. C.13 and C.14 and the answers are MA = 1.424 inches and Offset = 0.057 inches, quite close to the exact numbers. Of course, with a very small, fully illuminated region of the focal plane, these values approach MA = $T/F$ and Offset = $T/4F^2$.

# Appendix D

# Labeling of Diffraction Patterns

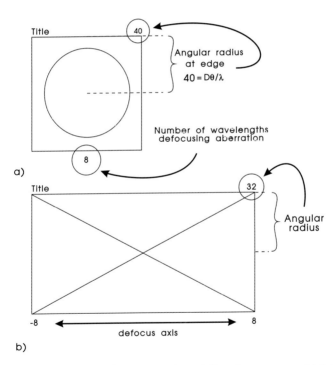

**Fig. D-1.** *Image notation: a) labels used on diffraction patterns, b) labels used on longitudinal slice patterns.*

Figure D-1a shows how the typical image pattern appearing in this book is labeled, and Fig. D-1b indicates the slight modifications to annotate slice patterns. In the upper left corner of any given pattern is a title, if one is present. In the upper right corner of a frame is a number that gives the reduced angular radius $D\theta/\lambda$ from the edge to the center of the square box.

In the case of the square diffraction pattern frame, this angle also applies to the horizontal axis. If the pattern had the number 1.22 here, the Airy disk of a focused perfect aperture would just be contained within the box (see Fig. D-2). Most of the focused patterns in the text have limits of 5 or 10, allowing us to inspect the ring structure as well as the central spot. Out-of-focus patterns are viewed at lower magnification, which accounts for the large numbers appearing in the upper right corners.

**perfect**                    **1.22**

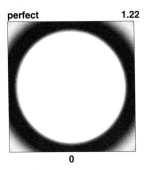

**0**

**Fig. D-2.** *A perfect Airy disk is barely contained within a box with a reduced angular dimension 1.22 from center to edge. The bright corners are the first diffraction ring.*

The centered number at the bottom of one of the square patterns is the number of wavelengths of defocusing aberration. The numbers at the lower corners of a slice pattern denote the value of defocus at each end of the box, with the defocus changing steadily between them. Longitudinal slice frames are defocused an equal distance inside and outside focus, with the best focus near the center. In all slice frames, the objective lens or mirror is to the left.

In some cases, clutter is reduced by labeling only one frame in a row or column. If a defocus value is missing, the value appears at the bottom of the column. If the angular coordinate is missing on a particular frame, it can be found on a row entry on the far right.

For composite figures with a focused image frame appearing to straddle two lower columns, the *inside* focus behavior is the column to the left (negative defocus values), while the *outside* focus behavior (positive) is in the middle column. Such figures have the behavior of perfect optics in the column to the far right. These unaberrated columns give only one side of focus; the other side is identical. See Fig. B-3.

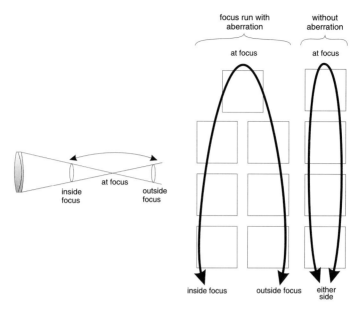

**Fig. D-3.** *A focus-run pattern shows how the frames "fold over" the region of focus. The perfect pattern to the right need not show both inside- and outside-focus images because they are identical.*

# Appendix E

# Eyepiece Travel and Defocusing Aberration

This book uses the generic unit of defocusing aberration when referring to distance out of focus. However, the most convenient way of thinking about defocus is in terms of eyepiece travel. Here, we wish to determine the amount of difference between two spheres at the aperture, one centered on focus $f$ and the other centered on a defocus position $f'$. We will then relate that very tiny distance at the aperture (the defocusing aberration) to the relatively large amount we have moved the eyepiece between $f$ and $f'$. This situation is depicted in Fig. 4-9.

The derivation proceeds from the difference between the two wavefront sagittae, or how much the wavefront is "cupped" at the aperture. Another common sagitta involves surface shape (or the shallow depth of the mirror itself). It is half the wavefront sagitta. Don't confuse surface sagitta with wavefront sagitta.

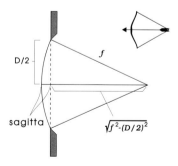

**Fig E-1.** *Geometry of the sagittal relation. Focal length $f$ is the radius of curvature of the wavefront.*

If the distance to a focus position is $f$ and if $D$ is the diameter of the aperture, then by the Pythagorean theorem, the sagitta $s$ is

$$s = f - \sqrt{f^2 - \left(\frac{D}{2}\right)^2}. \tag{E.1}$$

If the focal length is much greater than the aperture diameter, this equation may be approximated by performing a Taylor expansion. Such an approximation results in

$$s \cong \frac{D^2}{8f}. \tag{E.2}$$

Taking the difference between two different wavefront sagittae in Eq. E.2,

$$s - s' = \frac{D^2}{8f} - \frac{D^2}{8f'} = \frac{D^2}{8}\left(\frac{1}{f} - \frac{1}{f'}\right) = \frac{D^2}{8}\left(\frac{f' - f}{ff'}\right). \tag{E.3}$$

Next we demand that the quantity $s - s'$ be thought of as a certain number of wavelengths "$n\lambda$" out of focus, where $\lambda$ is the common symbol for wavelength. Noticing that $ff'$ is to a very high degree of precision just equal to the average focal length squared, then

$$s - s \equiv \Delta n\lambda = \frac{(f - f')}{8F^2}, \tag{E.4}$$

where $F$ is the focal ratio. The final change in focus as measured by advancing or pulling back the eyepiece is

$$f - f' = \Delta f = 8F^2 \Delta n\lambda. \tag{E.5}$$

As an aside, we can derive an expression for the depth of the shallow bowl in a mirror by noting that the focal distance $f$ in Eq. E.2 can be replaced by the radius of curvature $R = 2f$, or

$$s_d \cong \frac{D^2}{16f}. \tag{E.6}$$

# Appendix F

# Glitter in a Shiny Sphere

Figure F-1a shows a reflection in a small sphere. In its most general form, it is roughly shaped like a kidney bean, longer in the azimuthal direction than in the radial direction. Since the long axis of the bean is the limiting factor, an expression for this angle is derived first.

We wish to calculate $u$, the long axis of the glitter. If the glitter is far enough from the center, its approximate length is given by

$$\frac{u/2}{x} = \tan\left(\frac{\phi}{2}\right),$$  (F.1)

with $x$ being the radius of the circle containing the glitter seen in perspective and $\phi$ being the angle of the source of light. If we turn the sphere to view the situation from the side (Fig. F-1c), the radius $x$ is obtained from the great circle radius of the sphere $R$ and the light diversion angle $\theta_r$ as in

$$x = R\sin\left(\frac{\theta_r}{2}\right),$$  (F.2)

with the complete expression being

$$u = 2R\sin\left(\frac{\theta_r}{2}\right)\tan\left(\frac{\phi}{2}\right).$$  (F.3)

Thus, for a 1-inch sphere ($R = 0.5$ inch) and a reflection of the Sun ($\phi = 0.5° = 0.0087$ radians), a reflection angle ($\theta_r$) of 90° yields a glitter point 0.003 inches long. Thus, for a typical $\theta_r$, the gleam of a solar reflection will be smaller than $1/300$ the diameter of the sphere.

Similarly, we can obtain an expression for the short axis ($v$) of the bean. This dimension is obtained by perturbing Fig. F-1c around the average re-

a) front

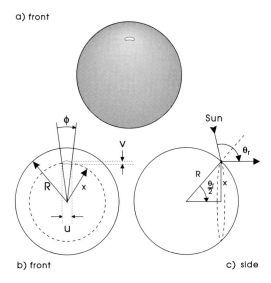

b) front                                              c) side

**Fig. F-1.** *The variables used to determine the size of the glitter reflected in a sphere.*

flection angle,

$$v = R \left[ \sin \left( \frac{\theta_r + \phi/2}{2} \right) - \sin \left( \frac{\theta_r - \phi/2}{2} \right) \right]. \qquad (F.4)$$

For the example situation, $v$ is 0.0015 inch. The glitter point is about twice as wide as it is long.

For a nearly centered bounce with the gleam appearing near the middle of the sphere ($\theta_r = 0$) and for a very small source angle $\phi$, the expression for $v$ is approximately

$$v \cong \frac{R\phi}{2}. \qquad (F.5)$$

If we want to figure the size of the round gleam where the 1-inch reflective sphere is placed opposite to the Sun, we could use this approximation. The numbers are inserted this way (the angle must be in pure number format, i.e., radians):

$$v = \frac{0.5 \text{ in } (.0087 \text{ radians})}{2} = 0.0022 \text{ in.} \qquad (F.6)$$

The glitter size shrinks to about $1/450$ the diameter of the sphere at its smallest aspect. The source of light is nearly behind the viewer's head and the reflection is approximately centered in the shiny sphere for this favorable condition to occur.

# Appendix G

# List of Common Symbols

Some symbols don't appear here at all because they are used in different ways in different locations (a good example is $N$). Some that do appear here occasionally are used in alternate ways. Most of symbols are used only in the way defined in this appendix, but if readers are unsure in any case, the immediate context takes precedence.

| | |
|---|---|
| $A_n$ | $n$th order coefficient of aberration. |
| $c$ | speed of light propagation. |
| CCD | acronym for charge-coupled device |
| CD | acronym for Compact Disc. |
| $D$ | diameter of the objective lens or mirror. |
| DAC | acronym for digital-to-analog converter. |
| $\Delta f$ | focus shift or change in focus. |
| $e$ | $2.71828\ldots$. |
| $E$ | energy. |
| EER$(\theta)$ | encircled energy ratio at angular radius $\theta$. |
| $f$ | effective focal length of the objective. |
| $F$ | the focal ratio as used in formulas. |
| $f, f',$ etc. | various focus positions. |
| $f/\#$ | the "$f$-number" or focal ratio. |
| $h$ | Planck's constant. |
| $i$ | $\sqrt{-1}$. |
| $i_s$ | the Strehl ratio. |
| $I(x', y')$ | intensity at image point $(x', y')$. |

| | |
|---:|:---|
| $J_0$ | the zeroth-order Bessel function. |
| $k$ | $k = 2\pi/\lambda$, called the "wave number." |
| $\lambda$ | the wavelength of light. |
| MA | the minor, or short axis of a Newtonian diagonal. |
| MTF | acronym for modulation transfer function. |
| Mult | the multiplier of focal lengths in the distance of the source $N$. |
| $\nu$ | frequency (time or spatial). |
| OTF | the optical transfer function. |
| $\varphi$ | reduced image angle $D\theta/\lambda$. |
| $\pi$ | $3.14159\ldots$ |
| $P(x,y)$ | the pupil function at position $(x,y)$. |
| $R$ | radius of curvature. |
| $r_{\text{Airy}}$ | radius of Airy disk. |
| RFT | acronym for richest-field telescope. |
| $\rho$ | radial coordinate of aperture (range 0 to 1). |
| RMS | acronym for root-mean-square deviation of wavefront. |
| $s$ | the sagitta in all but Appendix B. |
| $\sigma_{\text{RMS}}$ | RMS deviation of wavefront in wavelengths. |
| SNR | acronym for signal-to-noise ratio (S/N). |
| $T$ | distance from focal plane to center of tube. Ch. 6 and App. C. |
| $T(\rho)$ or $T(x,y)$ | transmission coefficient as a function of aperture radius. |
| $U(x',y')$ | complex scalar field value at point $(x',y')$. |
| $W(\rho)$ or $W(x,y)$ | aberration over the pupil in wavelengths. |
| $x$ or $y$ | usually the aperture coordinates. |
| $x'$ or $y'$ | usually the image coordinates. |

# Glossary

**Aberration** Any deviation from a spherically converging wavefront after the optical system has finished processing light is called an aberration. Aberration is commonly defined in one of two ways. The most convenient ray-optics usage expresses it as a deviation from the point of geometric focus. The wave optics convention defines it as deviation from a perfect converging sphere. These two seemingly different definitions are closely related. The slope of the wavefront determines the direction of ray propagation in a homogeneous medium.

**Accommodation** A biological adjustment to changing light or focusing conditions.

**Achromat** Literally meaning "without color," the term is used in astronomical optics to indicate a two-element refractor lens corrected for the dispersion of glass (chromatic aberration) over the color range of interest. The term achromat is a misnomer. For most doublets, only two colors are deliberately brought to a common focus, but the resulting folded spectrum offers much less dispersion than exists in simple lenses. (See *refractor, apochromat, secondary spectrum, dispersion,* and *chromatic aberration.*)

**Airy disk** (Named after early 19th century scientist Sir George Airy.) The appearance of the central peak in the focused diffraction pattern superficially resembles a disk. The illusion is made stronger since the peak is surrounded by a zero-intensity region. The disk has a soft edge, so the effective radius of the central diffraction spot varies with the brightness of the image. Brighter spots look bigger. (See *resolution.*)

**Analytic geometry** Originated by Pierre de Fermat and René Decartes in the early 17th century and further developed by later mathematicians, analytic geometry is a way of reducing geometrical relationships to algebra.

**Angle** A division of a circle. Four measures are common in this book: radians ("natural" or unitless), degrees, arcminutes, and arcseconds. The measure denoted in the upper left hand corner of the star-test plots is a reduced angle valid for all instruments, the angle in radians times the ratio $D/\lambda$. (See *resolution.*)

**Annealed** If materials are melted and allowed to cool below their solidification

343

temperature too quickly, they will exhibit permanent strains. Improperly annealed glass deforms under the influence of grinding and over time to make the surface shape uncontrollable. Almost never appearing in glasses made specifically for optical use, it often occurs in glass disks adapted for optics, but cast with another use in mind.

**Aperture** The opening through which parallel light enters the telescope. Aperture is typically measured as the diameter of the most restrictive opening of the telescope before the light is focused. Some confusion may exist with the abbreviated photographic terminology that uses the term "aperture" interchangeably with "focal ratio." Aperture is not used that way here.

**Aperture stop** A physical obstruction (usually a circular hole) placed somewhere in front of the telescope. The function of the aperture stop is to limit the aperture in a specific plane. (See *field stop*.)

**Apochromat** If three chosen colors are simultaneously focused, the lens is said to be apochromatic. The classical definition also includes corrections for spherical aberration and coma. Because three colors within the spectral range of interest are held to a common focus, secondary spectrum is markedly reduced. (See also *achromat, refractor, secondary spectrum*, and *chromatic aberration*.)

**Apodization** Shading the aperture to diminish diffraction rings. This term has come to refer to modifying the transmission and phase of the aperture to achieve any sort of diffraction pattern change.

**Arcminute** $1/60$ of a degree or $1/21{,}600$ of a full circle. (See also *arcsecond, degree, radian*, and *angle*.)

**Arcsecond** $1/60$ of an arcminute, $1/3600$ of a degree, or $1/1{,}296{,}000$ of a full circle. 1 arcsecond = $4.848 \times 10^{-6}$ radians. (See *arcminute, degree, radian*, and *angle*.)

**Aspheric surface** In optics, a concave or convex surface that superficially resembles a sphere but has another shape. Most commonly applied to conic sections.

**Astigmatism** An aberration that results from two radii of curvature oriented at right angles to one another on an optical surface. (See *aberration*.)

**Attenuation** A diminishing of wave intensity that includes diffraction, scattering, spreading of the beam, and absorption.

**Bandwidth/bandpass** The frequency range passed by a given filter.

**Barlow lens** A diverging lens placed near focus to increase the effective focal length of an instrument without appreciably increasing the telescope's physical size.

**Bench test** An indoor, laboratory-style test generally used during the fabrication of optics. Because of the necessarily compact nature of the testing geometry, most bench tests of astronomical instruments use secondary references or complicated data reduction procedures.

**Catadioptric** A mixed lens-mirror system that makes up the objective or main optical group.

**Caustic** A region where rays of light cross each other and pile up. Focus is a caustic, but this word also refers to the one-dimensional focusing that occurs with astigmatism or even the quasi-focusing that occurs in systems suffering from aberrations. In geometric optics, caustics are regions where the ray-tracing formalism breaks down.

**Chromatic aberration** Color error caused by the dispersion of light. Bringing the colors to different focus points has two debilitating effects on the image: all colors except those in focus are imaged as expanded disks, and magnifications vary with color. (See *refractor, achromat, dispersion,* and *apochromat.*)

**Collimation** Here, collimation is used to indicate achieving accurate alignment. More properly, it refers to the generation of a flat wavefront, but good alignment and a good wavefront are usually inseparable.

**Coma** An aberration that occurs when some optical systems are tilted. Rare in quality refractors, it is very common in reflectors and catadioptric systems. Coma results in a fan-like distortion. (See *aberration.*)

**Corrector** (See *Schmidt corrector* and *meniscus.*)

**Correlation** An expression of the similarity of two functions as they are offset from one another. If the functions are precisely the same, the maximum correlation is one.

**Criterion (resolution)** In astronomical optics, this term refers to a certain separation in resolved objects (as in "the stars were separated just at the Rayleigh criterion"). Colloquially, it has been also used for stating optical quality, as in "the 1/4-wavelength Rayleigh criterion," although this terminology is properly replaced by "the 1/4-wavelength limit." (See *Rayleigh tolerance* or *Rayleigh criterion.*)

**Curtate cycloid** A cycloid is the path followed by a point on the rim of a wheel. A curtate cycloid is the path of a point nearer the axle.

**Dawes criterion** A separation angle of about $1.02\lambda/D$. It occurs between the loose Rayleigh criterion and the tight Sparrow criterion.

**Decibel** A change in intensity of sound (or any signal) by a factor of 10 was originally termed "a bel." Since this change was too coarse, bels were never used. People much preferred the finer "decibel" measure. The dB level of $I_1$ referenced to $I_2$ is $10\log_{10}(I_1/I_2)$.

**Defocus** The amount of defocus as used here is more precisely the defocusing aberration measured in wavelengths of light. This number is not to be confused with defocus distance, or how far one must move the eyepiece to obtain defocusing aberration. (See Table 5-1.)

**Degree** $1/360$ of a full circle. The reason early mathematicians probably used such a peculiar number is because it can be divided into so many whole number portions: 180, 120, 90, 72, 60, 45, 36, 30, 20, 18, 16, 15, 12, 10, 8, 6, 5, 4, 3, and 2. This measure was very helpful before the decimal number system was invented (with its compact algorithm for long division). Also equal to $\pi/180$ or about $1/57.3$ radian. (See *arcminute, arcsecond, radian,* and *angle.*)

**Dielectric** A non-conducting material that becomes polarized in an electric field (i.e., that develops "electric poles" similar to "magnetic poles"). Many such materials are transparent to visible light. Glass, polyester, air, and quartz are all examples of dielectrics.

**Diffraction-limited** Used conventionally as an equivalent for the $1/14$-wavelength RMS wavefront deviation limit of Maréchal. Colloquially, it is used to mean the same thing as the $1/4$-wavelength Rayleigh limit, but that usage is only true for broadly-varying wavefront deformations such as correction error.

**Diopter** A measure of lens focusing strength. A lens having a strength of 2 diopters has a focal length of $1/2$ meter, 3 diopters has a focal length of $1/3$ meter, etc. Thus, the human eye, which is focused at a distance of about an inch, has a native strength of roughly 40 diopters. Focusing corrections typical in eyeglasses—1 to 4 diopters—are minor adjustments.

**Dispersion** Frequency or color dependence of optical effects. Dispersion in refractive materials leads to desirable effects in spectroscopes and undesirable effectos when white-light images are the goal. The phenomenon of chromatic aberration in lenses is a difference of focal lengths for light at various portions of the spectrum. It results in the breaking of white light into rainbow colors.

**Doublet** Two lenses placed in close proximity that act as if they were a single unit. Used to correct various single-lens defects, especially chromatic aberration. (See *achromat* and *chromatic aberration.*)

**Dynamic range** The intensity range over which a sensor or emitter is approximately linear. Dynamic range is typically written in decibels.

**Effective** *Effective* is applied to another quantity such as focal length or focal ratio. Complicated multi-element systems like Cassegrain telescopes or the use of a Barlow lens on a telescope demand some sort of leveling terminology to make their description comparable. "Effective focal length," for example, is the same as the fcal length if the complicated optics were replaced by a single thin lens. "Effective focal ratio" is determined by examining how precipitously the light cone converges to focus. Cassegrain telescopes are much shorter than their effective focal lengths and ratios indicate.

**Evanescent waves** Waves that can only occur at the interface between media of different optical characteristics. They cannot propagate away from the interface and are bound to that surface.

**Field stop** A mask defining the field near focus. It is usually visible in the eyepiece as a sharply defined circle. This circle is not the edge of the main lens or mirror, but is contained in the eyepiece itself. It can be seen in most eyepieces by removing the eyepiece and turning it upside down. It is the sharp-edge opening through which the lenses can be seen. (See *aperture stop*.)

**Figure** (Noun) The surface shape of an optical surface. (Verb) To perform polishing operations to achieve the proper shape.

**Focal length** If an infinitely distant target is imaged by a lens or mirror, the focal length of the optical element is the distance from the lens or mirror such that the sharpest image of the target is found. Here, if no other indication is given, the focal length refers to the effective focal length of the objective system, rather than the eyepiece.

**Focal ratio** The ratio between the effective focal length and the aperture is the focal ratio. It is written as $F = f/D$, where $F$ is the focal ratio, $D$ the diameter of the aperture, and $f$ the focal length. By convention, a 6-inch telescope with a focal length of 48 inches is referred to as an "f/8" system because $48/6$ equals 8.

**Fourier transform** A mathematical procedure used to derive the frequency content of a function.

**Foucault test** A test using an obscuring edge placed near a point or slit focus.

**Fraunhofer lines** Dark lines in the solar spectrum labeled by the alphabet.

**Fresnel zone** A conceptual device to keep track of the phase sign. At locations where the wave is above its average value, it is in a positive Fresnel zone, and where the wave is below its average value, it is in a negative Fresnel zone. Thus, a given Fresnel zone applies only at an instant of time and is only an approximation of what is really happening.

**Gaussian function** A function of form $Ae^{-x^2/w^2}$, with amplitude $A$ and $1/e$ half-width $w$. Random deviations often follow a Gaussian distribution, as does the well-known "bell curve."

**Geometric shadow** In the light-as-particles ray tracing approximation, the geometric shadow consists of the regions beyond the cone extending from the aperture and passing through focus.

**Grit** Loose particles of abrasive used in grinding optical surfaces. Grit sizes range from coarse sandlike grains to powdered finishing abrasives.

**Hyperboloid** A three-dimensional surface having a blunted cone shape.

**Incoherent** When two waves are added, they are said to be incoherent if they have no phase relationship with one another. At one instant, they may add constructively, and at the next, subtract destructively. Coherent light is usually derived from the same atomic transition or the same cavity resonance (in lasers), incoherent light from unrelated transitions. Severely restricting the geometry (as in focusing light on one or more slits) will often achieve approximate spatial coherence of even temporally incoherent light. In the star test, light is emitted from an insensibly small point, a star or a pinhole, so the Huygens-Fresnel principle treats it as coherent (See *interference.*)

**Index of refraction** (See *refractive index.*)

**Intensity** As used here, intensity is proportional to the wave value squared. Actually, this number is not intensity as defined radiometrically, but the misuse has become customary.

**Interference** When intensity is calculated from the sum of two coherent waves, it is figured something like this equation: $I = (W_1 + W_2)^2 = (W_1)^2 + (W_2)^2 + 2W_1W_2$. The term on the end of the equation is called the interference term. If $W_2 = -W_1$, this term completely cancels the first two. If $W_2 = W_1$, the intensity is doubled. For incoherent light, this term can be anything at a given instant, but it averages over longer times to zero.

**Iris** An aperture stop that is adjustable in diameter. The eye has an iris and most cameras have a leaf-type iris used to adjust the aperture ratio. An iris is typically placed in or near a pupil in an afocal beam of light. (See *aperture stop.*)

**Knife-edge test** Colloquial expression for the Foucault test.

**Lap** A contraction of "lapping tool," it is a disk coated with pitch and powdered polishing agent in a slurry of water. Laps are used to polish optics. Typically, they are crossed by trenches ("channels") that have been cut into the lap to ease conformance to the optical element being worked.

**Longitudinal** As used here, an orientation along the axis of the instrument. The opposite of transverse. The conventional image as viewed in an eyepiece is a transverse slice. A longitudinal slice is usually in a plane passing through the centers of the objective and eyepiece.

**Magnification** Literally, the object size divided by the image size. The usefulness of this term breaks down when we talk about very distant, very large objects. In astronomical telescopes, it is much more common to speak of *angular magnification*. Angular magnification refers to the angle subtended by the object in the eyepiece divided by the angle subtended without optical aid. Thus, if we look at the half-degree Moon in binoculars with a magnification of 7, we should see an image that extends an apparent 3.5 degrees.

**Magnitude** The magnitude difference between two stars is $-2.512 \log_{10}(I_1/I_2)$. Thus, if one star is 10 times brighter than another, it is only 2.5 magnitudes brighter. Magnitude is similar to the decibel scale used in electronics or sound and the Richter scale of earthquakes. For historical reasons, it increases with dimmer stars.

**Meniscus** Optically, a meniscus is a strongly bent lens with a great deal of curvature but little focusing power. In other words, its curvature on the rear side is very near that of its front. The corrector lens of a Maksutov telescope is a meniscus.

**Micrometer** A unit of measure equal to $10^{-6}$ meters. Twenty years ago, this unit was in common use as the "micron." Actually, by international convention, all metric units of length are denoted "-metre," but this convention is not followed here.

**Microripple** A surface roughness originating from a correlated area on the order of 1 mm across. Microripple is usually of very small amplitude.

**Model, modeling** Fitting a phenomenon to a mathematical system that may or may not be physically derived. The fit can be empirical, with no scientific basis, but the best and most extensible models are usually derived from fundamental theory.

**Modulation transfer function** MTF predicts the ability of an optical system to preserve light-dark contrast in periodic targets with finer and finer bar spacing.

**Newtonian telescope** The parabolic reflector was first announced by Sir Isaac Newton in 1672. It was not useful for astronomical purposes until John Hadley made the first approximately paraboloidal surface in 1721.

**Normalized** An integral that is normalized has been reduced to a value of one in an ideal case. Thus, an integral of, say, energy over the aperture is multipled by a constant to yield a value of 1.00. Such a procedure is useful in comparisons of imperfect apertures to perfect ones.

**Objective** The main image-forming element or group of elements in a telescope. Often, it is convenient to equate "objective" with "non-removable" optics in the system.

**Oblate spheroid** A conic surface of revolution that is flatter in the middle. An oblate spheroidal mirror focused at infinity has more spherical aberration than a sphere.

**Optical transfer function** Full complex form of the spatial-frequency transfer function. Its absolute value is the modulation transfer function. Gives the contrast and shift in position of a sinusoidal bar pattern.

**Overcorrected** A form of low-order spherical aberration in which marginal rays cross beyond the focus of central rays. In Newtonian telescopes, an overcorrected mirror is hyperboloidal. (See *undercorrected*.)

**Paraboloid** A theoretical curve between prolate spheroids and hyperboloids. Represents the ideal in making Newtonian telescope mirrors.

**Paraxial focus** The focus of rays incident at or near the center of the mirror and parallel to the axis of the instrument. Seldom the same as "best" focus.

**Photodetector** A sensor capable of detecting one or a few individual photons.

**Pit** An unpolished crater left over from the grinding process remaining in a polished surface.

**Polychromatic** Having many colors. White light is polychromatic.

**Primary aberrations** Pure low-order forms of aberrations. Examples include coma, spherical aberration, and astigmatism, etc. (Also called *Seidel aberrations.*)

**Primary ripple** Coarse, quasi-periodic roughness having a spacing about the same as the channels in the lapping tool. (See *lap.*)

**Prolate spheroid** A conic surface of revolution intermediate between a sphere and a paraboloid.

**Quantum mechanics** A name applied to the wave theory of matter. When wavelike particles are caught in a potential well (such as an electron in the Coulomb field of an atom), the requirement that the waves precisely fit in these wells demands that only certain energy states be occupied. Thus, energy can only be added or subtracted to such systems in discrete steps (called quanta).

**Radian** The measure of angle equal to moving one unit along the perimeter of a circle with unit radius. A radian is the "natural" measure of angle in that it is unitless. The word "radians" is actually a placeholder. A frequency of $2\pi$ radians/second is the same thing as $2\pi$/second. An angle of $2\pi$ means that one full cycle of a circle has been traversed. (See *angle, arcminute, arcsecond,* and *degree.*)

**Radiator** An elemental source of secondary waves used in the Huygens-Fresnel theory of diffraction.

**Rayleigh criterion** When a double star is separated by an amount equal to the radius of either star's Airy disk, the separation is said to be just at the Rayleigh criterion. Most observers are able to resolve stars separated by less than this amount, but they do so more by shape of the pair rather than darkening between them.

**Rayleigh tolerance or limit** Optics that satisfy Rayleigh's limit produce wavefronts that can be enclosed by concentric shells with radii differing by $1/4$ wavelength of yellow-green light. (See *RMS.*)

**Refractive index** The ratio of the speed of light in empty space to the speed of light in a material. Examples: water has a refractive index of 1.3 and most glasses are somewhere over 1.5. Refractive index varying with wavelength is a conventional way of describing dispersion.

**Resolution** A measure of optical quality that depends solely on whether two equally bright incoherent points or bands of light are distinguishable. (See *modulation transfer function* and *optical transfer function.*)

**RMS** Stands for "root mean square," or the square root of the averaged deviations squared. In telescopes, RMS is used as a measure of surface quality of optical elements, with lower values for more perfect optics.

**Rouge** (or *Jeweler's rouge*) A powdered oxide of iron used in polishing compounds.

**Scattering** Diffraction from randomly distributed optical defects or obstructions.

**Schiefspiegler** A German word meaning "oblique reflector." A schiefspiegler is a telescope that avoids the additional diffraction of central obstruction by using tilted, round mirrors.

**Schmidt corrector** A plate placed in the incoming parallel beam to introduce an equal and opposite amount of spherical aberration to that produced by the rest of the optical system. The typical curve defining a Schmidt corrector is a 4th-order radial polynomial.

**Secondary spectrum** The residual chromatic aberration that exists in the bright portions of the spectrum (among the deliberately corrected wavelengths) even after a good attempt has been made at fixing color error. (See *chromatic aberration, achromatic, apochromatic,* and *dispersion.*)

**Seidel aberrations** The earliest formal description of spherical aberration, coma, astigmatism, field curvature, and distortion using polynomials and trigonometric functions. Also called the "primary" aberrations, or the first non-trivial components of a generalized aberration expansion.

**Shading** (See *apodization.*)

**Signal-to-noise ratio (SNR)** A comparison between the amount of interesting information to the amount of non-interesting information as it is transferred through a system. Because the noise power is usually so much less than the signal power, the SNR is usually given in decibels. Higher SNRs are desirable. (See *decibels.*)

**Sparrow criterion** If the separation of two points of light is set to where the diffraction structure creates a flat isthmus bridging them, then they are said to be separated by the Sparrow criterion.

**Speckles** Little points of light surrounding the image produced from rough surfaces or turbulent media. Speckles are caused by interference.

**Spherical aberration** When the converging wavefront is subtracted from a sphere centered on best focus, any remainder described by radial polynomials of low order is called "spherical aberration."

**Strehl ratio** The ratio of the maximum central brightness of an aberrated aperture's image to what it would be if the aberration were removed. A Strehl ratio of 0.8 is associated with the $1/4$-wavelength Rayleigh tolerance.

**Substrate** A telescope mirror is a layer of metal about 100 nanometers thick. The glass holding it is properly termed the "substrate."

**Superposition** If the combined effects of two waves are no more complicated than the simple sum of the waves, the system is called linear, and the net effect is called a linear superposition of the two waves. In other words, no effect arises from one wave's influence on the other. Intense light beams do not obey superposition in nonlinear media. All optical phenomena in this book are assumed to be linear. (See *interference*).

**Telephoto** A rear lens element that lengthens the effective focal length. Differs from a Barlow lens primarily in that it cannot be removed and was specifically designed to work with the optical system.

**Undercorrected** As used here, a type of low-order spherical aberration in which marginal rays cross nearer to the objective than the central rays.

**Wave function** The three-dimensional function describing a wave, generally including its amplitude, phase, and direction of propagation.

**Wavelet** Here, this term refers to the tiny subsequent waves emitted by the Huygens-Fresnel radiators. It also refers to a mathematical method used in signal processing, but that usage does not apply in this book.

**Wedge** A prismatic aberration of refractor lenses. Although wedge can result from a lens that is actually thicker on one side, it can also result from a decentered symmetric lens.

**Zones** A contraction of "zonal defects," they are a special case of spherical aberration. "Zones" can be thought of as localized circular corrugations on the surface.

# References

**Allred and Mills 1989** Daniel B. Allred and James P. Mills, "Effect of aberrations and apodization on the performance of coherent optical systems. 3: The near field," *Applied Optics,* vol. 28, no. 4, pp. 673–681, 15 Feb. 1989.

**Bachynski and Bekefi 1957** M.P. Bachynski and G. Bekefi, "Study of Optical Diffraction Images at Microwave Frequencies," *Journal of the Optical Society of America,* vol. 47, no. 5, pp. 428–438, May 1957.

**Baker 1992** Lionel Baker, *Selected Papers on Optical Transfer Function: Measurement,* SPIE Milestone Series Volume MS 60, SPIE Optical Engineering Press, 1992.

**Baker and Copson 1950** Bevan B. Baker and E.T. Copson, *The Mathematical Theory of Huygens' Principle,* Oxford Clarendon Press, Oxford UK, 1950.

**Barakat 1962** Richard Barakat, "Solution of the Luneberg Apodization Problems," *J. Opt. Soc. Am.,* vol. 52, no. 3, pp. 264–275, March 1962.

**Bell 1922** Louis Bell, *The Telescope,* McGraw-Hill, 1922, Dover reprint, 1981.

**Berry 1979** M.V. Berry, "Diffractals," *J. Phys. A: Math. Gen.,* vol. 12, no. 6, pp. 781–797, 1979.

**Berry and Blackwell 1981** M.V. Berry and T.M. Blackwell, "Diffractal echoes," *J. Phys. A: Math. Gen.* vol. 14, pp. 3101–3110, 1981.

**Berry 1992** Richard Berry, "How to build a portable artificial star," *Sky & Telescope* (Gleanings for ATMs), p. 572, November 1992.

**Beyer and Clune 1988** Louis M. Beyer and Laverne C. Clune, "Intensity and encircled energy for circular pupils obscured by strut supported central obscurations," *Applied Optics,* vol. 27, no. 24, 15 Dec. 1988.

**Born and Wolf 1980** Max Born and Emil Wolf, *Principles of Optics,* 6th ed., Pergamon Press, 1980.

**Brigham 1988** E. Oran Brigham, *The Fast Fourier Transform and its Applications,* Prentice-Hall, Englewood Cliffs, NJ, 1988.

**Buchdahl 1970** H.A. Buchdahl, *An Introduction to Hamiltonian Optics,* pp. 232–234, Cambridge University Press 1970 (republished by Dover Publications in 1993).

354

**Buchroeder 1994** R.A. Buchroeder, private correspondence, 1994.

**Burch 1985** D.S. Burch, "Fresnel diffraction by a circular aperture," *American Journal of Physics,* vol. 53, no. 3, pp. 255–260, March 1985.

**Cagnet et al. 1962** M. Cagnet, M. Francon, J.C. Thrierr, *Atlas of Optical Phenomena,* Springer-Verlag, Göttingen and Heidelberg 1962.

**Capers et al. 1991** Robert S. Capers, Eric Lipton, and staff writers "The Looking Glass—How a flaw reflects cracks in space science" March 31 to April 3, 1991, *The Hartford Courant,* Hartford Connecticut.

**Ceravolo et al. 1992** Peter Ceravolo, Terence Dickinson, and Douglas George "Optical Quality in Telescopes," *Sky & Telescope,* vol. 83, no. 3, pp. 253–257, March 1992.

**Conrady 1957** A.E. Conrady, *Applied Optics and Optical Design,* Dover Publications, Part One–1957 (Part Two–1960).

**Cornejo and Malacara 1970** A. Cornejo and D. Malacara, "Ronchi Test of Aspherical Surfaces, Analysis, and Accuracy," *Applied Optics,* vol. 9, no. 8, Aug. 1970, pp. 1897–1901.

**CRC 1973** *Handbook of Chemistry and Physics,* 54th Ed., ed. by Robert C. Weast, The Chemical Rubber Company Press, 1973.

**Danjon and Couder 1935** André Danjon and André Couder, *Lunettes et Télescopes,* Éditions de la Revue D'Optique Théorique et Instrumentale, Paris, 1935. [in French]

**Delvo 1985** Pierino Delvo, "Point-Diffraction Interferometry Made Easy" *Sky & Telescope* (Gleanings for ATM's), February 1985.

**Dakin 1962** R.K. Dakin, "Placing and Aligning the Newtonian Diagonal," *Sky & Telescope* (Gleanings for ATM's), pp. 368–369, Dec. 1962. *erratum* p. 114, Feb. 1963.

**di Francia 1952** G. Toraldo di Francia, "Super-Gain Antenna and Optical Resolving Power," *Supplemento al Volume IX,* Serie IX del Nuovo Cimento, no. 3, 1952.

**Dolph 1946** C.L. Dolph, "A Current Distribution of Broadside Arrays Which Optimizes the Relationship Between Beam Width and Side-Lobe Level," *Proc. Inst. Radio Eng.,* vol. 34, p. 335, June 1946.

**Edberg 1984** Stephen J. Edberg, "Apodizing Screens: A Critical Evaluation," *Telescope Making #24,* p. 12, Fall 1984.

**Erkkila and Rogers 1981** John H. Erkkila and Mark E. Rogers, "Diffracted fields in the focal volume of a converging wave," *J. Opt. Soc. Am.,* vol. 71, no. 7, pp. 904–905, July 1981.

**Goodman 1968** J.W. Goodman, *Introduction to Fourier Optics,* McGraw-Hill, 1968.

**Gordon 1984** Rodger W. Gordon, "Apodizing and Metzger," Letters, *Telescope Making #24,* p. 47, Fall 1984.

**Harrington 1987** Steven Harrington, *Computer Graphics, A Programming Approach,* 2nd ed., McGraw-Hill, New York, 1987.

**Hecht 1987** Eugene Hecht, *Optics,* 2nd ed., Addison-Wesley, Reading, MA, 1987.

**Hufnagel 1993** Robert E. Hufnagel, "Propagation Through Atmospheric Turbulence," Chap. 6 in *The Infrared Handbook,* ed. by William L. Wolfe and George J. Zissis, Infrared Information Analysis Center, Environmental Research Institute of Michigan, 4th printing, 1993.

**Ingalls 1976** *Amateur Telescope Making Book One,* 4th ed., edited by Albert G. Ingalls, Scientific American, Inc., 1976 (originally published 1935). Book Two–1978 (org. 1937) and Book Three–1953 by the same publisher.

**Jacquinot 1958** Pierre Jacquinot "Apodization" (Appendix E) *Concepts of Classical Optics,* by John Strong, Freeman and Co., 1958.

**Jacquinot and Roizen-Dossier 1964** P. Jacquinot and B. Roizen-Dossier, "Apodisation," [alternate spelling] *Progress in Optics Vol III,* ed. by E. Wolf, p. 29, North-Holland, 1964.

**Kestner 1981** Bob Kestner, "Grinding, Polishing, and Figuring Thin Telescope Mirrors," Part 1–Grinding, *Telescope Making #12,* pp. 30–35, Summer 1981 (Part 2: *TM#13*; Part 3: *TM#16*).

**King 1955** Henry C. King, *The History of the Telescope,* Charles Griffin and Co., 1955, Dover reprint, 1979.

**Kingslake 1948** R. Kingslake, "The Diffraction Structure of the Elementary Coma Image," *Proc. Phys. Soc.,* vol. 61, p. 147, 1948.

**Kingslake 1978** R. Kingslake, *Lens Design Fundamentals,* Academic Press, Inc., 1978.

**Kinsler et al. 1982** Lawrence E. Kinsler, Austin R. Frey, Alan B. Coppens, and James V. Sanders, *Fundamentals of Acoustics,* 3rd Ed., John Wiley and Sons, New York, 1982.

**Leonard 1954** Arthur S. Leonard, in "The Amateur Astronomer" column of *Scientific American,* ed. by Albert G. Ingalls, p. 104, June 1954.

**Li 1982** Yajun Li, "Dependence of the focal shift on Fresnel number and f number," *J. Opt. Soc. Am.,* vol. 72, no. 6, pp. 770–774, June 1982.

**Luneburg 1964** R.K. Luneburg, *Mathematical Theory of Optics,* University of California Press, Berkeley & Los Angeles, 1964. (Luneburg's name was misspelled "Luneberg" in the 1944 first edition; unfortunately, this spelling was propagated in the literature.)

356

**Mahajan 1981** Virendra N. Mahajan, "Zernike annular polynomials for imaging systems with annular pupils," *J. Opt. Soc. Am.,* vol. 71, no. 1, Jan. 1981.

**Mahajan 1982** Virendra N. Mahajan, "Strehl ratio for primary aberrations: some analytical results for circular and annular pupils," *J. Opt. Soc. Am.,* vol. 72, no. 9, Sept. 1992.

**Mallick 1978** S. Mallick, "Common-Path Interferometers" in *Optical Shop Testing,* ed. by Daniel Malacara, Wiley 1978.

**Mandelbrot 1983** B.B. Mandelbrot, *The Fractal Geometry of Nature,* W.H. Freeman, San Francisco, 1983.

**Maréchal 1947** André Maréchal, "Études des effets combinés de la diffraction et des aberrations géométriques sur l'image d'un point lumineux," *Revue d'Optique,* vol. 26, no. 9, pp. 257–277, 1947.

**Maurer 1991** Andreas Maurer, "Measuring Resolution Indoors," *Sky & Telescope* (Gleanings for ATM's), September 1991.

**Mobsby 1974** E.G.H. Mobsby, "A Ronchi Null Test for Paraboloids," *Sky & Telescope* (Gleanings for ATM's), November 1974.

**Muirden 1974** James Muirden, *The Amateur Astronomer's Handbook,* Crowell, New York, 1974.

**Murata 1965** Kazumi Murata, "Instruments for the Measuring of Optical Transfer Functions," *Progress in Optics V,* ed. by E. Wolf, North Holland, 1965.

**Nienhuis and Nijboer 1949** K. Nienhuis and B.R.A. Nijboer, "The Diffraction Theory of Aberration. Part III: general formulae for small aberrations: experimental verification of the theoretical results," *Physica,* vol. 14, no. 9, pp. 590–608, Jan. 1949.

**Osterberg and Wilkins 1949** Harold Osterberg and J. Ernest Wilkins, Jr., "The Resolving Power of a Coated Objective," *Journal of the Optical Society of America,* vol. 39, no. 7, p. 553, July 1949.

**Park 1974** David Park, *Introduction to Quantum Mechanics* 2nd ed., McGraw-Hill, Inc., 1974.

**Parrent and Thompson 1969** George B. Parrent, Jr. and Brian J. Thompson, *Physical Optics Notebook,* Society of Photo-Optical Instrumentation Engineers (SPIE), Redondo Beach, CA, 1969.

**Peitgen and Saupe 1988** *The Science of Fractal Images,* ed. by H. Peitgen and Deitmar Saupe, Springer-Verlag, New York, Berlin, 1988.

**Peltier 1965** Leslie C. Peltier, *Starlight Nights,* pp. 215–216, Sky Publishing, Cambridge, Massachusetts, 1965.

**Peters and Pike 1977** W.T. Peters and R. Pike, "The Size of the Newtonian Diagonal." *Sky & Telescope* (Gleanings for ATMs), p. 220, March 1977.

**Press et al. 1986** William H. Press, Brian P. Flannery, Saul A. Teukolsky, and William T. Vetterling, *Numerical Recipes: The Art of Scientific Computing (Fortran),* Cambridge University Press, Cambridge, 1986.

**Prugna 1991** F.D. Prugna, "A Monte Carlo Approach to the Ronchi Test," *Sky & Telescope* (Astronomical Computing), April 1991.

**Roddier 1981** F. Roddier, "The Effects of Atmospheric Turbulence in Optical Astronomy," *Progress in Optics,* ed. by E. Wolf, vol. XIX, pp. 281–376, North-Holland 1981.

**Ronchi 1964** Vasco Ronchi, "Forty Year of History of a Grating Inteferometer," *Applied Optics,* vol. 3, no. 4, pp. 437–450, April 1964.

**Rutten and van Venrooij 1988** H.G.J. Rutten and M.A.M. van Venrooij, *Telescope Optics: Evaluation and Design,* Willmann-Bell, Inc. 1988.

**S&T 1990** "Hubble's Flaw Pinpointed," *Sky & Telescope,* November 1990, p. 470.

**Schroeder 1987** Daniel J. Schroeder, *Astronomical Optics,* Academic Press, Inc., 1987.

**Schultz 1980** S. Schultz "The Macalester Four-Goal System of Mirror Making and the Ronchi Test," *Telescope Making #9,* Fall 1980.

**Sidgwick 1955** J.B. Sidgwick, *Amateur Astronomer's Handbook,* 4th ed., Enslow Publishers, Hillside New Jersey (1980).

**Sinnott 1990** "HST's Magnificent Optics... What Went Wrong?" *Sky & Telescope,* October 1990, p. 356.

**Sinnott 1991** R.W. Sinnott, "Focus and Collimation: How Critical?" *Sky & Telescope* (Astronomical Computing), May 1991.

**Smartt and Strong 1972** R.N. Smartt and J. Strong "Point Diffraction Interferometer" (Abstract) *J. Opt. Soc. Am.,* vol. 62, p. 737, 1972.

**Smartt and Steel 1975** R.N Smartt and W.H. Steel, "Theory and Application of Point-Diffraction Interferometers," *Proc. ICO Conf. Opt. Methods in Sci. and Ind. Meas.,* Tokyo, 1974 Japan. *J. Appl. Phys.* vol. 14, (1975), Suppl. 14–1.

**Strong and Plitnick 1992** William J. Strong and George R. Plitnick, *Music Speech Audio,* Soundprint, Provo UT, 1992.

**Suiter 1983** D. Suiter, "Star Testing Your Telescope," *Astronomy,* April 1983.

**Suiter 1986a** D. Suiter, "Modifications to the Diffraction Image Caused by the Surface Roughness in Mirrors," *Telescope Making #28,* p. 24, Fall 1986.

**Suiter 1986b** D. Suiter, "Changing the Aperture Pupil," *Telescope Making #29,* p. 34, Winter 1986/87.

**Suiter 1987** D. Suiter, "Letter to a Beginner," *Deep Sky* vol. 5, no. 1, Spring 1987.

**Suiter 1988** D. Suiter, "Testing Paraboloidal Mirrors," *Telescope Making #32,* Spring 1988, p. 4.

**Suiter 1990** D. Suiter, "Test Drive Your Telescope," *Astronomy,* pp. 56–61, May 1990.

**Taylor 1983** H. Dennis Taylor, *The Adjustment and Testing of Telescope Objectives,* 5th ed., first published 1891, Adam Hilger Press, 1983.

**Taylor and Thompson 1958** C.A. Taylor and B.J. Thompson, "Attempt to Investigate Experimentally the Intensity Distribution near the Focus in the Error-Free Diffraction Patterns of Circular and Annular Pupils," *J. Opt. Soc. Am.,* vol. 48, no. 11, pp. 844–850, November 1958.

**Terebizh 1990** V.Yu. Terebizh, "A New Ronchi Null Test for Mirrors," *Sky & Telescope* (Gleanings), Sept. 1990.

**Texereau 1984** Jean Texereau, *How to Make a Telescope,* 2nd ed., (first published 1951), Willmann-Bell, Inc., 1984.

**Twyman 1988** F. Twyman, *Prism and Lens Making,* 2nd ed., (originally published 1952), portion on roughness abstracted from work by Texereau, Adam Hilger, Bristol, 1988.

**van de Hulst 1981** H.C. van de Hulst, *Light Scattering by Small Particles,* p. 107, Dover Publications, 1981 (originally appeared in 1957).

**Van Nuland 1983** J. Van Nuland, "More on Apodizing," Letters, *Telescope Making #21,* p. 4, Winter 1983.

**Walker 1977** Jearl Walker, *The Flying Circus of Physics With Answers,* probs. 4-13, 4-15, Wiley and Sons, New York, 1977.

**Welford 1960** W.T. Welford, "On the Limiting Sensitivity of the Star Test for Optical Instruments," *Journal of the Optical Society of America,* vol. 50, no. 1, pp. 21–23, Jan. 1960.

**Welford 1978** W.T. Welford, "Star Tests," ch. 11 of *Optical Shop Testing,* ed. by D. Malacara, pp. 351–379, John Wiley and Sons, New York 1978.

**Zmek 1993** W.P. Zmek, "Rules of Thumb For Planetary Scopes–I," *Sky & Telescope* (Telescope Making), July 1993; "Rules of Thumb For Planetary Scopes–II," *Sky & Telescope,* Sept. 1993.

# Index

## A

aberration function,
    astigmatism 254
    medium-scale roughness 241
    misalignment 106
    pinching 147
    small-scale roughness 247
    spherical aberration 174
    tube currents 139
    turbulence 131
    turned edge 211
    zones 205
accommodation 19, 79, 93
accordion box 91
achromatic lens 222
achromatism, Isaac Newton 222
aggregate error 265
air, index of refraction 129
Airy disk 11, 334
alignment 17, 22, 104, 266
    Newtonian 109
    refractor 121
    Schmidt-Cassegrain 125
aperture, as fundamental filter 37
APERTURE program 307, 316
apochromatic lens 226
apodization 160–166
artificial source 77, 82
    at night 90
    color correction 90
    disadvantages 83
    distance 83
    distance for Schmidt-Cassegrains 86
    example 97–100
    flashlight illumination 90
    induced spherical aberration 83
    modifying separation 98
    mounting 91
    size 86
    size, reflected in sphere 89, 339

artificial source (cont.)
    spherical reflector 88
aspherical figuring 202
astigmatism 5, 32, 251
    diagnosing cause 258
    in star test 90, 258–260
ASYMM program 317
atmospheric turbulence 129
audio analogy 38

## B

bandpass, optical system 46
black spheres 90
boundary-value problem 58, 308

## C

calculation methods 307
Cassegrain design 171
causality 62
caustic test 284
caustic 170
Ceravolo's mirrors 267
chromatic aberration 219
    eyepiece 232
    in eye 231
clean optics 168
clips, mirror 25, 114
collimation 17, 22, 104
colored filters in star test 93, 227
coma 23, 106
    mix with astigmatism 104
complain, how to 273
contrast reversal 52
convective cell 131
coordinates of light 57
cycloid, curtate 147, 345

## D

Dall-Kirkham-Cassegrain 171

Danjon and Couder conditions 8
Dawes criterion 286
decentering error 228
defocus distance 20, 78, 337
defocused, definition 2
defocusing aberration 75, 173
deformed optics 145
depth of focus 79
diagonal size, excessive cures 156
diffraction rings 10
diffraction, and focusing 65
diffraction 55
dispersion 220
dog biscuit 236
Dollond, John 223
dust and scratches 166

**E**

electronic pop 61
encircled energy ratio (EER) 197
encircled energy
    secondary obstruction 154
    spherical aberration 177
example star tests
    8″ f/6 Newtonian 94
    16″ f/4 Newtonian 97
    6″ f/12 apochromatic refractor 98
    8″ f/10 Schmidt-Cassegrain 100
eye, automatic focus 93
    roughness 240
eyeglasses 18, 252
eyepiece motion, 77–81
    internal focusing mechanisms 81
    table of 80
eyepiece, in star test 17

**F**

fast Fourier transform 314
field stop 9
filter, colored 93, 98, 227
fine-alignment 117
fixed eyepiece viewpoint 9
fixing telescope flaws 269
fluorescent lights 41
focus accommodation 19, 79, 93
focus position with artificial source
    83–86
focus trick 93
focus, types 174
focuser motion, in star test 18, 78
focusing error, fix first 272
Foucault test 167, 239, 278

Fourier 62, 71
Fraunhofer 26
    approximation 310
    lines 224
Fresnel approximation 310
Fresnel zones 66–70
Fresnel-Kirchhoff formula 308

**G**

Gaussian pupil transmission 161
geometric Ronchi test 289–297
geometric shadow 56
grinding, astigmatism 5
guitar string 70

**H**

Hall, Chester Moor 223
Hartmann test 284
Heisenberg indeterminacy 60
HST (Hubble Space Telescope) 172
Huygens, Christian 63
Huygens-Fresnel principle 307
Hz (hertz), definition 39

**I**

image evaluation, blind test 267
image processing 41
image, as reproduction 35
impulse response function 62
indeterminacy principle 60
interferometer tests 298
iridescence 298

**K**

knife-edge test 167, 239, 278

**L**

labeling of image frames 333
location, in star test 17, 138, 243
longitudinal slice 73, 187–190
lowpass filters 42

**M**

magnification as oversampling 42
Maksutov telescope 171
maps and surface error 236
Maréchal's tolerance 7, 9, 238
microripple 237, 246
microscopy 38
microwave oven 72

midpoint-displacement fractal
    algorithm 131
misalignment 17, 22, 104, 109, 121,
    125, 266
MTF (modulation transfer function) 9,
    46
    as autocorrelation 315
    astigmatism 256
    definition 47
    defocusing 51
    higher-order spherical aberration
        194
    lower order spherical aberration
        176
    medium-scale roughness 242
    multiple optical problems 52, 267
    obstruction 155
    of symmetric apertures 313
    pinched optics 147
    small-scale roughness 247
    spiders 158
    tube currents 140
    turbulence 136
    turned edge 211
    zones 205
mythology of telescopes 15

**N**

Newtonian reflector, quality 28
nodes and antinodes 70–74
null test 172, 304
numbering in image frames 333
numerical model, limitations 320

**O**

obstruction mask, 33% 94
obstruction 20, 153
    tolerance 155
offset, diagonal 114
ordering of diagnosis 19
OTF/MTF as autocorrelation 315
other tests 277
out-of-focus, definition 2
overcorrection 171
oversampling 41

**P**

paraboloid 171
perfect optics, diffraction pattern
    characteristics 11, 14
perspective compression 38

photographic plates 284
physical optics 15
Pickering's seeing scale 136
pinched optics 25, 145
pinch
    horizontal star test 92
    in thin-mirror reflectors 151
pinholes 83–88
pitch
    operating principles 5
    physical characteristics 5
    polishing 28
point-spread function 62
point-diffraction interferometer 302
Poisson, S.D. 21
power conservation 11
primary ripple 236
printing image frames 324
propagation, definition 63
pupil function 74
pupils, Gaussian 161
pupils, super-resolution 160

**R**

radial bar target 52
radiators 64
radio telescope 40
ray tracing (geometric optics) 22, 56
Rayleigh criterion 286
Rayleigh tolerance 6
Rayleigh-Taylor instability 130
rear-view mirrors 89
red dot effect 230
refractive/reflective optics 26
remedies, turned edge 217
residual chromatic aberration 224
resolution, audio 39
resolving power test 286
resonance, cause for dispersion 224
Ritchey-Chrétien-Cassegrain 172
Ronchi test 289–297
rough surface 28, 235
roughness in the eye 240
roughness scales 238

**S**

sagitta 78, 337
sampling errors in calculations 320
scaled accuracy of wavefront 3
schiefspiegler 79
Schmidt-Cassegrain 171
scratches and dust 166

secondary sources 64
secondary spectrum 224
"seeing" filters 165
sensitivity of star test 78, 81–82
shading 160
shrinkage with cooling 146
signal-to-noise ratio (SNR) 43, 167,
        249
signature of reproduction device 62
simple lenses 219
site modification 14, 138
site selection 91
skyglow 38
snap test 18, 93, 98
SNR 43, 167, 249
soap bubbles 298
Sparrow's criterion 287
spatial frequency response 45
spherical aberration 26, 170, 174
spherical reflector as an artificial
        source 88
spiders 157–160
stack of filters 35
star, as target 18
star test 17
        2:1 criterion for spherical
                aberration 190–192
        apochromats and advanced
                designs 231
        astigmatism 258
        chromatic aberration 227
        conventional doublets 229
        Ellison's variant 179
        Gaussian pupil 163
        higher-order spherical aberration
                194
        inequalities of focus 311
        low-order spherical aberration
                178
        medium-scale roughness 243
        obstruction 155
        pinched optics 148
        spider diffraction 159
        tube currents 142
        turbulence 136
        turned edge 211
        zones 207
star-test etiquette 273
strained optics 25, 145
Strehl ratio 9, 148, 198, 238
subwoofer 40
surface deformation at microscopic
        scale 4

surface roughness 235

**T**

temperature effects 25, 187
torus 252
transmission, negative 161
tube currents 24, 139
turbulence cells, origin 23
turbulence, ground 91, 138
turbulence 23, 129
turned edge 5, 31, 203, 209
twinkling 24

**U**

undercorrection 171

**V**

vignetting 85

**W**

"warm" colors 41
wave sum 67
wavefront error, measure of quality 6
wedge error 228
Welford's 20 focal length rule 83
white light diffraction pattern 13
wire test 284

**Z**

Zernike polynomials 174
zonal aberration 31, 201

# Optional Software

APERTURE is the IBM-PC program written by Dick Suiter to calculate most of the diffraction patterns appearing in his book *Star Testing Astronomical Telescopes*. With APERTURE you can investigate the most common aberrations, including spherical aberration (low and high order), zones and turned-down edges. It easily defocuses the image to show the actual perceived behavior on either side of focus. Users can specify many transmission patterns, such as obstruction and apodized pupils. If the many built-in aberrations and transmissions are not enough, you can construct your own. Sold only to purchasers of the book.

APERTURE has fewer approximations than ray-tracing routines. It shows the spreading of energy into the Airy disk caused by the wave nature of light. APERTURE displays images with a smooth 256-level gray scale (VGA monitors only). It also performs many other auxiliary calculations including the optical transfer function, field phase, and encircled energy function (EGA, VGA and Hercules-compatible monitors).

APERTURE accepts input from Suiter's Foucault test-reduction program ADMIR (also available from Willmann-Bell for $19.95 plus $1.00 handling for domestic orders), so you can knife-edge test an imperfect paraboloid and then feed the results directly to APERTURE. You can thus derive the actual diffraction pattern produced by that optical surface as well as its ability to preserve contrast. A PostScript utility program is provided to generate the same sort of images that appeared in the book.

APERTURE works on a 286 MS-DOS machine, although it is best on a 386 processor or higher. A coprocessor is recommended. It supports EGA and Hercules-compatible monitors, but a VGA board and color monitor are required for gray scale displays.

Turn page for order form.

364

## Order Form

◯ APERTURE for the IBM-PC at $24.95 each.           $_____
   ◯ 5.25-inch 360K   ◯ 3.5-inch 720K

◯ ADMIR for the IBM-PC at $19.95 each.              $_____
   ◯ 5.25-inch 360K   ◯ 3.5-inch 720K

                            Handling[1]           **1.00**

                        **TOTAL**           $_____

I wish to pay with:
◯ **Check** ◯ **Money Order**
◯ **Visa**   ◯ **MasterCard**   ◯ **American Express**

Card No._____

Card expiration date_____

Signature_____

Name (Please Print)_____

Street_____

City, State, ZIP_____

### Willmann–Bell, Inc.
P.O. Box 35025
Richmond, Virginia, 23235
Voice (804) 320-7016 FAX (804) 272-5920

**Prices Subject To Change Without Notice**

**This Book's Serial Number is**   028775 _____

---

[1]Foreign orders: shipping charges are additional. Write for proforma invoice which details your exact costs for various shipping options.